THE GLASS ELECTRODE

THE GLASS ELECTRODE

Methods, Applications, and Theory

BY

MALCOLM DOLE

Associate Professor of Chemistry
Northwestern University

NEW YORK

JOHN WILEY & SONS, Inc.

London: CHAPMAN & HALL, Limited

1941

PRINTED IN U. S. A.

PRESS OF
BRAUNWORTH & CO., INC.
BUILDERS OF BOOKS
BRIDGEPORT, CONN.

To

GRINNELL JONES

Teacher, Counselor, Friend

PREFACE

To the field of hydrogen ion concentration and of aqueous solution phenomena the nineteenth century contributed the discovery of the existence of ions, the thermodynamic laws that govern ionic equilibria, and the development of many of the fundamental experimental methods used today. The special significance of the hydrogen ion was not realized, however; the proton was unknown and unnamed, and its influence in biologic as well as inorganic and organic reactions little understood. As experimental technique improved, as measurements became more precise and accurate, as biologists and biochemists became more skilled in the ever advancing theories and methods of physical chemistry, the subtle activity and reactions of the hydrogen ion were noticed, studied, and quantitatively estimated. Thus in the period 1900 to 1920 the pH was first defined and accurate methods for its measurement were first developed; the activity coefficient and the corresponding practical thermodynamic methods of G. N. Lewis were discovered, and the whole subject of ionic equilibria put on a fairly sound basis. Between 1920 and 1930 pH measurements by means of indicators and by means of the quinhydrone and hydrogen electrode reached a high state of perfection, but this decade was chiefly characterized by the epochal publications of Debye and his school concerning the influence of interionic electrical attractions upon the properties of ionic solutions. At the same time the true thermodynamic significance, or perhaps I should say the lack of thermodynamic significance, of the pH concept finally became understood. Yet the glass electrode was practically unknown.

With the perfection of theory and experiment it might have appeared that further important changes in pH methods and technique were hardly possible; nevertheless the decade that has just passed actually witnessed the most valuable development from a practical standpoint that has ever been made in the field of pH, namely, the invention of glass electrode pH electrometers which have literally swept the country and are now so extensively used that they are manufactured by mass production methods. In many respects the glass electrode makes possible the ideal measurement, a measurement in which the glass bulb is inserted into the solution whose pH is to be determined, a switch pressed and the pH immediately read off the dial; as simple and as quick as the measurement of temperature with a mercury thermometer. However, the very ease and speed of the method may lead the unwary scientist into a deluded sense of experimental security; it is not always possible or usually advisable to rely uncritically upon the pH reading of these convenient measuring instruments.

Clearly the time has now come for a detailed review and discussion of the glass electrode, of its limitations and difficulties, of its methods and applications and of its mechanism and theory. In this monograph I have tried to include all pertinent material concerning pH as measured with the glass electrode, such as types of glass, electrodes and cells, special applications, difficulties and techniques, methods of calculating or avoiding errors, as well as related discussions on the significance of pH and the standardization of the pH scale. A brief review of other methods of pH measurement with a list of the advantages and disadvantages of these methods is also given, so that the position which the glass electrode occupies in the pH realm can be correctly understood.

Thermionic amplifiers which today have practically displaced electrostatic electrometers in the laboratories of physicists and chemists, thanks to the development of new types of vacuum tubes, are described in considerable detail in Chapter 3. Directions for building accurate and serviceable electrometers of this type should prove to be of value to physical scientists who are interested in the measurement of the e.m.f. of any system having a high resistance as well as that of glass electrode cells. The discussion of commercial pH electrometers had to be omitted from this monograph, not only because many of the details of these instruments are carefully guarded trade secrets, but also because there are so many different types commercially available that an excessive amount of space would be required to describe them all.

Dr. C. A. Crowley, Director of Research of the Technical Service Bureau in Chicago, first urged me to undertake the task of writing this book, and also kindly offered to attempt to obtain for me information concerning the glass electrode which had been accumulated by research chemists working in industrial laboratories. Because of his many industrial contacts and his energy in sending out letters of inquiry, it has been possible to tap this vast reservoir of unpublished material and to include in the book industrial applications and methods which otherwise would not have been available. The names of the men who generously responded to the letters of inquiry sent out mostly by Dr. Crowley are appended to this preface.

The importance of the glass electrode in the world of biology and biochemistry has become so great that any book on the glass electrode that did not treat fully this aspect of the subject would be incomplete. Fortunately, Dr. J. Sendroy, Jr., Chairman of the Department of Experimental Medicine of the Loyola Medical School, Mercy Hospital, Chicago, and an expert in this field, kindly consented to contribute a detailed account of the measurement of the pH of blood and to read critically the whole chapter on biological applications. For his able review I wish to extend my sincere thanks. I also wish to acknowledge the aid of Dr. A. O. Beckman and Dr. S. E. Hill, who not only submitted manuscripts of unpublished material, but also carefully read over and criticized several chapters of the book.

In our own researches on the glass electrode I have been aided by Miss Charlotte Erwin (Mrs. Ralph Munch), Dr. J. L. Gabbard, Dr. C. E. Holley, Jr., Dr. R. M. Roberts, Dr. B. Z. Wiener, Mr. R. Hernandez Corzo, and Mr. R. B. Haller, to whom I express my indebtedness. Financial assistance for our experimental work has been received from the Bache Fund of the National Academy of Sciences, the Penrose Fund of the American Philosophical Society, the Research Funds of the National Research Council and of the Society of Sigma Xi, and from Northwestern University. Without this support, much of the data of this monograph would never have been obtained. For my original introduction to the problems of the glass electrode in the laboratories of Dr. D. A. MacInnes of the Rockefeller Institute for Medical Research, New York, I am most grateful.

MALCOLM DOLE

EVANSTON, ILLINOIS
March, 1941

ACKNOWLEDGMENT

The author wishes to acknowledge gratefully the kind cooperation of the following scientists:

W. E. Baier	J. C. Krantz, Jr.
A. O. Beckman	E. P. Laug
J. S. Blair	H. F. Launer
I. H. Blank	J. M. Lupton
D. R. Briggs	D. A. MacInnes
D. H. Cameron	W. T. McGeorge
A. L. Chaney	E. B. Newton
L. Clifcorn	R. C. Newton
E. D. Coleman	W. J. Nungester
L. W. Elder, Jr.	A. E. Osterberg
S. B. Ellis	A. Passinski
A. N. Finn	A. I. Rambo
L. Giraut-Erler	D. B. Sabine
M. M. Haring	T. D. Sanford
W. H. Harrison	J. Sendroy, Jr.
P. J. Hartsuch	D. M. Smith
S. E. Hill	K. C. Swan
D. I. Hitchcock	T. L. Swenson
D. Hubbard	W. C. Taylor
G. H. Joseph	M. R. Thompson
H. Kahler	D. S. Villars
H. L. Kahler	H. C. Wall
E. F. Klem	L. W. Wells
F. Kraissl	J. Wyman, Jr.

CONTENTS

PAGE

CHAPTER 1. SIGNIFICANCE OF HYDROGEN ION CONCENTRATION. DEFINI-
TIONS AND CONVENTIONS.................................... 1

1·1 The Ionization Theory of Acidity............................. 1
1·2 The Mechanism of Ionization and the Nature of the Hydrogen Ion.. 3
1·3 The Debye Interionic Theory, The Activity Coefficient and the Ionic
Strength.. 6
1·4 The Work of Sörensen and the Early Definition of pH............. 9
1·5 Sign and Cell Conventions.................................... 11

CHAPTER 2. REVIEW OF METHODS OF pH MEASUREMENT INCLUDING THE
EARLY HISTORY OF THE GLASS ELECTRODE................. 14

2·1 The Hydrogen Electrode....................................... 14
2·2 The Quinhydrone Electrode.................................... 18
2·3 Indicators.. 22
2·4 The Development of the Glass Electrode........................ 25

CHAPTER 3. E.M.F. MEASURING CIRCUITS............................. 32

3·1 Galvanometers, Potentiometers, and Standard Cells.............. 32
3·2 Galvanometer-Potentiometer Circuits for Glass Electrode E.M.F.
Measurements... 38
3·3 Electrostatic Electrometers................................... 39
3·4 General Theory of Vacuum Tube pH Electrometers.............. 41
3·5 Single Vacuum-Tube Amplifying Circuits....................... 46
3·6 Insulation, Shielding, and Constructional Details............... 54
3·7 Multiple Tube Thermionic Amplifiers.......................... 58

CHAPTER 4. TYPES OF GLASS ELECTRODES AND GLASSES................. 64

4·1 Types of Glass for Glass Electrodes............................ 64
4·2 Water Content of Glass. Durability and Treatment of the Glass
Surface.. 78
4·3 Bulb Types of Glass Electrodes................................ 85
4·4 Insulation of Glass Electrode Stems........................... 89
4·5 Capillary and Thin Membrane Types of Glass Electrodes.......... 92

CHAPTER 5. REFERENCE ELECTRODES FOR GLASS ELECTRODE CELLS....... 98

5·1 Internal Electrodes for Glass Electrodes. The Silver Chloride
Electrode.. 98
5·2 The Calomel Reference Electrode.............................. 101

CHAPTER 6. CELL ASSEMBLIES AND LIQUID-JUNCTION POTENTIALS......... 105

6·1 The Theory of the Liquid-Junction Potential.................... 105
6·2 Experimental Studies of the Liquid-Junction Potential.......... 109
6·3 Liquid Junctions in Glass Electrode Cells and Cell Assemblies...... 114
6·4 Derivation of Eq. 6·1·5.. 120

xiii

PAGE

CHAPTER 7. LIMITATIONS OF GLASS ELECTRODE IN ALKALINE pH RANGE.. 123

7·1   Introduction... 123
7·2   An Experimental Method of Measuring Glass Electrode Error...... 124
7.3   Errors of the Glass Electrode in Alkaline Solutions................ 128
7·4   Methods of Avoiding Alkaline Errors........................... 135
7·5   Qualitative Explanation of Alkaline Errors...................... 137

CHAPTER 8. LIMITATIONS OF THE GLASS ELECTRODE IN ACID AND NONAQUE-
            OUS SOLUTIONS... 139

8·1   Introduction... 139
8·2   Experimental Data in Acid and Nonaqueous Solutions............ 140
8·3   Methods of Avoiding Acid and Nonaqueous Solution Errors........ 144
8·4   Qualitative Explanation of the Negative Errors of the Glass Electrode. 145
8·5   The pH of Emulsions of Sulfonated Oils........................ 145

CHAPTER 9. TEMPERATURE EFFECTS IN GLASS ELECTRODE CELLS......... 151

9·1   Electrical Resistance of Glass as a Function of Temperature........ 151
9·2   High Temperature Stability of Glass Electrodes................... 153
9·3   Assymmetry Potential as a Function of Temperature.............. 154
9·4   Alkaline Errors as a Function of Temperature.................... 155
9·5   Acid and Nonaqueous Solution Errors as a Function of Temperature. 158
9·6   Temperature Coefficient of Glass Electrode Surface e.m.f.......... 159
9·7   Temperature Coefficient of the Inner Reference Electrode.......... 162
9·8   Temperature Coefficient of Saturated Calomel Reference Electrode
      and of the Complete Cell...................................... 165
9·9   Methods of Avoiding Temperature Difficulties................... 168

CHAPTER 10. SOME SPECIAL APPLICATIONS OF THE GLASS ELECTRODE...... 169

10·1 Determination of the pH of Unbuffered and Slightly Buffered Solu-
      tions.. 169
10·2 Study of Reaction Rates Using the Glass Electrode................ 175
10·3 The Use of the Glass Electrode in the Tropics and Under Conditions
      of High Humidity... 176

CHAPTER 11. SPECIAL APPLICATIONS OF THE GLASS ELECTRODE IN BIOLOGICAL
             CHEMISTRY.. 179

11·1 Introduction... 179
11·2 The Measurement of Blood pH in Vitro......................... 180
11·3 The Measurement of the pH of Blood in Vivo................... 192
11·4 The Measurement of pH in Vitro.............................. 194
11·5 The Measurement of pH in Vivo............................... 194

CHAPTER 12. APPLICATIONS OF THE GLASS ELECTRODE IN INDUSTRIAL
             RESEARCH AND CONTROL LABORATORIES.................... 203

12·1 The Glass Electrode in Food Industries.......................... 203
12·2 The Glass Electrode in the Rubber and Leather Industries......... 212
12·3 Miscellaneous Applications of the Glass Electrode................ 219

CONTENTS   XV

CHAPTER 13. CONTINUOUS pH RECORDERS AND AUTOMATIC pH CONTROL
WITH A GLASS ELECTRODE.............................. 229

13·1 Continuous Recording of pH................................. 229
13·2 Automatic Control of pH................................... 232

CHAPTER 14. MICRO METHODS WITH GLASS ELECTRODE................. 238

14·1 Introduction.. 238
14·2 Micro Apparatus for pH Determination........................ 238

CHAPTER 15. POTENTIOMETRIC TITRATIONS WITH THE GLASS ELECTRODE... 242

15·1 Glass Electrode Titration Cells.................................. 243
15·2 Differential Titration Cells..................................... 247
15·3 Analysis of Acid Mixtures...................................... 251
15·4 Uses of the Glass Electrode in Nonaqueous Solution Titration...... 254

CHAPTER 16. THE THEORY OF THE GLASS ELECTRODE.................. 256

16·1 Thermodynamics of the Glass Electrode.......................... 256
16·2 The Electrode Reaction Mechanism of the Glass Electrode......... 261
16·3 Theory of the Glass Electrode in Basic Solutions.................. 267
16·4 Theory of the Glass Electrode in Acid and Nonaqueous Solutions... 276

CHAPTER 17. SIGNIFICANCE AND STANDARDIZATION OF pH SCALE.......... 280

17·1 Why do we measure pH Numbers?............................. 280
17·2 Sörensen's First Standardization of pH Scale..................... 282
17·3 Scatchard's Standardization of the pH Scale..................... 285
17·4 Cohn's Method of pH Standardization........................... 289
17·5 Glass Electrode Standardization Recommendations................ 296
17·6 Glass Electrode Standardization Recommendations for Nonaqueous
Solutions... 299
17·7 Significance of pH... 300

APPENDIX
    I   Definition of Symbols... 305
   II   Values of the General Physical Constants....................... 307
  III   Values of $2.3026\ RT/F$.. 308
   IV   Some Standard Electrode Potentials............................ 309
    V   Potassium and Sodium Salt Error Corrections at 25° C........... 310
   VI   Lithium and Barium Salt Error Corrections at 25° C............. 311
  VII   Temperature Correction Curves for Uncompensated pH Meters..... 312
 VIII   Dissociation Constants of Acids at 25° C....................... 313
   IX   Dissociation Constant of Water................................ 314
    X pH Values of Standard Buffer Solutions........................ 315

LOGARITHMS... 316

AUTHOR INDEX... 319

SUBJECT INDEX.. 325

CHAPTER 1

SIGNIFICANCE OF HYDROGEN-ION CONCENTRATION
DEFINITIONS AND CONVENTIONS

1·1. The Ionization Theory of Acidity

In the eighteenth century acids were believed to be composed of "pointed particles" which "affect the taste in a sharp and piercing manner" and which could be recognized by their ability to turn syrup of violets red; alkaline or lixivial particles being substances which turn that syrup green.[1]

During most of the nineteenth century, only the total quantity of acid both ionized and unionized per unit of volume was measured by titration analyses; no attempt to determine hydrogen-*ion* concentration, that is, the ionized-acid concentration, was or could be made, not only because the existence of ions in the absence of an electric current had not even been postulated, but also because the importance and significance of acidity in influencing chemical reactions, physiological processes and bacterial growth were not realized. In the years preceding 1879 Pasteur [2] recognized empirically the effect of the acidity of the solution in the wine and the beer industries, but the exact connection between hydrogen-ion concentration or acidity and chemical activity awaited the advent of the ionization theory (1882–87). In fact it was Arrhenius' attempt to understand the constitution of acid solutions as revealed by his measurements of the equivalent conductance of dilute solutions in relation to the chemical strength of acids that led him to his theory.[3]

Concentrated solutions of acids had been studied before, but by focusing his attention on dilute solutions Arrhenius discovered that the relationships between equivalent solutions of different acids were considerably simplified so that the generalization could be made that the acids acted as if all the molecules became "conducting molecules" at the lowest concentrations. Arrhenius made the further important

---

[1] Samuel Johnson, "Dictionary," Fourth Edition, W. Strahan, London, 1773.
[2] L. Pasteur, "Studies on Fermentation," translated by F. Faulkner and D. C. Robb, London, 1879.
[3] S. Arrhenius, *J. Am. Chem. Soc.* **34**, 353 (1912).

1

discovery that of two acids the one which had the better conductivity in equivalent solutions of the same solvent was also the stronger acid chemically. He therefore postulated that the bodies in solution producing the chemical properties must be the same as the particles responsible for the conductivity. Thus he identified the hydrogen ion as being the significant entity in acids and demonstrated its importance not only in regard to the electrical conductivity of solutions, but what has since proved to be of even greater moment, also in regard to the chemical activity of acids. The "pointed particles" of Samuel Johnson are thus seen to be the hydrogen ions; it is they which "affect the taste in a sharp and piercing manner," which turn syrup of violets a red color and which produce all the properties of the substances we now associate with the word "acid."

Arrhenius' theory can be briefly explained as follows: In aqueous solution acetic acid, for example, ionizes according to the equilibrium

$$CH_3 COOH \rightleftarrows CH_3 COO^- + H^+ \qquad [1·1·1]$$

which is shifted to the right on dilution with water so that the acetic acid becomes relatively more ionized with decreasing concentration, although the hydrogen-ion concentration actually becomes smaller. The acid properties are due only to the hydrogen ion, H^+, whose concentration may be calculated from conductance measurements by means of the following equations:

$$N_{H^+} = \alpha N \qquad [1·1·2]$$

$$\alpha = \frac{\Lambda}{\Lambda_0} \qquad [1·1·3]$$

where N is the stoichiometric normality of the acid, N_{H^+} the normality (equivalents per liter of solution) of the hydrogen ion, α the fraction of acetic acid ionized, Λ the equivalent conductance at the normality N, and Λ_0 the equivalent conductance at zero concentration (for the definition of all symbols used see Appendix I). Equations 1·1·2 and 1·1·3 are valid in pure solutions of acetic acid, but can only be used with exactness in dilute solutions and only after certain corrections have been applied. Obviously, electrical conductance measurements are not of much help in the practical problem of hydrogen-ion concentration determinations.

At this point we wish to emphasize most strongly the difference between the total acid concentration (its normality or stoichiometric concentration, which is such a property of the solution that twice as much base would be required to neutralize an acid whose normality is twice as great as another) and the hydrogen-ion concentration existing at any moment in the solution, an *intensive* property.   There is no necessary connection between the hydrogen-ion concentration and the amount of base required for neutralization since a base neutralizes all the acid both in its ionic and unionized form.   Referring to Eq. 1·1·1 the hydrogen-ion concentration is represented by N_{H^+}, but the normality of the acid, N_A, is equal to $(N_{CH_3COOH} + N_{H^+})$.

Before continuing our discussion of methods of hydrogen-ion determination, we shall next consider the mechanism of ionization and the present day concept of the nature of acid solutions.

1·2. The Mechanism of Ionization and the Nature of the Hydrogen Ion

Thanks to the discovery of the electron by Sir Joseph John Thomson [4] in 1897 and his experimental proof of the existence of the electron in all substances, and thanks to the Lewis-Langmuir-Kossel electronic theory of chemical activity, we now believe that chlorine ion in solution has become an ion by the acquisition of an electron and that the negative chlorine ion with eighteen electrons about its nucleus has entirely different chemical properties from neutral atomic chlorine with seventeen electrons about its nucleus.   But it is more difficult to understand why the chlorine atom can become an ion at all.   From spectroscopic measurements it can be calculated that 3.8 electron-volts of energy are gained when the chlorine atom in the gaseous state adds an electron to become Cl^-; if, however, this electron is taken from a sodium atom, 5.11 electron-volts of energy must be supplied.[5]   There is thus an energy deficiency of 1.3 electron-volts or 30,000 cal. per g. ion in the process and the reaction

$$Na + Cl \rightarrow Na^+ + Cl^- \qquad [1·2·1]$$

will, therefore, not of itself occur.

In aqueous solution we have the possibility of an additional reaction and it is just this reaction which supplies the energy necessary for ionization to take place, produces such a decrease in potential energy that the system becomes stable, like a rock rolling down a hill into a valley beneath, and also provides the energy necessary to make the salt soluble; the reaction referred to is the hydration of the ions,

$$Na^+ + x\, H_2O \rightarrow Na^+ \cdot x\, H_2O + 115,000 \text{ cal./g. ion} \qquad [1·2·2]$$

$$Cl^- + y\, H_2O \rightarrow Cl^- \cdot y\, H_2O + \ \ 64,400 \text{ cal./g. ion} \qquad [1·2·3]$$

---

[4] Sir Joseph John Thomson, "Recollections and Reflections," Macmillan, New York, 1937, p. 339.

[5] R. W. Gurney, "Ions in Solution." Cambridge, 1936, p. 201.

yielding a total of 179.4 kg.-cal.   The hydration energy is due to the great attraction between the water dipoles and the positive and negative ions.   (In the "polar" water molecule there is a permanent separation of the centers of gravity of positive and negative electricity, so that although the water molecule as a whole is neutral, there exist enormous electrical forces in the immediate vicinity of the positive and negative ends of the molecule, forces which may be so high as to be equivalent to a field of 70,000,000 v. per cm.)   Energetically, therefore, we can say that ionization in aqueous solution is quite possible.   Furthermore, the hydration energy is sufficient to overcome the lattice energy of ionic crystals so that salts will dissolve, but the lattice energy of some salts like silver chloride is so high that it dissolves only to a negligible extent.   Yet some molecules like the organic acids are bound together so firmly that even the high energy of ionic hydration is insufficient to produce appreciable ionization, and for still other molecules no ionization at all can occur.   Before considering the reasons for the weak ionization of the organic acids, a subject of vital importance for pH measurements, let us consider the mechanism by which ionization takes place.[6]

On solution of the salt or organic molecule, the undissociated substance is subjected to bombardment by solvent molecules.   If the ions in the molecule are bound together by weak enough forces, the collision with the solvent molecule can produce ionization.   This fundamental idea, originally due to Bjerrum, has recently been tested by Kraus and Fuoss who were able to show in some beautiful experiments that the electrical binding force between ions given by the equation of Coulomb's law

$$f = \frac{q_+ \cdot q_-}{Dr^2} \qquad\qquad [1\cdot2\cdot4]$$

is insufficient to hold the molecule together for most salts if the dielectric constant is greater than about 43.6; ordinary salts are completely dissociated, therefore, in pure water whose dielectric constant is 78.6 at 25° C., and only partially dissociated in solvents of dielectric constant below 43.6.   In the case of a salt dissolved in pure water, one may picture the ions first being knocked apart by collisions with the solvent and then held apart by the attractive forces existing between the ions and the water dipoles.

We now have to ask ourselves why is it that while most salts are

---

[6] For a more detailed account and references see M. Dole, "Experimental and Theoretical Electrochemistry," McGraw-Hill Book Co., New York, 1935, p. 20. Also L. P. Hammett, "Physical Organic Chemistry," McGraw-Hill Book Co., 1940.

completely ionized in water solution, there are many weakly dissociated substances? At the same time we might also ask, why is it that the mercurous ion exists in aqueous solution as the diatomic mercurous ion Hg_2^{++}? One of the most important contributions of the quantum mechanics to chemistry is the concept of "exchange forces" due to "resonance." In fact, the chemical bond of greatest frequence in organic chemistry, the electron-pair bond, arises because of this type of force. In the hydrogen molecule, for example, the exchange force owing to the electrons encircling or exchanging between the nuclei is the chief force holding the molecule together; it is many times greater than the comparatively weak Coulombic (electrostatic) forces. In the case of the diatomic mercurous ion, Hg_2^{++}, the repulsive force between the two positive mercurous ions is reduced to a low value when the ion is dissolved in water of high dielectric constant (compare Eq. 1·2·4), but the exchange force of the electron pair bond between the two mercury atoms is presumably independent of the dielectric constant of the solvent so that the attractive forces due to the electron pair bond outweigh the electrostatic repulsion forces and the molecule is stable.[7] Reduce the dielectric constant of the solvent and the ion Hg_2^{++} dissociates as the electrostatic forces increase and become larger than the oppositely directed exchange forces. In the case of organic acids, exchange forces binding the ionizable hydrogen ion to the remainder of the molecule may be large in which case the acid will be very weakly dissociated like carbolic acid, or they may be smaller and only slightly greater than the electrostatic force, in which case the acid will be more strongly dissociated, formic acid, for example. (For a table of dissociation constants, see Appendix VIII.)

Up to this point we have been talking rather glibly about the hydrogen ion without specifying whether we mean by this term the nucleus of the hydrogen atom, the proton, p^+, whether we mean the hydrated proton, $p(H_2O)^+$, or whether we mean the proton hydrated with an indefinite number of water molecules, $p(H_2O)_x^+$. There is considerable evidence that the proton cannot exist in aqueous solution, that the solution of hydrogen chloride to form hydrochloric acid, for example, should be written

$$HCl + H_2O \rightarrow H_3O^+ + Cl^- \qquad [1·2·5]$$

We shall call the ion, H_3O^+, the hydrogen ion, and shall designate it by the symbol H^+, reserving the symbol p^+ for the unhydrated proton. The hydrogen ion, H^+, is estimated to be about the size of the potassium ion and is further hydrated for the same reasons that the potas-

[7] R. W. Gurney, *J. Chem. Phys.* **6**, 499 (1938).

sium ion is hydrated. But in speaking of the hydrogen ion, H^+, we mean the ion H_3O^+ and shall refer to it in the same way that one refers to the sodium ion or any other ion, without including in its symbol the extra water of hydration.

At this point we should recall to the reader Brönsted's definition of an acid as any molecule, A, that can donate a proton, and a base as any molecule, B, that can accept a proton, e.g.,

$$A \rightleftarrows B + p^+ \qquad\qquad [1\cdot2\cdot6]$$

Thus, the hydrogen ion, the acetic acid molecule, and the ammonium ion are acids, while the hydroxyl ion, OH^-, ammonia, and the acetate ion are bases.   These statements are true irrespective of the solvent. Brönsted's concept is quite general and is particularly useful in describing the acid-base chemistry of nonaqueous solutions.

1·3. The Debye Interionic Theory, the Activity Coefficient, and the Ionic Strength

Proof of the Arrhenius theory of an ionization existing at equilibrium is demonstrated graphically by means of the titration curves for weak acids given in Chapter 15, but many quantitative discrepancies as well as failure of the theory to account for the properties of "strong electrolytes" (salt solutions, strong acids, and bases) convinced leading physical chemists that the electrical forces existing between ions in solution should be considered.   This was not done by Arrhenius.   Debye and Hückel[8] in 1923 supplied the necessary mathematical description of these forces, obtaining explicit equations for the activity coefficient, a function first introduced into thermodynamics by G. N. Lewis in 1901.[9]

The role of the activity coefficient in electrochemistry is perhaps best understood by considering the method by which it can be calculated from electrochemical data; at the same time we shall become familiar with the common procedure in estimating standard electrode potentials—a subject of importance in pH standardization—as well as with a good example of the value of the Debye theory in solution chemistry.   Consider the electrochemical cell composed of the hydrogen and silver chloride electrodes immersed in hydrochloric acid; when the cell operates spontaneously to pass one faraday of electricity, the following electrode reactions will occur:

[8] For references and a more detailed account of this theory see the author's "Experimental and Theoretical Electrochemistry," McGraw-Hill Book Co., New York, 1935.   Chapters VI and XVIII.

[9] G. N. Lewis, *Proc. Am. Acad.* **37**, 49 (1901).

At the hydrogen electrode:

$$\tfrac{1}{2}H_2 \rightarrow H^+(m) + \epsilon^- \qquad [1\cdot3\cdot1]$$

At the chloride electrode:

$$\epsilon^- + AgCl \rightarrow Cl^-(m) + Ag, \qquad [1\cdot3\cdot2]$$

the net cell reaction being

$$\tfrac{1}{2}H_2 + AgCl \rightarrow H^+(m) + Cl^-(m) + Ag \qquad [1\cdot3\cdot3]$$

where $H^+(m)$ signifies one mole of hydrogen ion at a concentration m moles per 1000 g. of solvent. The total change in chemical potential $\Delta\mu$, is

$$\Delta\mu = \mu_{H^+} + \mu_{Cl^-} + \mu_{Ag} - \tfrac{1}{2}\mu_{H_2} - \mu_{AgCl} \qquad [1\cdot3\cdot4]$$

The relation between the change in chemical potential and the cell electromotive force (e.m.f.) is

$$\Delta\mu = - FE \qquad [1\cdot3\cdot5]$$

where F is the faraday and E the e.m.f. If the hydrochloric acid were an ideal solution, the chemical potential would be given in terms of the concentration by the equation

$$\mu = \mu^o + RT \ln m$$

but since no solutions are exactly ideal, the activity coefficient γ must be introduced to make the equation thermodynamically valid,

$$\mu = \mu^o + RT \ln m\gamma \qquad [1\cdot3\cdot6]$$

where μ^o is a constant at constant temperature and solvent. Introducing Eqs. $1\cdot3\cdot5$, and $1\cdot3\cdot6$ into Eq. $1\cdot3\cdot4$ and rearranging we have

$$E = E^o - 2\frac{RT}{F} \ln m_{HCl}\, \gamma_{\pm HCl} \qquad [1\cdot3\cdot7]$$

In Eq. $1\cdot3\cdot7$ E^o is the standard electrode potential of the silver chloride electrode (since E^o for the hydrogen electrode is by definition zero), and $\gamma_\pm$ is the so-called "mean" activity coefficient of hydrochloric acid,

$$\gamma_\pm = \sqrt{\gamma_{H^+} \cdot \gamma_{Cl^-}} \qquad [1\cdot3\cdot8]$$

Separating measurable quantities in $1\cdot3\cdot7$ we obtain

$$E + \frac{2RT}{F} \ln m_{HCl} = E^o - \frac{2RT}{F} \ln \gamma_{\pm HCl} \qquad [1\cdot3\cdot9]$$

From the Debye theory of solutions

$$\ln f_\pm = - z_+ z_- \frac{\epsilon^3}{(DkT)^{3/2}} \sqrt{\frac{\pi N}{1000} \sum_i c_i z_i^2} \qquad [1\cdot3\cdot10]$$

or more simply at 25° C.   (For numerical values of the constants of Eq. 1·3·10 see Appendix II.)

$$\log f_\pm = - 0.358 \, z_+ \cdot z_- \sqrt{\sum_i c_i z_i^2} \qquad [1\cdot3\cdot11]$$

or

$$\log f_\pm = - 0.506 \sqrt{c}. \qquad [1\cdot3\cdot12]$$

In Eqs. 1·3·10 to 1·3·12 c is concentration in moles per liter of solution and f is the activity coefficient based on that concentration unit; in dilute aqueous solutions there will be an insignificant difference between these quantities and m and γ of the preceding equations. Making use of Eq. 1·3·12, Eq. 1·3·9 becomes at 25° C.

$$E + 0.1183 \log m_{HCl} = E^\circ + 0.0599\sqrt{m} \qquad [1\cdot3\cdot13]$$

If the Debye theory is correct, a plot of the left-hand side of Eq. 1·3·13 as a function of the square root of the concentration should yield a

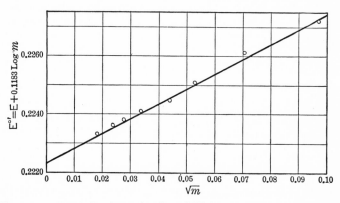

FIG. 1·1.   Graph for determination of E° for the AgCl/Ag electrode.

straight line extrapolating to E° at zero concentration.   Once E° has in this way been determined, activity coefficients at *all* finite concentrations are easily and correctly calculated using Eq. 1·3·9.   Thus a plot of $E + 0.1183 \log m_{HCl}$ results not only in E° and from E°, $\gamma_{\pm HCl}$, but it also illustrates graphically the validity of the Debye theory.   Such a plot is shown in Fig. 1·1.

Equation 1·3·10, known as the "limiting law," is usually valid from zero to 0.001 or 0.01 normal concentration; other equations for the activity coefficient which have been used at higher concentrations are, at 25° C.

$$\ln \gamma_{\pm} = - \, 0.358 \, z_+ \cdot z_- \sqrt{\sum_i c_i z_i^2} \pm B(c_i z_i^2) \qquad [1\cdot3\cdot14]$$

$$\ln \gamma_{\pm} = \frac{- 0.358 \, z_+ \cdot z_- \sqrt{\sum_i c_i z_i^2}}{1 + A \sqrt{\sum_i c_i z_i^2}} \pm B(c_i z_i^2) \qquad [1\cdot3\cdot15]$$

where A and B are empirical factors chosen so as to make the equations agree with the data as closely as possible.

At this point it can be seen that the Debye equations give a theoretical basis for the ionic strength principle discovered by Mellanby [10] and by Lewis and Randall.[11] This principle states that the activity coefficient is a function of the ionic strength, μ,

$$\mu = \tfrac{1}{2}\Sigma m_i z_i^2 \qquad [1\cdot3\cdot16]$$

where m_i is the concentration of any specified ion and z_i is its valence, rather than a function of the concentration.

In concluding this very brief outline of modern solution theory we should point out that the Debye equation for the ionic activity coefficient, γ_i, is

$$\ln \gamma_i = - \, z_i^2 \, \frac{\epsilon^3}{(DkT)^{3/2}} \sqrt{\frac{\pi N}{1000} \sum_i c_i z_i^2} \qquad [1\cdot3\cdot17]$$

Since the deviation of activity coefficient from unity is a measure of the imperfectness of the solution, the activity coefficient is unity at zero concentration where all solutions are ideal.

1·4. The Work of Sörensen and the Early Definition of pH

Considerable time elapsed after Arrhenius' discovery of the connection between hydrogen-ion concentration and chemical strength of acids before scientists began to realize the importance of the role of the hydrogen ion in influencing chemical and biological behavior; thus in 1909 Sörensen wrote [12] that in studying and describing enzymatic reactions biological chemists rarely, if ever, took into consideration the degree of dissociation of acid or base in the enzyme solution,

[10] J. Mellanby, *J. Physiol.* **33**, 373 (1905).
[11] G. N. Lewis and M. Randall, *J. Am. Chem. Soc.* **43**, 1112 (1921).
[12] S. P. L. Sörensen, *Biochem. Z.* **21**, 131, 201 (1909).

but were content to record merely the total amount of acid or base added. Even more rarely did they consider the possibility of the ingredients of the solution, such as proteins, combining with the added acid or base and thus changing its concentration. Sörensen pointed out that two solutions made by adding first, 1 g. and second, 5 g. of a protein to 100 cc. 0.1 N. HCl might differ appreciably in their "actual acidity"; that is, in their hydrogen-ion concentration. Sörensen clearly realized that the use of any method of measuring the acidity was unsound if the method produced a change of hydrogen-ion concentration during the measurement.

In his great papers of 1909, Sörensen reviewed the experimental procedures that might be used for the determination of hydrogen-ion concentration (these methods are not to be confused with analytical titrations which give one only the total acid concentration); he then proceeded to develop the colorimetric method, to study buffer solutions for use as standards, to compare the colorimetric method with the electrometric (hydrogen electrode) method, to define the pH symbol and concept and to standardize the pH scale, and finally to demonstrate the importance of the pH in determining the rate of enzyme hydrolysis (cleavage). Realizing the awkwardness of such expressions as "hydrogen-ion concentration of 0.0000056 N," he concluded that it would be better to express the hydrogen-ion concentration as some power of ten and to introduce a new concept and symbol, the pH, which he defined as the negative of the exponent of ten necessary to give the normality.   Thus

$$0.0000056 \ N = 1 \times 10^{-5.25} \ N$$

or

$$p\text{H} = 5.25.$$

In remembering that the definition of the ordinary or Briggsian logarithm of a number is the exponent of ten necessary to give the number, it is obvious that the pH can be defined as the negative of the logarithm of the hydrogen-ion normality, $e.g.$,

$$-\log (0.0000056) = 5.25, \text{ or in general}$$

$$-\log N_{\text{H}^+} = p\text{H}. \qquad [1\cdot4\cdot1]$$

As a matter of fact, this definition of pH is not precise, nor did Sörensen actually calculate his pH values from Eq. 1·4·1; instead, he found them from e.m.f. measurements which is the modern usage.   As will be pointed out in Chapter 17, the error in Eq. 1·4·1 enters when we try to calculate the hydrogen-ion normality from the pH; we shall learn that it is thermodynamically impossible to do this, because a certain unavoidable difficulty due to liquid-junction potentials cannot be eliminated in our pH measurements, although it can be made very small. There is the further difficulty that we never deal with "perfect" solutions as we never deal with "perfect" gases, with the result that even if the pH could be determined without error, we could not calculate the hydrogen-ion concentration from it by Eq. 1·4·1. For most medical and industrial practice today the pH data are accepted and interpreted as such without trying to go beyond them to the hydrogen-ion concentration. Later on we shall try to estimate the accuracy with which the hydrogen-ion concentration can be calculated from pH measurements.

After Sörensen's pioneering work and comprehensive papers we find a rapid increase in pH measurements and technique; in Germany Michaelis' book "Die Wasserstoffionen Konzentration" appeared in 1914 and in this country W. M. Clark and H. A. Lubs published their important papers on "The Colorimetric Determination of Hydrogen-Ion Concentration and Its Applications in Bacteriology" in 1917. The first edition of Clark's well known treatise "The Determination of Hydrogen Ions" followed in 1920.

The importance of pH measurement and control is so well recognized at the present time that we do not need to dwell on it further; instead we shall pass to a brief comparison of the various methods of pH measurements (Chapter 2) after we have listed in the following section the conventions in regard to sign and current flow of electrochemical cells.

1·5. Cell and Sign Conventions

In the preceding section an electrochemical cell composed of the hydrogen and silver chloride electrodes with hydrochloric acid as the electrolyte was mentioned; the conventions used in writing down these cells in as concise a form as possible and the sign to be assigned to the e.m.f. and to each electrode will now be introduced so that they may easily be referred to during the reading of subsequent chapters. They are as follows:

1. A single vertical line represents a boundary between two solid or two immiscible liquid phases, between a solid and liquid phase, or between a liquid and a gaseous phase.

2. A double vertical line represents a boundary such as a liquid junction between two solutions having the same solvent but different concentrations or compositions; it does *not* signify that the liquid-junction potential has been eliminated.

3. The right-hand electrode is *always* the positive electrode as measured unless specifically stated to the contrary.

4. The total e.m.f. of the cell is *always* considered positive when the cell is written down with the right-hand electrode positive.

5. When the right-hand electrode is positive, and when the cell operates to generate an e.m.f., positive current flows through the cell from left to right (as one reads). Remembering this convention, it is easy to formulate the electrochemical reaction occurring in the cell when the current flows.

6. Standard electrode potentials will be given in reference to the standard hydrogen electrode potential taken as zero at each temperature. The sign given to the standard electrode potential is the measured sign of the electrode when measured in a cell with reference to the standard hydrogen electrode at the left so that the right-hand electrode can be either positive or negative.

As an example of these conventions, the hydrochloric-acid cell of Sec. 1·3 would be written

$$\text{Pt, H}_2 \mid \text{HCl } (m) \mid \text{AgCl} \mid \text{Ag} \qquad [1 \cdot 5 \cdot \text{A}]$$

the silver chloride electrode being positive and positive current passing through the cell from left to right. When we remember these conventions the confusing problems of signs become clarified.

Later in this book we shall frequently need to refer to the so-called asymmetry potential of the glass electrode which will now be defined.

By asymmetry potential we mean the potential which exists across the glass membrane when the glass is in contact with the same solution on both the inside and outside surface of the membrane. It is easily measured by measuring the e.m.f. of the cell,

$$\text{Ag} \mid \text{AgCl} \mid 0.1 \ N \text{ HCl} \mid \boxed{\text{glass}} \mid 0.1 \ N \text{ HCl} \mid \text{AgCl} \mid \text{Ag} \qquad [1 \cdot 5 \cdot \text{B}]$$

where the e.m.f.'s of the two silver chloride electrodes can be canceled out if they are equal, but any finite difference between the two should be subtracted, leaving the asymmetry potential as the net e.m.f. of the cell. We shall call the sign of the asymmetry potential positive if the outside surface of the glass is positive with respect to the inside; that is, if the e.m.f. of cell $1 \cdot 5 \cdot$ B is positive as written (with the inside of the glass electrode on the right). Some authors of glass electrode papers have failed to state the sign of the asymmetry potential in relation to the inside or outside of the electrode, compelling us to make the best decision we can regarding the sign of their measurements of asymmetry potential on the basis of our own experiences with the glass electrode. The sign convention we have adopted gives to the asymmetry potential the sign of the glass electrode as actually measured in cell 1·5·B.

The following is an example of asymmetry potential sign convention. Consider the cell

$$^{-}\text{Pt, H}_2 \ \left| \begin{array}{c} \text{Soln. of} \\ p\text{H } 6.90 \end{array} \right. \ \boxed{\text{glass} \mid 0.1 \ N \ \text{HCl} \mid \text{AgCl} \mid \overset{+}{\text{Ag}}} \quad [1\cdot5\cdot\text{C}]$$

which gives an e.m.f. of 0.3521 v. if no asymmetry potential exists.[13] To measure the asymmetry potential, a cell similar to 1·5·B was set up which gave an e.m.f. (asymmetry potential) of −0.0017 v. Hence the actually measured cell corresponding to 1·5·C was

$$^{-}\text{Pt, H}_2 \ \left| \begin{array}{c} \text{Soln. of} \\ p\text{H } 6.90 \end{array} \right. \ \boxed{\overset{-}{\text{glass}} \mid \overset{+}{0.1} \ N \ \text{HCl} \mid \text{AgCl} \mid \overset{+}{\text{Ag}}} \quad [1\cdot5\cdot\text{D}]$$

and the measured e.m.f. was 0.3504 v. The correction to the e.m.f. of cell 1·5·D is +0.0017 v. to bring its e.m.f. to the theoretically correct value given by cell 1·5·C.

To realize that the sign of the asymmetry potential is negative, consider the analogous cell

$$+ \ \text{Ag} \mid \text{AgCl} \mid .1 \ N \ \text{HCl} \mid\mid \text{Sat. KCl} \mid\mid 0.01 \ N \ \text{HCl} \mid \text{H}_2, \text{Pt} -$$

$$\text{Pt, H}_2 \mid 0.1 \ N \ \text{HCl} \mid \text{AgCl} \mid \overset{-}{\text{Ag}} \quad\quad\quad [1\cdot5\cdot\text{E}]$$

in which hydrogen electrodes take the place of the two glass surfaces. Positive electricity tends to flow from right to left so that the electrode on the right is negative (if the flow of current had been from left to right, the electrode on the right would have been positive, by the conventions we have adopted). Hence a negative asymmetry potential is equivalent to a lower hydrogen-ion concentration in the solution at the outside surface of the glass electrode.

[13] D. A. MacInnes and D. Belcher, *J. Am. Chem. Soc.* **53**, 3315 (1931).

CHAPTER 2

REVIEW OF METHODS OF pH MEASUREMENT INCLUDING THE EARLY HISTORY OF THE GLASS ELECTRODE

2·1. The Hydrogen Electrode

Practically of no great application but theoretically of the utmost importance is the hydrogen-electron method for determining the pH; this is because the hydrogen electrode gives the standard pH values to which all other methods must be referred and by which all standard solutions, new types of electrodes and new pH methods must be checked. The relation between e.m.f. and concentration in a cell with liquid junction we owe to Nernst.[1] Bjerrum[2] in 1905 invented the "salt bridge" to connect the hydrogen electrode with a reference electrode in such a way that the liquid-junction potential is nearly eliminated; he also developed a hydrogen-electrode vessel.

In 1909, Sörensen[3] further developed the hydrogen electrode, Clark[4] in 1915 invented his "rocking" hydrogen electrode cell and many other workers have made significant contributions to hydrogen electrode technique.

What do we mean by the "hydrogen electrode"? What does it look like? How is it constructed? How does it function and how are pH data calculated from the results? The word electrode usually conveys the picture of a metal electrode immersed in a solution containing ions of the metal, with "equilibrium" existing between the forces owing to the ions of the metal lattice, to the ions in the solution and the electrostatic forces at the interface. Hydrogen, however, is a gas, but it can be bubbled through a solution which is in contact with a noble inert metal like platinum. The latter adsorbs the hydrogen, particularly if it is covered with a catalytic surface of platinum black, and the adsorbed hydrogen then acts as the electrode; its atoms can give up electrons to the metal, leave the metal surface

---

[1] W. Nernst, *Z. physik. Chem.* **4**, 129 (1889).

[2] N. Bjerrum, *Z. physik. Chem.* **53**, 428 (1905).

[3] S. P. L. Sörensen, *Biochem. Z.* **21**, 131 (1909).

[4] W. M. Clark, *J. Biol. Chem.* **23**, 475 (1915).

and become attached to water molecules in the solvent, or the reverse process can take place.

The e.m.f. of the hydrogen electrode is proportional to the pressure of the hydrogen gas, becoming more negative with increase of hydrogen gas pressure; it changes with the temperature and with the concentration of hydrogen ions in the aqueous solution, becoming more positive with increase of hydrogen-ion concentration. When the pressure of the hydrogen gas is 760 mm. of Hg and when the concentration of the hydrogen ions is such that $m_{H^+}\gamma_{H^+}$ is equal to unity (about 1.2 N HCl, for example), the e.m.f. by definition is taken as zero at each temperature so that we can say that by this definition of the standard zero of potential, the hydrogen electrode has no temperature coefficient (for the standard state).

The hydrogen electrode is constructed by fusing a platinum wire to a square piece of platinum foil and sealing the wire into a soft glass tube in which mercury can later be poured, thus making electrical connection with the platinum. The fusing of the wire to the foil is done simply by heating both to white heat and then pounding them together with a hammer. The metal electrode is sealed in the glass tube in such a way that the soft glass flows over a bit of the platinum foil; by this procedure the mechanical support of the foil does not depend on the thin wire which is easily broken, but on the relatively strong upper edge of the foil itself. After cleaning by standing in a cleaning solution, a mixture of concentrated sulfuric acid and potassium dichromate, the electrode is washed and covered with platinum black electrolytically deposited. The method of depositing the colloidal platinum is not particularly important. Of great importance is the hydrogen gas used in the experiment. This must be as free of oxygen as possible because platinum adsorbs traces of oxygen tenaciously and the electrode assumes a too positive potential if oxygen is present. Purify commercial tank hydrogen by passing it over hot copper at 600° C., the hot copper being made by reducing copper oxide, wire form. The hydrogen gas system should be free of leaks, all connections should be sealed with mercury.

In Fig. 2·1 is illustrated the Clark rocking electrode cell for pH measurements using the hydrogen electrode; practically any type of vessel is suitable if air can be rigidly excluded and if the electrodes and solution can be conveniently inserted, but the Clark cell has the advantage of giving good results if the hydrogen gas is not entirely free of oxygen since after hydrogen gas has been swept through the cell the hydrogen is turned off and the cell is rocked by means of the eccentric I to allow the hydrogen remaining in the cell to clean up traces of the oxygen on the catalytic platinum surface. More recently DuNoüy [5] has described a cell whose half-immersed electrode rotates about an inclined axis.

The total cell whose e.m.f. is measured can be written down as follows:

Pt, H_2 | Unknown Solution || Saturated KCl | Hg_2Cl_2 | Hg [2·1·A]

In Fig. 2·1 M is the "saturated calomel" reference electrode (see Sec. 5·2), N a reservoir of saturated potassium chloride, and P several accurately made 0.1 N KCl calomel electrodes for standardizing the

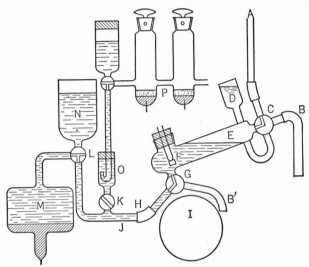

FIG. 2·1.   The Clark rocking hydrogen electrode cell.

somewhat variable electrode M. The broad liquid junction between the saturated potassium chloride salt bridge and the unknown solution is made at H.

The e.m.f. of the cell is given by the equation

$$E_{2·1·A} = E^{o,\prime} - 2.3 \frac{TR}{F} \log m_{H^+} \gamma_{H^+} + E_X \qquad [2·1·1]$$

Defining the "theoretical pH" by the equation

$$\text{"theoretical } p\text{H"} = -\log m_{H^+} \qquad [2·1·2]$$

we can write

$$E_{2·1·A} = E^{o,\prime} + E_X + 2.3 \frac{RT}{F} (p\text{H} - \log \gamma_{H^+})(\text{theoretical}) \quad [2·1·3]$$

[5] P. LeC. DuNoüy, *Compt. rend.* **193**, 1417 (1931); **195**, 1265 (1932).

where E_X is the unknown liquid-junction potential existing at the junction of the saturated potassium chloride and unknown solutions, and $E^{o,\prime}$ is the so-called standard electrode potential of the saturated calomel electrode. This latter potential is the potential of the saturated calomel electrode with respect to the standard hydrogen-electrode potential which we take as zero by definition.

The method of determining $E^{o,\prime}$ and of eliminating E_X or of determining $E^{o,\prime} + E_X$ will be considered in Chapter 17 where the subject will be investigated in detail because of its importance to pH measurements and to the standardization of the pH scale and the glass electrode. Here we shall write

$$E^{o,\prime} + E_X = E^o \qquad\qquad [2·1·4]$$

and

$$p\text{H} = \frac{E_{2·1·A} - E^o}{2.3RT/F} \qquad\qquad [2·1·5]$$

Values of E^o valid for different temperatures are given in Table 9·5. In Eq. 2·1·5 the pH is not the "theoretical pH" of Eq. 2·1·2 but pH as calculated by Eq. 2·1·5 from the measurements. We shall consider this the true pH and in talking of pH in this book we mean the pH as obtained from the e.m.f. of cells like 2·1·A by means of equations similar to 2·1·5. By studying Eq. 2·1·5 it can be seen that the pH is directly proportional to the e.m.f.; the greater the e.m.f. the greater the pH. Sörensen's symbol is thus seen to have added significance and usefulness.

The advantage of the hydrogen electrode over other pH measuring devices is that very accurate standard pH values are obtained. All other methods must be calibrated by the hydrogen electrode method; all solutions of standard pH, the buffer solutions, must have their pH confirmed by it. The hydrogen electrode is also superior to other electrodes in that it exhibits no error in ordinary alkaline solutions where the pH is high; the quinhydrone electrode cannot be used above a pH of 8 or 9 while the glass electrode often gives large errors in basic solutions. There are so many disadvantages to the hydrogen electrode, however, that it is never used as a routine instrument; it is never used if the pH can possibly be measured in some other way. Its disadvantages are as follows:

1. It cannot be used in the presence of air or of oxygen.

2. It cannot be used in the presence of oxidizing and reducing agents.

3. It cannot be used to measure the pH of solutions containing elements below hydrogen in the electromotive series of elements.

4. It cannot be used to measure the pH of solutions in the neighborhood of the neutral point unless the pH is strongly stabilized by the use of buffer solutions.

5. It gives difficulties when the solution whose pH is being measured contains some other gas than hydrogen, such as carbon dioxide, or ammonia.

6. The catalytic platinum black deteriorates and must be renewed daily.

9. It is slow in coming to equilibrium and one must usually wait an hour or two before all oxygen has been swept out of the system.

10. The measurement of the pH of minute quantities of material is extremely difficult with the hydrogen electrode.

11. Colloidal solutions are likely to give difficulties with the hydrogen electrode as may other substances such as unsaturated hydrocarbons which are adsorbed on the platinum surface.

The difficulty due to the unknown liquid-junction potential is common to all types of electrode systems and must be understood to exist even if it is not specifically listed in the discussion of individual electrode properties. Liquid-junction potentials are discussed in detail in Chapter 6.

2·2. The Quinhydrone Electrode

There are many organic oxidizing and reducing agents such as the quinones and the hydroquinones of various types whose oxidation-reduction potentials, when measured by an inert electrode made of platinum or gold, are functions of the hydrogen-ion concentration of the solution. Benzoquinone and benzohydroquinone (hereafter the prefix "benzo" will be omitted) are particularly suitable for pH measurements since these two substances crystallize together in equal molecular proportions to form a solid substance quinhydrone (for the structure of solid quinhydrone see J. S. Anderson.[6]) This, when later used to saturate a solution whose pH is to be determined, gives to the solution equal concentrations of quinone, $C_6H_4O_2$, which we shall designate by Q, and of its reduction product hydroquinone, $C_6H_4(OH)_2$, or QH_2.

Thus
$$Q \cdot QH_2 \rightleftarrows Q \cdot QH_2 \rightleftarrows Q + QH_2 \qquad [2\cdot2\cdot1]$$
$$\text{Solid} \qquad \text{Solution} \qquad \text{Solution}$$

Since QH_2 is a weak acid and enters into the dissociative equilibria
$$QH_2 \rightleftarrows QH^- + H^+ \qquad [2\cdot2\cdot2]$$
$$QH^- \rightleftarrows Q^= + H^+ \qquad [2\cdot2\cdot3]$$

[6] J. S. Anderson, *Nature*, **140**, 583 (1937).

it is obvious that the concentration of the reducing ion $Q^=$ will be a function of the hydrogen-ion concentration, as will the potential of the quinhydrone-platinum electrode. Therefore, by measuring the e.m.f. of the latter in the solution under investigation it is possible to determine the pH.

Haber and Russ [7] first measured the e.m.f. of a cell containing quinhydrone. In 1921 Granger and Nelson [8] also studied similar cells, but were interested only in the oxidation-reduction potentials of the system as a function of the concentration of quinone and hydroquinone. To Biilmann [9] (1921) goes the credit for discovering in the quinhydrone electrode a possible method for measuring the pH; he and his students have been largely responsible for the development of the quinhydrone electrode and for the elucidation of its properties, its advantages, and its errors. (See the review by Biilmann, [10] 1927.)

In using the quinhydrone electrode, an inert electrode made of bright platinum or of bright gold is immersed in the solution of unknown pH, a pinch of solid quinhydrone is added, and the mixture stirred until the solution becomes saturated with the quinhydrone. The e.m.f. can then be measured with reference to some standard electrode such as the saturated calomel electrode. The cell measured is

Pt, $Q \cdot QH_2$ | Unknown Solution || Saturated KCl | Hg_2Cl_2 | Hg [2•2·A]

and the pH is calculated from the equation

$$pH = \frac{E_{2 \cdot 2 \cdot A} - E^o_{2 \cdot 2 \cdot A}}{2.3RT/F} \qquad [2 \cdot 2 \cdot 4]$$

In Eq. 2·2·4 the $E_{2 \cdot 2 \cdot A}$ is given the sign of the calomel electrode which, in contrast to the calomel electrode in the hydrogen electrode cell, may take on either positive or negative values depending on the pH. The standard electrode potential of cell 2·2·A is equal to the standard electrode potential of the saturated calomel electrode less that of the quinhydrone electrode because in this cell the quinhydrone electrode is written on the left and its standard electrode potential is given the opposite sign to those listed in Appendix IV. There all the standard electrode potentials are based on the convention that the electrode is written at the right. Thus at 25° C.

$$E^o_{2 \cdot 2 \cdot A} = 0.2445 - 0.6997 = -0.4552$$

[7] F. Haber and R. Russ, Z. physik. Chem. **47**, 257 (1904)
[8] F. S. Granger and J. M. Nelson, J. Am. Chem. Soc. **43**, 1401 (1921).
[9] E. Biilmann, Ann. chim. [9] **15**, 109 (1921).
[10] E. Biilmann, Bull. soc. chim. [4] **41**, 213 (1927).

and the pH as measured by cell 2·2·A is calculated at 25° C. from the equation

$$pH = \frac{E_{2\cdot2\cdot A} + 0.4552}{0.05915} \qquad [2\cdot2\cdot5]$$

The theory on which Eq. 2·2·4 is based can be briefly outlined as follows: The electrode reaction of the quinhydrone electrode is essentially an oxidation-reduction reaction and can be written

$$Q + 2\epsilon^- \rightleftarrows Q^= \qquad [2\cdot2\cdot6]$$

where $Q^=$ is the completely ionized form of hydroquinone (cf. Eq. 2·2·2 and 2·2·3).

The equation for the e.m.f. of cell 2·2·A is

$$E_{2\cdot2\cdot A} = E^{0,'}_{2\cdot2\cdot A} - 2.3 \frac{RT}{2F} \log \frac{m_Q \cdot \gamma_Q}{m_{Q^=} \cdot \gamma_{Q^=}} \qquad [2\cdot2\cdot7]$$

provided we assume that the quinhydrone electrode reaction concerns only Q and the anion $Q^=$ and not the ion QH^- or the undissociated molecule QH_2.

From equilibrium 2·2·3 we have the thermodynamically correct L.M.A. (law of mass action) equation

$$m_{Q^=} \cdot \gamma_{Q^=} = K_2 \cdot \frac{m_{HQ^-} \cdot \gamma_{HQ^-}}{m_{H^+} \cdot \gamma_{H^+}} \qquad [2\cdot2\cdot8]$$

and from 2·2·2

$$m_{HQ^-} \cdot \gamma_{HQ^-} = K_1 \cdot \frac{m_{H_2Q} \cdot \gamma_{H_2Q}}{m_{H^+} \cdot \gamma_{H^+}} \qquad [2\cdot2\cdot9]$$

Eliminating $m_{HQ^-} \cdot \gamma_{HQ^-}$ from these last two equations

$$m_{Q^=} \cdot \gamma_{Q^=} = K_1 \cdot K_2 \cdot \frac{m_{H_2Q} \cdot \gamma_{H_2Q}}{(m_{H^+} \cdot \gamma_{H^+})^2} \qquad [2\cdot2\cdot10]$$

which on introduction into Eq. 2·2·7 yields the equation

$$E_{2\cdot2\cdot A} = E^{0,'}_{2\cdot2\cdot A} - 2.3 \frac{RT}{2F} \log \frac{m_Q \cdot \gamma_Q}{m_{H_2Q} \cdot \gamma_{H_2Q}}$$

$$+ 2.3 \frac{RT}{2F} \log K_1 K_2 - 2.3 \frac{RT}{F} \log m_{H^+} \cdot \gamma_{H^+}. \qquad [2\cdot2\cdot11]$$

In acid solutions the ionization of the hydroquinone will be almost completely repressed (because K_1 and K_2 are very small) so that the concentration of the quinone and undissociated hydroquinone may be set equal to each other. Under these conditions the second term of the right-hand side of Eq. 2·2·11 drops out because it is reasonable to assume that the activity coefficients of quinone and hydroquinone are also equal. Equation 2·2·11 reduces, therefore, to

$$E_{2 \cdot 2 \cdot A} = E^o_{2 \cdot 2 \cdot A} - 2.3 \frac{RT}{F} \log m_{H^+} \cdot \gamma_{H^+} \qquad [2 \cdot 2 \cdot 12]$$

from which Eq. 2·2·4 is readily obtained.

The advantages of the quinhydrone electrode are as follows:

1. It is simpler to use than the hydrogen electrode, requires no carefully purified hydrogen gas, and can be used in the presence of air.

2. It can be used for "micromeasurements" of pH.[11, 12]

3. It comes to equilibrium more rapidly than does the hydrogen-electrode system.

The disadvantages of the quinhydrone electrode are as follows:

1. The quinhydrone electrode is only accurately applicable to solutions having a pH lower than 8.5 because the ionization of QH_2 cannot be neglected in more basic solutions and the concentration of Q can no longer be set equal to QH_2.

2. In basic solutions the quinhydrone decomposes or is oxidized by the oxygen of the air. This is indicated by the progressive darkening of the color of the solution with time and rising pH.

3. The quinhydrone electrode is subject to a "salt error" which arises from the effect of salts in changing the activity coefficients of the quinone and hydroquinone by different amounts; i.e., in some highly concentrated salt solutions γ_Q is not equal to γ_{H_2Q}. As an example of this error, Amis and Gabbard [13] found the error of the quinhydrone electrode to be one millivolt in 2 c $MgSO_4$ solution buffered, and about eight millivolts in 1.87 c $MgSO_4$, unbuffered at pH 5.88. The quinhydrone electrode error in the unbuffered solution was less in solutions of lower pH.

4. The quinhydrone electrode cannot be used in solutions containing oxidizing and reducing agents although in some solutions, such as those containing dilute nitric acid or unsaturated hydrocarbons, correct results are obtained, presumably because the pH measurements can be made before the nitric acid or unsaturated hydrocarbons have time to act on the hydroquinone or quinone and so upset the equality

[11] F. Fuhrmann, *Mikrochemie*, Festschr. von Hans Molisch, 1936, p. 130.

[12] J. A. Pierce, *J. Biol. Chem.* **117**, 651 (1937).

[13] E. S. Amis and J. L. Gabbard, *J. Am. Chem. Soc.* **59**, 557 (1937).

in their concentration. The quinhydrone electrode gives erroneous pH measurements of soils if the soils contain manganese dioxide.[14]

5. The quinhydrone electrode is subject to "protein errors" although in certain protein solutions correct values are obtained. The author measured, with the glass electrode, the pH of a thick, turbid casein solution prepared by the late Dr. Erich von Gebauer-Fuelnegg, and much to his surprise, obtained a result identical with that previously obtained by Dr. von Gebauer-Fuelnegg using the quinhydrone electrode. Some proteins may combine with the quinone or hydroquinone.

6. The preparation and drying of pure quinhydrone presents some difficulty. Clark [15] recommends repeated recrystallization from acid solution with decreasing concentrations of acid as the product becomes purer, and with a final washing with pure water in the absence of air. The quinhydrone must be carefully dried to prevent the sublimation of quinone.

7. At high temperatures the quinhydrone becomes more unstable and more susceptible to attack. At 37° C. in 0.6 N HCl the potential of the quinhydrone electrode falls at the rate of 0.3 mv. per hour, but in 0.1 N HCl the potential is more stable.

8. The addition of the quinhydrone to an unbuffered solution may change the pH of the solution, and produce, therefore, an erroneous reading.[16] (For an extensive comparison of the quinhydrone and glass electrodes in fruit juices see Sec. 12·1.)

There are other electrodes for pH determination, such as the antimony-antimony oxide electrode, but these electrodes are relatively unimportant and so we shall not discuss them here, but shall pass to a consideration of the colorimetric method of pH measurement.

2·3. Indicators

Since the early years of the twentieth century when Friedenthal and Salm [17] developed the first quantitative colorimetric method for the estimation of hydrogen-ion concentration, the use of indicators for quickly and easily determining pH has become almost universal. Indicators are those organic weak acids or bases which have a definite color in the acid or basic state of ionization or molecular form and

[14] J. A. Naftel, *Soil Research*, **4**, 41 (1934).

[15] W. M. Clark, "The Determination of Hydrogen Ions," Third Edition. Williams and Wilkins Co., Baltimore, 1928.

[16] M. R. Thompson, *J. Research Natl. Bur. Standards*, **9**, 833 (1932).

[17] Friedenthal, *Z. Elektrochem.* **10**, 113 (1904); E. Salm, *ibid.*, **10**, 341 (1904); **12**, 99 (1906); E. Salm and H. Friedenthal, *ibid.*, **13**, 125 (1907).

another color in the opposite state. For example, let us consider the indicator phenol red (phenolsulfonephthalein),

$$C\begin{cases} C_6H_4OH \\ C_6H_4{=}O \end{cases}$$

$$-SO_2OH$$

Yellow

which has in acid form the structure [18]

$$C\begin{cases} C_6H_4OH \\ C_6H_4{=}O \end{cases}$$

$$-SO_2O^- \qquad + H^+$$

Yellow

since the sulfonic hydrogen is completely ionized; and in solution made basic with sodium hydroxide, for example, the structure

$$C\begin{cases} C_6H_4O^- \\ C_6H_4{=}O \end{cases} \qquad + 2Na^+$$

$$-SO_2O^-$$

red

The color change reaction can then be written

$$HIn^- \rightleftarrows In^= + H^+ \qquad\qquad [2\cdot3\cdot1]$$
$$\text{Yellow}\quad\text{Red}$$

where $In^=$ represents the organic ion given above.

In acid solutions the above equilibrium is shifted to the left with the result that the red ion disappears leaving only the yellow form in solution, whereas in basic solutions the reverse shift occurs with the appearance of the red ion $In^=$ and the disappearance of the yellow undissociated ion, HIn^-.

Applying the mass action law in its ideal form, i.e., activity coeffi-

---

[18] I. M. Kolthoff, "Acid-Base Indicators" translated by Charles Rosenblum, Macmillan, New York, 1937.

cient omitted, to 2·3·1 we obtain, letting brackets represent concentrations

$$K_{In} = \frac{[H^+]\,[In^=]_{red}}{[HIn^-]_{yellow}}$$ [2·3·2]

When the indicator is half neutralized or half turned in color, $[In^=]_{red}$ equals $[HIn^-]_{yellow}$, and

$$K_{In} = [H^+]$$

or

$$pK_{In} = pH$$

Thus for each indicator there will be a definite pH at which the color of the indicator is exactly that produced by a 50–50 mixture of the acid and basic forms, and for a short range of pH, about one pH unit, on either side of this particular pH the indicator is capable of changing its color with change of pH. Each indicator can serve, therefore, to indicate the pH by comparison of the color produced by a definite concentration of indicator in the unknown solution with the color produced by the same concentration of indicator in a standard solution of known pH. (The neglect of activity coefficients produces the salt effect error which may amount to 0.3 pH unit or more, but which may be corrected for.)

In Sörensen's [19] and Clark and Lubs' [20] great works on the determination of pH by the indicator method, indicators for various pH ranges were developed and tested and standard buffer solutions of known pH prepared. Sörensen's conclusions in regard to the colorimetric method may be listed as follows:

1. All indicators are not equally sharp (because of differences in the magnitude of their extinction coefficients as a function of wave length) nor are they all equally applicable under all conditions.

2. Indicators must be chosen critically and with consideration of the system under investigation.

3. Indicators of the methyl violet group are especially sensitive to neutral salts. Furthermore, their intensity of color will change on standing, because of chemical reactions, and the more rapid the change the more acid is the solution under investigation.

4. Some basic indicators such as benzol-azo-diphenylamine partially precipitate from solution on long standing, but it is possible to increase the solubility by the addition of alcohol.

[19] S. P. L. Sörensen, *Biochem. Z.* **21**, 131 (1909).
[20] W. M. Clark and H. A. Lubs, *J. Bact.* **2**, 1, 109, 191 (1917).

5. Most indicators are useless in the presence of significant amounts of pure proteins; however, certain indicators may be used to advantage, such as methyl violet, phenolphthalein, etc.

6. Most indicators are applicable to solutions containing decomposition products of proteins, but certain of the azo-indicators produce considerable errors.

Finally, Sörensen states that in applying the colorimetric method to any doubtful case, that is, to solutions whose effect on the chosen indicator is unknown, it is absolutely necessary to compare the pH determined in this way with the results given by the electrometric method.

Clark and Lubs [20] were particularly interested in the influence of hydrogen-ion concentration on bacterial growth. They developed a new series of excellent indicators applicable to bacterial systems, but they conclude that the chief advantage of the colorimetric method for the determination of pH of these media lies in the rapidity with which unknown fields may be explored, in the ease with which a large number of significant but not highly accurate results may be obtained. They recognized that protein and salt errors can invalidate the results. Furthermore, they found that optical effects may interfere, and that the method in general is not capable of very great precision. Although visually the colorimetric method is not applicable to highly colored solutions or to turbid suspensions, the modern use of spectrophotometers makes possible not only the determination of pH of many colored solutions, but also increases the accuracy of the colorimetric method to 0.001 pH unit in certain favorable cases.

2·4. The Development of the Glass Electrode

In 1906 Cremer [21] measured the e.m.f. of the following two cells

$$\text{Zn}\left|\begin{array}{c}\text{ZnSO}_4\\\text{Soln.}\end{array}\right|\left|\begin{array}{c}0.6\%\text{ NaCl}\\+0.01\text{ }N\text{ H}_2\text{SO}_4\end{array}\right|\text{Glass}\left|\begin{array}{c}0.6\%\\\text{NaCl}\end{array}\right|\left|\begin{array}{c}\text{ZnSO}_4\\\text{Soln.}\end{array}\right|\text{Zn} \qquad [2\cdot4\cdot A]$$

$$\text{Zn}\left|\begin{array}{c}\text{ZnSO}_4\\\text{Soln.}\end{array}\right|\left|\begin{array}{c}0.6\%\text{ NaCl}\\+\text{ dil. H}_2\text{SO}_4\end{array}\right|\text{Glass}\left|\begin{array}{c}0.6\%\text{ NaCl}\\+\text{ dil. NaOH}\end{array}\right|\left|\begin{array}{c}\text{ZnSO}_4\\\text{Soln.}\end{array}\right|\text{Zn} \quad [2\cdot4\cdot B]$$

using the bulb type of glass electrode, and found for the first cell the large e.m.f. of 190 mv. and for the second the even larger e.m.f. of 550 mv.! He was much astonished at these results, but it remained for Haber and Klemensiewicz [22] three years later to make a careful study of

[21] M. Cremer, *Z. Biol.* **47**, 562 (1906).
[22] F. Haber and Z. Klemensiewicz, *Z. physik. Chem.* **67**, 385 (1909).

the electric potentials developed on glass surfaces, to show under what conditions glasses could function as hydrogen-ion electrodes and to prove that the glass electrode potentials varied with the pH in the correct hydrogen electrode manner. The glass electrode of Haber and Klemensiewicz is illustrated in Fig. 2·2, where the glass bulb, through whose walls the current flows during a measurement, is the glass electrode. The beaker was hung on silk threads for electrical insulation, the glass stirrer handle was of hard rubber surrounded by a layer of tin foil. The e.m.f. of the glass electrode-calomel reference electrode cell was measured over a range of pH values of the solution under

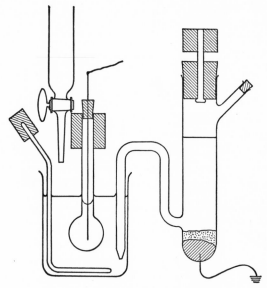

FIG. 2·2   Haber's glass electrode cell.

investigation by noting the deflections of a quadrant electrometer. Their solutions were made from 10 cc. of 1 N acid or base diluted with 90 cc. of water, and the pH was varied by dropping into the solution 1 N base or acid 1 cc. at a time. A typical titration curve, measured e.m.f. plotted versus cc. of titrant added, is illustrated in Fig. 2·3 and because of the similarity in shape of this curve with that obtained with the hydrogen electrode, Haber concluded that the glass electrode was a perfect hydrogen electrode. When we use the expression "the glass electrode acts as a perfect hydrogen electrode," we mean that the e.m.f. developed on the surface of the glass changes with change of pH in exactly the same way as the hydrogen electrode e.m.f. changes. He did not compare the two types of electrode directly in the same solution and because he used chiefly potassium hydroxide as the base he failed to discover the sodium error of the glass electrode. The slight downward drop in his titration curve, which

he observed in the alkaline range using sodium hydroxide as the base (see Fig. 2·4) he attributed to experimental error.

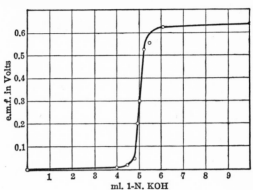

Borelius,[23] apparently ignorant of the work of Haber and Klemensiewicz, also discovered in 1914 the hydrogen electrode function of glass surfaces.

FIG. 2·3. Titration curve obtained with glass electrode. Data of Haber and Klemensiewicz (1909).

In their comparison of the thermodynamic and ζ potentials in 1920, Freundlich and Rona [24] confirmed the work of Haber and Klemensiewicz and discovered that the addition of the capillary-active substance crystal violet to a buffer solution did not change the glass electrode potential.

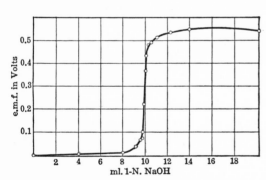

FIG. 2·4. Titration curve obtained with glass electrode. Data of Haber and Klemensiewicz (1909).

In 1922 we find an important paper published by Hughes [25] who directly compared the glass with the hydrogen electrodes using a quadrant electrometer as a null-point indicating instrument. He concluded that "the glass surface potential is not a linear function of the logarithm of the hydrogen-ion concentration except when the hydrogen-ion concentration is greater than 10^{-11}. Even then this linear relationship is only approximate." He discovered the extremely important fact that the glass-electrode potentials were independent of

[23] G. Borelius, *Ann. Physik* [4] **45**, 929 (1914).
[24] H. Freundlich and Rona, *Sitz.ber. preuss. Akad. Wiss.* **20**, 397 (1920).
[25] W. S. Hughes, *J. Am. Chem. Soc.* **44**, 2860 (1922).

oxidation-reduction potentials in the system, and that capillary-active ions like Th^{++++}, had no effect on glass electrode potentials. He proved in a direct way the electrical conductance of glass by showing that the charge on the electrometer needle leaked off immediately when grounded through a glass electrode, and he found that a one per cent gelatin solution caused the glass and hydrogen electrodes to differ by several hundredths of a volt. The first statement quoted above from his paper indicates that he was the first person to realize the sodium error of the glass electrode.

In 1923 Horovitz [26] demonstrated that the glass surface could exhibit electrode functions of other ions in addition to that of the hydrogen ion; he found that certain glasses could act as sodium, potassium, silver, and zinc electrodes. But it should be pointed out that he did not compare his glass electrodes with sodium, potassium, or zinc electrodes, with the result that we do not know with what accuracy the glass surfaces reproduced the e.m.f. properties of the metal electrodes. Horovitz's idea was that the glass surface could take up hydrogen, sodium, potassium, silver, or zinc ions, depending on the solution they were immersed in, because of an "exchange adsorption" giving a "mixed" electrode with variable "solution pressure."

Schiller,[27] a student of Horovitz, obtained in 1924 substantially the same results as Horovitz; he proved the sodium electrode function of certain glasses, but found the zinc- and potassium-ion functions only partly developed. All his glasses behaved as hydrogen electrodes in acid solutions; but in regions of low hydrogen-ion concentration other ions began to affect the glass electrode potentials.

In 1924 we find published for the first time two papers specifically devoted to the determination of the hydrogen-ion concentration by means of the glass electrode, the papers of Brown [28] and von Steiger.[29] Working in A. V. Hill's Laboratory of Physiology, University College, London, Brown proved the absence of salt and protein errors of the glass electrode up to a pH of 10. von Steiger advocated the use of the glass electrode in solutions containing alkaloids because of the disturbing effect of the latter on the hydrogen electrode and indicators. He showed the glass electrode e.m.f. to be independent of the thickness of the glass, but if the glass electrode was allowed to stand in concentrated sodium chloride solution, its potential became irregular

[26] K. Horovitz, Z. Physik **15**, 369 (1923).
[27] H. Schiller, Ann. Physik [4] **74**, 105 (1924).
[28] W. E. L. Brown, J. Sci. Instruments, **2**, 12 (1924).
[29] A. L. von Steiger, Z. Elektrochem. **30**, 259 (1924).

and required two days of soaking in pure water to regain its original value. During 1925 and 1926 Mrs. Kerridge [30] continued the London development of the glass electrode with the invention of a cup type of glass electrode by means of which the pH of small quantities of solution could be measured. This electrode is illustrated in Fig. 2·5.

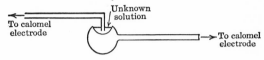

FIG. 2·5. The Kerridge glass electrode.

Beginning with the year 1928 several major developments of glass-electrode technique took place in the United States. Morton,[31] Elder,[32] and Partridge [33] devised vacuum-tube potentiometers to take the place of quadrant electrometers as null-point indicating instruments, as did also Stadie,[34] Hill,[35] Fosbinder,[36] Van Dyke and Bennett,[37] DeEds,[38] etc. This was extremely important work as commercial glass electrode apparatuses modeled particularly after the instruments of Goodhue [39] and of Ellis and Kiehl [40] employing vacuum tubes were soon designed and manufactured, making possible the rapid expansion of the use of the glass electrode throughout the United States. While this development was taking place, MacInnes [41] and the author made a systematic study of the effect of composition of the glass on the properties of the glass electrode, and discovered the best glass for pH measurement; in this research they were able to obtain consistent results by working with a thin membrane type of glass electrode.[42] More recently the alkaline or high pH errors of the glass electrode were measured in a variety of solutions and a mathematical theory developed for their explanation.[43, 44]

[30] P. M. T. Kerridge, *Biochem. J.* **19**, 611 (1925); *J. Sci. Instruments* **3**, 404 (1926).

[31] C. Morton, *Trans. Faraday Soc.* **24**, 14 (1928); *J. Chem. Soc.*, 1931, 2983. Actually Morton first used his vacuum-tube potentiometer in connection with hydrogen electrode measurements.

[32] L. W. Elder, Jr., and W. H. Wright, *Proc. Natl. Acad. Sci.* **14**, 936 (1928); L. W. Elder, Jr., *J. Am. Chem. Soc.* **51**, 3266 (1929).

[33] H. M. Partridge, *J. Am. Chem. Soc.* **51**, 1 (1929).

[34] W. C. Stadie, *J. Biol. Chem.* **83**, 477 (1929).

[35] S. E. Hill, *J. Gen. Physiol.* **12**, 813 (1929).

[36] R. J. Fosbinder, *J. Phys. Chem.* **34**, 1294 (1930).

[37] Van Dyke and Bennett, *J. Lab. Clin. Med.* **17**, 1268 (1932).

[38] F. DeEds, *Science*, **78**, 556 (1933).

[39] L. D. Goodhue, *Iowa State Coll. J. Sci.* **10**, 7 (1935).

[40] S. B. Ellis and S. J. Kiehl, *Rev. Sci. Instruments*, **4**, 131 (1933).

[41] D. A. MacInnes and M. Dole, *J. Am. Chem. Soc.* **52**, 29 (1930).

[42] D. A. MacInnes and M. Dole, *Ind. Eng. Chem., Anal. Ed.* **1**, 57 (1929).

[43] M. Dole, *J. Am. Chem. Soc.* **53**, 4260 (1931).

[44] M. Dole, *J. Chem. Phys.* **2**, 862 (1934).

In 1931 Buchböck [45] and MacInnes and Belcher [46] discovered that the glass electrode gave erroneous results in very acid solutions, and in 1932 it was proved that the same type of error existed in very concentrated salt solutions and in alcoholic solutions even at intermediate *p*H values. [47] A theoretical (quantitative) explanation of these errors has also been given. A detailed account of other recent and important papers on the glass electrode will be found elsewhere in this volume, in addition to further discussions of the papers already mentioned.

In concluding this introductory chapter we shall list the advantages and disadvantages of the glass electrode for comparison with the comments on the hydrogen and quinhydrone electrode and colorimetric methods given above. The advantages of the glass electrode are:

1. Over the aqueous *p*H range 0–10 the glass electrode functions accurately as a hydrogen electrode. In some rare instances it may be used in solutions having *p*H values as high as 13.

2. It usually comes to equilibrium immediately, allowing *p*H measurements to be made with great rapidity.

3. It can be used in the presence of air, or of any other gas.

4. It requires no hydrogen or any other agent which must be added to the solution. The glass electrode can be inserted and the *p*H measured without changing the *p*H of the solution and without changing the solubility of gases such as carbon dioxide, sulfur dioxide, etc.

5. The glass electrode gives potentials which are not affected by oxidation-reduction potentials existing in the solution.

6. It has no salt or protein error.

7. It can be used in turbid, colored solutions, in solutions of colloids, in oil emulsions containing water, and in other types of heterogeneous systems.

8. It is not affected by the ions of elements below hydrogen in the electromotive series.

9. It can be used to measure the *p*H of unbuffered salt solutions, of tap water and if the proper technique is used, even of distilled water.

10. Micro-*p*H measurements can be easily made.

11. The glass electrode does not deteriorate appreciably with age, does not have to be renewed, unless broken, and on the whole its use is most convenient and easy.

[45] G. Buchböck, *Z. physik. Chem.* **156A**, 232 (1931).
[46] D. A. MacInnes and D. Belcher, *J. Am. Chem. Soc.* **53**, 3315 (1931).
[47] M. Dole, *J. Am. Chem. Soc.* **54**, 2120, 3095 (1932).

Unfortunately the glass electrode is not perfect, it does have some limitations and its use is hampered by some difficulties, although most of the difficulties and limitations can be overcome.

1. It is fragile and easily broken, but certain rugged types of glass electrodes have been designed.

2. The glass wall has a high electrical resistance, from 1 to 100 megohms (meg = million) total resistance, usually, so that the e.m.f. of a glass electrode cell cannot be measured by the ordinary potentiometer-galvanometer circuits. Here again, however, glass electrodes have been designed with such low electrical resistance that no e.m.f. measuring difficulties with ordinary galvanometers are encountered. Furthermore, commercial apparatus for the measurement of the e.m.f. of high-resistant glass electrodes is now available.

3. A special type of low-melting, soda-lime glass must be used. This glass slowly gives off alkali on standing which may change the pH of unbuffered solutions if the solution remains in contact with the glass for an appreciable length of time. This difficulty has been overcome and the pH of unbuffered solutions and of pure water has been accurately measured.

4. Extraneous potentials, called asymmetry potentials, exist across the walls of some glass electrodes. This potential changes slowly with time, but can be corrected for.

5. The glass electrodes give irregular results if allowed to dry out or to stand in nonaqueous solutions; for this reason they are usually kept in distilled water.

The above difficulties of the glass electrode can all be overcome; the limitations listed below are more serious since they seem to be inherent in the glass itself.

1. Above a pH of 8, 9, 10 or 11, depending upon their concentration, sodium, lithium, potassium, calcium, and barium ions affect the potential of the glass electrode, causing the measured pH to be too low, although this difficulty can be nearly eliminated by using a new type of glass. Ammonium ions give little error. This is also true for large size positive ions such as the tetramethyl-ammonium ion.

2. The glass electrode gives too high a pH in very acid solutions, and is also in error when used in concentrated salt solutions and in nonaqueous solutions in which the vapor pressure of water is low.

In the chapters that follow, detailed discussion of all phases of glass electrode technique, applications, and theory are given.

CHAPTER 3

E.M.F. MEASURING CIRCUITS

3·1. Galvanometers, Potentiometers, and Standard Cells

Probably the most inconvenient property of the glass electrode is the high electrical resistance across its glass membrane, a property that forces us to use special electrical equipment in measuring the e.m.f. of glass electrode cells. In this chapter we describe in some detail vacuum-tube amplifiers, electrometers, and other auxiliary equipment used in glass electrode researches before beginning the detailed discussion of the glass electrode itself.

It is unnecessary here to explain the principles involved in the operation of moving-coil galvanometers, ammeters, or voltmeters, as these instruments are usually used as null or impulse meters. Instead we shall list the precautions to be followed in their use.

1. Avoid subjecting the instruments to mechanical shock as the jewel bearings may be cracked or broken, the fine wire suspensions broken, the magnetism of the permanent magnets partially annulled, and delicate contacts and connecting wires broken.

2. Keep instruments clean and free from dust by covering when not in use. Dust may lodge in the air gap in the moving-coil instruments possibly producing magnetic disturbances; dust accumulating on the outside walls of the instrument cases may also affect the readings magnetically. Dust and dirt on the contact points of switches are, of course, inadmissible.

3. Stray magnetic and electric fields should be avoided, very strong stray magnetic fields may produce permanent alterations in the instruments. Direct-current stray magnetic fields cause a percentage change throughout the scale in the readings of moving-coil ammeters and voltmeters; alternating fields would have no effect. By rereading the instrument after turning it through an angle of 180°, the presence of stray fields may be detected. Stray fields due to heavy currents in the leads may be avoided by twisting the leads together and keeping the twisted strand straight.

4. Temperature inequalities in an electric circuit may produce thermoelectric e.m.f.'s. This difficulty is only serious in very accurate work. Shifts in the room temperature have practically no effect on the readings of voltmeters and ammeters.

5. Galvanometers should be carefully leveled by means of a spirit level until the moving coil swings freely without touching either the pole pieces or the soft iron core.   They should be supported from a vibration-free wall or pier, or on a Julius suspension,[1] or similar vibration-eliminating support.   Galvanometers should also be protected from drafts by enclosure in a box containing a window.   Figure 3·1 illustrates a possible galvanometer arrangement [2] which is simple, maintains a constant level, and effectively eliminates vibration.   Furthermore, the solid framework which serves as the support of the suspended cage may also be used as the foundation for an electrical shield or for an enclosing box made of Celotex or other material to protect the galvanometer from air currents in the room.   Johnson and Nottingham state

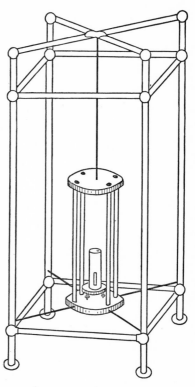

FIG. 3·1.   Galvanometer support of Johnson and Nottingham.

" We have a rigid instrument support or cage made of two iron disks joined by four half-inch steel rods 20 inches long hung at the center of the upper disk by a piece of 37 mil steel piano wire about two feet long. Small rubber bands [3] stretched horizontally from the corners of the frame to the bottom of the cage damp out rotation.   The instrument is placed on the floor of the cage, and electrical connections are made with very flexible coils of small copper wire. . . The rubber bands should not be so tense as to transmit vibrations from the frame to the bottom of the cage.   It is not necessary to place the instrument precisely in the center, nor is the height of the instrument with respect to the bottom of the cage particularly important. . . Damping by means of radial vanes hung from the

[1] W. H. Julius, *Wied. Annalen* **56**, 151 (1895).

[2] R. P. Johnson and W. B. Nottingham, *Rev. Sci. Instruments* **5**, 191 (1934). Professor F. T. Gucker and co-workers have successfully used a similar galvanometer suspension in the Northwestern Laboratories.   They built their Celotex box about, not on, the framework illustrated.

[3] Loosely coiled weak brass springs are better than rubber bands as the latter harden in time.

bottom of the cage and immersed in a vessel of oil decreases the time taken for the system to come to rest after it has been violently disturbed, but does not contribute to eliminating subsequent random vibrations. . . Satisfactory results are obtained when the cage is hung from a cross-bar between two ordinary laboratory supports."

Julius suspensions which involve a cage supported by three wires and which require careful centering of the point of support of the moving coil of the galvanometer at the center of gravity of the suspended cage may be purchased at several apparatus supply houses. They are hung from the ceiling and make possible a stable index line on the galvanometer scale even when vibrating machinery is attached to the same ceiling structure.

The e.m.f. of glass electrode cells is usually measured by means of potential-balancing methods involving the use of Poggendorf potentiometers. The principle of the method can be explained very simply by saying that the unknown e.m.f. is placed in opposition to a known e.m.f. or potential difference, and the magnitude of the latter varied by means of the potentiometer until some indicating device demonstrates equality between the e.m.f. and p.d. at which moment the desired voltage can be read off the potentiometer. Poggendorf's scheme

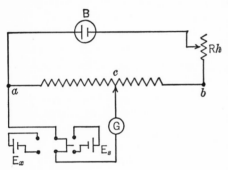

FIG. 3·2.   Schematic diagram of simple potentiometer-galvanometer circuit.

for accomplishing this result is schematically illustrated in Fig. 3·2 where acb represents a slide wire of uniform resistance (this slide wire is usually used for the fine adjustment after rough equality has been attained through the use of resistance coils), B a working battery to provide a steady flow of current through acb, and therefore a constant potential drop (p.d.) along acb, G the current indicating device, E_s a standard cell and E_x the unknown cell. To obtain the known p.d. which is to be balanced against the unknown e.m.f. E_x, a switch (not shown) connects the battery B to the slide wire acb; E_s is then connected to the slide wire through the variable contact c so that the p.d. between ac as read off the instrument dial is equal to the e.m.f. E_s, the variable resistance R_h is next altered until no current is detected by G; then the p.d. ac is exactly equal to the known e.m.f. E_s and the current through the slide wire has become adjusted to its correct value.   The double-pole, double-throw switch is then thrown over so that E_x is connected to acb through G and the point of contact c again moved until no current is detected flowing through G.   At this moment the p.d. ac read off the instrument is exactly equal to the e.m.f. E_x, if the working current which flows continuously through the slide wire acb has not dropped since its original adjustment; however, this possibility can be readily tested by repeating the calibration with the standard cell E_s.   If the measurements are made quickly, usually no alteration in the setting of R_h is necessary, but if some time has elapsed or if the e.m.f. to be measured is nearly as large or larger in magnitude than the e.m.f. E_s, then the adjustment of the working current must be repeated.   In most commercial high-grade potentiometers the standard-cell-slide-wire comparison can be performed without changing the setting of the e.m.f. dial, since a separate switch or tapping key is provided.   It is advisable to turn on the battery B, a half hour or an hour before making measurements.

The chief precaution in using a potentiometer is to keep the slide wire and contacts free of dust and dirt by avoiding the accumulation of dust and by periodically wiping off the slide wire and contacts with a clean cloth impregnated with petroleum jelly.   Much valuable time can be wasted by failure to observe most scrupulously this simple precaution; commercial potentiometers with exposed contacts and slide wires are particularly bad in this respect as they require more frequent cleaning.

High-grade commercial potentiometers reading to 0.01 mv. do not have to be calibrated since fluctuations and irregularities in glass-electrode cells are greater than the uncertainties in the potentiometer readings; when bad contacts or other effects cause potentiometers to give erroneous results, they can be readily detected.   However, commercial glass-electrode pH electrometers with built-in potentiometer circuits are not constructed to be as accurate as their more elegant prototypes, and should be calibrated occasionally at two or more pH or e.m.f. points on the dial; this is especially necessary to discover changes in voltage of the standard cell as the commercial electrometers will not give the correct pH change if their standard cell is in error as described below.

Blair [4] has calibrated a commercial pH electrometer by comparing

---

[4] Private communication from Dr. J. S. Blair, American Can Company, Maywood, Illinois. O. E. Lanford and S. J. Kiehl, *J. Phys. Chem.* **45**, 300 (1941) recently measured the glass electrode pH of potassium ferrocyanide solutions using a Type K potentiometer and a commercial pH electrometer finding little difference between the two sets of data.

its pH readings with standard voltages given by a Type K potentiometer with the finding that the dial of the commercial electrometer
may be as much as 0.04 pH unit in error. Blair's data are given in
Table 3·1; by "True" pH, Blair means "the reading which would
have been obtained had the resistance of the 'pH' coil been strictly
uniform, and properly calibrated, from the point at pH 0.39."

TABLE 3·1

CALIBRATION OF A COMMERCIAL pH ELECTROMETER

DATA OF BLAIR

Volts Type K	Electrometer pH Reading	ΔpH	Slope	True pH Reading	Error
0.3000	0.39	. . . . . .	. . . . . .	. . . . . .	. . . . . .
0.4000	2.10	1.71	0.0585	2.08	+0.02
0.5000	3.79	1.69	0.0592	3.77	+0.02
0.6000	5.49	1.70	0.0588	5.47	+0.02
0.7000	7.19	1.70	0.0588	7.16	+0.03
0.8000	8.86	1.67	0.0599	8.85	+0.01
0.9000	10.53	1.67	0.0599	10.54	−0.01
1.0000	12.27	1.74	0.0575	12.23	+0.04
1.1000	13.93	1.66	0.0602	13.93	0
		Average slope = 0.0591			

From the data of Table 3·1 it is evident first that one can not be sure
of the correct pH to ±0.03 pH unit and second, that the dial error will
depend upon the pH of standardization when using a commercial
electrometer (unless, of course, a calibration of the instrument is
carried out as above and a correction table prepared).

Since e.m.f. cells containing glass electrodes are chiefly characterized by their high resistances, we should consider the influence, if any,
of their high internal resistance on the measured e.m.f. If E_x is the
true e.m.f. of the cell, R_x its resistance, and I_x the current flowing
through the cell, then the e.m.f., E_p, as measured on the potentiometer
will be given by the equation

$$E_x - I_x R_x = E_p \qquad [3·1·1[$$

but in the Poggendorf potentiometer method, I_x is zero (provided G,
the current-indicating device, is functioning properly) and the correct
e.m.f. is observed. There are certain types of current-amplifying
devices, however, which do not indicate null current, and they give
incorrect glass electrode e.m.f. readings, as will be discussed later.

Each potentiometer circuit should be isolated from all other electrical measuring equipment; thus it is *not* permissible to connect two potentiometers to a single working battery, nor is it advisable to place the potentiometer close to a high-voltage source. The relative humidity of the surrounding air should be kept as low as possible.

The standard cell commonly used in America is the Weston secondary standard cell,

$$\text{Hg, Cd (12.5\%)} \mid \begin{array}{c} \text{CdSO}_4 \\ \text{Sat. at} \\ 4^\circ \text{ C.} \end{array} \mid \text{Hg}_2\text{SO}_4 \mid \text{Hg}$$

the pure mercury electrode being positive and the voltage close to 1.01864. This cell has a negligible temperature coefficient, long life, good constancy and reproducibility of e.m.f., but it should be calibrated by the Bureau of Standards or compared with a recently calibrated cell about once a year. In commercial *p*H electrometers, the quality of the standard cell is also important; even though the standardization of an instrument whose "built-in" standard cell e.m.f. is erroneous, a solution of known *p*H automatically corrects the instrument at that single *p*H to the proper *p*H reading. At all other points on the *p*H dial, the instrument would be in error, the error increasing, the greater the difference between the calibrating *p*H and the *p*H of the test sample. In this connection we wish to quote from some experiences obtained in the actual plant operation of a commercial electrometer.[5]

"The type of standard cell used in the electrometer does not give a constant voltage over a period of time, which leads to serious errors in the readings obtained, particularly if the instrument is standardized at a *p*H of 4.1 (according to the instructions furnished with the instrument), and then determinations are made at a *p*H distant from the *p*H used for standardization. This error, of course, would be true of any potentiometer circuit using a standard cell which has an unknown error in voltage.

"Our method of checking this error is to set the asymmetrical potential knob so that the electrometer indicates the *p*H of a buffer solution, which has been checked on the quinhydrone cell, at about *p*H 4.0. Buffers of *p*H 5.0 and 6.0 are checked on the quinhydrone cell and then the observed readings obtained on the same buffers, found by the electrometer without further change of the asymmetric potential knob, are plotted against the readings of the quinhydrone cell and the curve extrapolated into the alkaline range.

"Readings obtained from the glass cell are corrected by means of this curve. If the error found is small, and all the solutions to be tested are in a narrow range,

[5] Private communication from H. C. Wall, Chief Chemist, Longview Fibre Co., Longview, Wash.

we sometimes standardize with a buffer near the pH of the unknowns by adjusting the asymmetric potential knob so that the electrometer will give the correct pH directly from its scale.

"Unreliable results have been obtained when the battery voltages of the electrometer had decreased. As this difficulty does not always become immediately apparent, we have adopted the procedure of frequently measuring the voltage of the batteries."

Precautions to be observed in the use of standard cells may be listed as follows: [6]

1. Standard cell voltages may decrease at the rate of 0.1 mv. per year; hence the necessity for the yearly calibration mentioned above.

2. The temperature coefficient of the cell as a whole is low owing to a balancing of two rather large coefficients in the two arms; accordingly, if the temperature of one arm of the cell becomes different from that of the other, errors will enter into the measurement. For this reason, the cell should not be touched with the hand shortly before a measurement; it should neither be exposed to drafts, nor to rays of the sun, nor to radiated heat.

3. Abrupt temperature changes, even if uniform, may change its voltage momentarily, by as much as several hundredths of a per cent.

4. Excessive heating or cooling of the cell may damage it; keep it between 4 and 40° C.

5. Never connect the cell to a voltmeter nor polarize it by allowing 0.0001 amp. or more to pass through it.

3·2. Galvanometer-Potentiometer Circuits for Glass Electrode E.M.F. Measurements

Although the resistance of the glass-electrode membrane is usually too high to permit the use of ordinary galvanometers for the indicating device G of Fig. 3·2, nevertheless a number of workers beginning with Robertson,[7] followed by Michaelis,[8] Mouquin and Garman,[9] and Nichols and Schempf,[10] have succeeded in constructing glass electrodes of sufficiently low resistance to make pH measurements accurately to 0.01 pH with even the most common type of galvanometer. Robertson's arrangement of apparatus is illustrated in Fig. 3·3 where P is a "student-type" potentiometer whose dial reads directly to 1 mv., R is a variable resistance to control the current from the working

[6] G. W. Vinal, *Trans. Electrochem. Soc.* **54**, 255 (1928).

[7] G. R. Robertson, *Ind. Eng. Chem., Anal. Ed.* **3**, 5 (1931).

[8] L. Michaelis, *Science*, **83**, 213 (1936).

[9] H. Mouquin and R. L. Garman, *Ind. Eng. Chem., Anal. Ed.* **9**, 287 (1937).

[10] M. L. Nichols and J. Schempf, *ibid.* **10**, 286 (1938).

battery B, $S.C.$ is the standard cell, G_1 a pointer-type galvanometer of low sensitivity, and G_2 a "type R" galvanometer of sensitivity equal to 0.0001 microampere per mm. scale reading. Switch S_4 is merely a galvanometer short-circuiting switch to stop the motion of the galvanometer and is used instead of the critical damping resistance of 10,000 ohms. Robertson made bulb-type electrodes of 8 to 10 cc. capacity whose resistances were as low as 2 to 3 megohms, whose average wall thickness was 0.03 mm., and whose surface area was about 14 sq. cm. For a potential difference of 1 mv. applied across a resistance of 3 megohms we have by Ohm's law a current of 3×10^{-10} amp. or a scale deflection

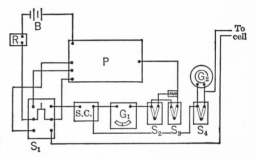

of 3 mm. in Robertson's outfit. Thus Robertson could make glass electrode measurements better than to 1 mv. without using enough current to polarize the electrodes; when he deliberately polarized the glass surface by depressing the tapping key S_3 for sev-

FIG. 3·3. Arrangement of student type poten-

eral seconds with the poten-tiometer and ordinary galvanometer for glass

tiometer unbalanced to the electrode cell—e.m.f. measurements.

extent of 100 mv., a few seconds were required for the glass electrode e.m.f. to return to normal on releasing the key S_3.

Using a galvanometer of sensitivity equal to 0.00025 microampere per mm. scale division, "Type K" potentiometer whose dial reads directly to 0.1 mv., and glass electrodes of a type devised by him (see Sec. 4·5) with resistances from 4 to 10 megohms, Michaelis was able to estimate the e.m.f. of glass-electrode cells to several tenths of a millivolt. Observations agreed almost perfectly with theoretical expectations. Mouquin and Garman's glass electrodes (see Sec. 4·5) were of such low resistance, 0.01 to 0.1 megohm, that e.m.f. readings to better than 1 mv. could be made using a portable lamp and scale-enclosed galvanometer whose sensitivity was only 0.025 microampere per scale division. Nichols and Schempf succeeded in duplicating Mouquin and Garman's result with a somewhat different type of glass electrode.

3·3. Electrostatic Electrometers

All of the earlier glass electrode studies were carried out using some form of electrostatic electrometer, most frequently of the quadrant type [11] but at the present time the tendency appears to be in the direction of the increasing use of vacuum-tube or thermionic electrometers; hence we shall mention the electrostatic instruments only very briefly.

Dolazalek, Lindemann, and Compton quadrant electrometers have been used, the last by MacInnes and the author.[12,13,14,15] Figure 3·4 illustrates the wiring diagram of an electrometer circuit. During measurements, the tapping key of the potentiometer should be locked closed and the galvanometer binding posts short-circuited. X is the glass electrode cell, s_1 a reversing switch and s_2 a highly insulated tapping key. A good quadrant electrometer is more expensive and slightly less sensitive than a good thermionic amplifier, and it is correct to say that, in general, electrometers require greater skill to set up than do thermionic amplifiers. Furthermore, thousands of portable thermionic amplifiers have been built, but the author knows of no portable instruments containing electrostatic electrometers.[16] Many excellent e.m.f. measurements of glass-electrode

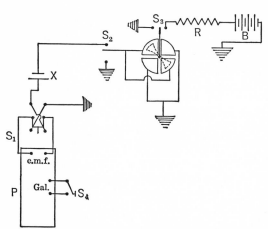

FIG. 3·4. Wiring arrangement for glass electrode e.m.f. measurements using a quadrant electrometer.

cells have been made, however, with quadrant electrometers. These are particularly good for research experiments where the electrometer need not be disturbed and where a stable zero over long periods of time is essential.

[11] For the theory of the quadrant electrometer see "Electricity and Magnetism" by S. G. Starling, Fifth Edition, Longmans, Green and Co., New York, 1929, p. 158.

[12] P. T. Kerridge, *Biochem. J.* **19**, 611 (1925).

[13] A. E. Mirsky and M. L. Anson, *J. Biol. Chem.* **83**, 581 (1929).

[14] D. A. MacInnes and M. Dole, *J. Am. Chem. Soc.* **52**, 29 (1930).

[15] The Wien-Harms "Handbuch der Experimental-Physik," Leipzig, 1930, Vol. 10, pp. 42–97, gives complete and detailed description of all types of quadrant electrometers.

[16] Such a portable instrument could be made using a Lindemann electrometer as the needle is suspended so tightly in these electrometers that they do not have to be leveled. Microscopic observation of the needle deflections is required.

3·4. General Theory of Vacuum Tube pH Electrometers

Glass electrode e.m.f.-measuring circuits employing vacuum tubes are by far the most important type of pH electrometer, for they can be made accurate and more sensitive than any other type, or they can be made rugged, portable, simple and almost foolproof in operation. Furthermore, they are not too expensive to build since fairly large scale production methods can be used. Thousands of them are in daily use. For all these reasons, we shall discuss the general theory, construction, and manipulation of the instruments in some detail, but at the same time we find it necessary to avoid describing commercial pH electrometers to any great extent, not only because of the ignorance of the author concerning the exact specifications of many of the different circuits, but also because the variety of instruments on the market makes it impossible to describe them all in an adequate way.[17]

The fundamental mechanism of vacuum tube operation may be explained with the aid of the vacuum tube-potentiometer circuit first introduced by Goode,[18]

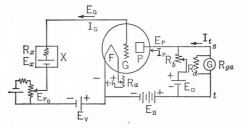

FIG. 3·5. Schematic diagram of vacuum tube –potentiometer circuit.

and illustrated as shown in Fig. 3·5 without E_v. Current of 1.06 amperes from the A-battery of 6 v. heats the filament F of the UV 201 tube hot enough to emit electrons which are drawn to the plate P with the aid of the positive potential of the 22.5 v. B-battery. The magnitude of the filament to plate current is determined to a

[17] The different companies in this country manufacturing glass electrode pH electrometers which have come to the author's attention may be listed as follows:

American Instrument Co., Silver Springs, Md.

Cambridge Instrument Co., 3512 Grand Central Terminal, New York, N. Y.

Coleman Electric Co., 310 Madison St., Maywood, Ill.

Eisendrath Memorial Laboratories, Racine, Wis. (Cameron).

Hellige, Inc., 3702 Northern Blvd., Long Island City, N. Y.

Leeds and Northrup Co., 4902 Stenton Ave., Philadelphia, Pa.

E. Leitz, Inc., 730 Fifth Ave., New York, N. Y.

National Technical Laboratories, 330 E. Colorado St., Pasadena, Calif. (Beckman).

Palo-Myers, Inc., 81 Reade St., New York, N. Y.

Thwing-Albert Instrument Co., 3339 Lancaster Ave., Philadelphia, Pa.

The Bristol Company, Waterbury, Conn.

[18] K. H. Goode, *J. Am. Chem. Soc.* **44**, 26 (1922); **47**, 2483 (1925).

great extent by the potential existing on the grid G by virtue of the control this grid potential has upon the electric space charge existing within the tube. When G becomes positively charged, destroying the negative space charge, electrons flow freely from filament to plate, giving rise to a relatively large plate current; conversely, a negative grid allows the negative space charge in the tube to increase to such an extent that the plate current becomes much smaller, as illustrated in Fig. 3·6 where we have plotted the plate current of the important FP–54 tube of the General Electric Company as a function of control-grid voltage.[19]

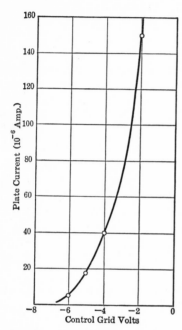

The slope of this curve, when taken with a constant plate potential, is called the "mutual conductance" of the tube, G_m, and defined mathematically by the equation

$$G_m = \left(\frac{\partial I_P}{\partial E_G}\right)_{E_p} \qquad [3\cdot4\cdot1]$$

Suppose now that the unknown e.m.f. to be measured is connected between the grid and the filament or the unknown cell-potentiometer combination is so connected [20] as in Fig. 3·5, that the grid will acquire the potential of the cell and the plate current will be correspondingly modified. To detect this change in the plate current a galvanometer is connected as in the illustration where R_d is a galvanometer shunt resistance, R_b is a variable resistance of 3000 ohms, and E_D, the e.m.f. of a dry cell. When the unknown e.m.f., E_x, is zero and the grid is connected usually through a "biasing" battery to the negative end of the filament, the current through the galvanometer is brought to zero by proper adjustment of the variable resistance R_b; at this point the potential at s will equal that at t and

$$I_P R_b = E_D \qquad [3\cdot4\cdot2]$$

On introduction of X into the grid-filament circuit, the plate current

FIG. 3·6. Plate current of FP–54 tube as a function of grid voltage.

[19] G. F. Metcalf and B. J. Thompson, *Phys. Rev.* **36**, 1489 (1930).
[20] As was first done by C. Morton, *Trans. Faraday Soc.* **24**, 14 (1928).

I_P will be altered, the equality expressed by Eq. 3·4·2 will be upset and a current will flow through the galvanometer. Usually the vacuum-tube electrometer is used as a null-point indicating instrument in which case the potentiometer is balanced against the unknown cell X until the galvanometer image on the scale returns to its zero setting.

There are many difficulties with the simple circuit shown in Fig. 3·5, the chief one, as far as glass electrode e.m.f. measurements are concerned, being the existence of a grid current flowing through the cell even at zero balance. As already explained in Sec. 3·1, the observed e.m.f. will be less than the true e.m.f. by an amount equal to $I_G R_X$ where I_G is the grid current and R_X the internal resistance of the unknown cell; ordinarily R_X is relatively small so that this complication does not exist, but in glass electrode cells whose resistances may be as high as 10^8 ohms or even higher, $I_G R_X$ may amount to 0.1 v. if I_G is of the order of magnitude of 10^{-9} amp. Six possible sources of the grid current, even when the grid is sufficiently negative to repel all electrons, have been listed by Metcalf and Thompson: [19]

(1) Leakage over glass or insulation.

(2) Ions formed by gas present in the tube.

(3) Thermionic grid-emission due to heating of grid by energy radiated from the hot filament.

(4) Positive ions emitted by the filament.

(5) Photo-electrons emitted by the grid under action of light from the filament.

(6) Photo-electrons emitted by the control grid under action of soft x-rays produced by the normal anode current.

Of these sources of grid current the leakage over glass or insulation is usually the least important and can be made negligibly small by keeping the tube clean and by housing it in a chamber desiccated by some sort of drying agent. This is usual procedure. Another suggestion is to place just above the base of the tube a guard ring having a potential equal to that of the operating potential of the grid (the lead to the grid is usually brought out through the top of the tube).

Stadie [21] points out that for relative pH measurements the extraneous p.d. due to the grid current cancels out, but this is only true when the resistance of the unknown cell is always the same; two different glass electrodes of different resistances would not give the same pH reading unless each one is separately calibrated. It is much better to make use of a special circuit which eliminates this difficulty by the introduction of a condenser in the grid circuit or by the use of special

[21] W. C. Stadie, *J. Biol. Chem.* **83**, 477 (1929).

compensating devices or by the use of a tube whose grid current can be made sufficiently low such as the General Electric FP–54 tube, the Westinghouse electrometer tube RH–507, the A. E. G. T–114 tube, the Western Electric D–96475 tube.

Before describing in detail the modern pH electrometers, a few words concerning the sensitivity of thermionic amplifiers will be given according to Nottingham.[22]

Considering the input or the grid circuit of Fig. 3·5 where E_x represents the e.m.f. to be measured, E_{P_o} the potentiometer p.d., and E_V the grid-"biasing" voltage, the following equation must necessarily hold by virtue of Kirchhoff's law (we are measuring all voltages with respect to the negative end of the filament),

$$E_x + E_{P_o} + E_V = E_G + R_X I_G \qquad [3·4·3]$$

Holding E_X and E_V constant, we find for a small variation of E_{P_o}

$$\frac{\partial E_G}{\partial E_{P_o}} + R_X \frac{\partial I_G}{\partial E_{P_o}} = 1 \qquad [3·4·4]$$

Since the reciprocal of the slope of the grid current-grid voltage curve is defined as the "grid impedance," Z_G, we have

$$\frac{1}{Z_G} = \frac{\partial I_G}{\partial E_G} \qquad [3·4·5]$$

which when substituted into Eq. 3·4·4 gives, after rearranging,

$$\frac{\partial E_G}{\partial E_{P_o}} = \frac{1}{1 + \dfrac{R_X}{Z_G}} \qquad [3·4·6]$$

Equation 3·4·6 tells us that the rate with which the grid voltage changes with change of the potentiometer setting, or the sensitivity of the circuit, is a maximum when R_x is small in comparison to the always positive quantity Z_G. Thus again we see that electrometer tubes should have a large internal resistance, or large grid impedance, for use with glass electrodes since the R_x of glass-electrode circuits is always large.

We can express the final sensitivity of the electrometer in terms of galvanometer coil angular deflection θ in the following way: Let I_P represent plate current and Z_P plate impedance, and assume the cor-

[22] W. B. Nottingham, *J. Franklin Inst.* **209**, 287 (1930).

rectness of the following equation which is sufficiently accurate for our purposes,

$$I_P = \frac{1}{Z_P}(E_P + \mu E_G + E_o) \qquad [3·4·7]$$

where E_o is a constant and μ the voltage amplification, $-\left(\dfrac{\partial E_P}{\partial E_G}\right)_{I_P}$.

From a consideration of additional minor circuits or "meshes" of Fig. 3·5, we can also write down the equations

$$I_t = I_d + I_{ga} \qquad [3·4·8]$$

$$E_P = E_B - I_t R_t \qquad [3·4·9]$$

$$\frac{1}{R_t} = \frac{1}{R_d} + \frac{1}{R_{ga}} \qquad [3·4·10]$$

$$E_D = I_P R_b - I_t (R_b + R_t) \qquad [3·4·11]$$

and

$$I_{ga} = I_t \left(\frac{R_d}{R_d + R_{ga}}\right) \qquad [3·4·12]$$

From Eqs. 3·4·7, 3·4·9, and 3·4·11 we have

$$I_t = \frac{\dfrac{1}{Z_P}(E_B + \mu E_G + E_o) - \dfrac{E_D}{R_b}}{1 + R_t\left(\dfrac{1}{Z_P} + \dfrac{1}{R_b}\right)} \qquad [3·4·13]$$

which on differentiation yields (remembering the definition of G_m given by Eq. 3·4·1)

$$\frac{\partial I_t}{\partial E_G} = \frac{G_m}{1 + R_t\left(\dfrac{1}{Z_P} + \dfrac{1}{R_b}\right)} \qquad [3·4·14]$$

But the substitution of Eqs. 3·4·10 and 3·4·12 into Eq. 3·4·14 gives

$$\frac{\partial I_{ga}}{\partial E_G} = \frac{G_m}{1 + R_{ga}\left(\dfrac{1}{Z_P} + \dfrac{1}{R_b} + \dfrac{1}{R_d}\right)} \qquad [3·4·15]$$

which reduces to

$$\frac{\partial I_{ga}}{\partial E_G} = \frac{G_m}{1 + \dfrac{R_{ga}}{R_{cd}}} \qquad [3·4·16]$$

if R_b and R_d are adjusted to produce critical damping of the galvanometer. The critical damping resistance, R_{cd}, is given by the equation

$$\frac{1}{R_{cd}} = \frac{1}{Z_P} + \frac{1}{R_b} + \frac{1}{R_d}$$ [3·4·17]

The angular deflection of the galvanometer, θ, is related to the galvanometer current by the equation

$$\frac{\partial\theta}{\partial I_{ga}} = C_s$$ [3·4·18]

which when substituted in 3·4·16 and the latter combined with 3·4·6 results in the final equation for the sensitivity, S, of the amplifier,

$$S \equiv \frac{\partial\theta}{\partial E_{Po}} = \frac{C_s}{1 + \dfrac{R_{ga}}{R_{cd}}} \cdot \frac{G_m}{1 + \dfrac{R_x}{Z_G}}$$ [3·4·19]

The first factor of Eq. 3·4·19 depends only on the galvanometer constants while the second factor depends both on the tube characteristics and the resistance of the unknown cell R_x. These equations are applicable only to the circuits like that of Fig. 3·5, but they indicate the general ideas involved in the determination of amplifier sensitivity.

With this brief introduction into the theory of vacuum tube action, we pass on to a detailed consideration of tube circuits.

3·5. Single Vacuum-Tube Amplifying Circuits

Of the many early (from 1928 to 1935) thermionic amplifiers which now can be seen to have been of great pioneer and exploratory importance but which at the present time have chiefly historic interest we shall have little to say; instead we shall try to choose the most reliable circuit of each type from the many that have been proposed, and to give the specifications of these circuits in sufficient detail for the reader to duplicate them if he so desires.[23]

For measurement of pH with a limiting accuracy of ± 0.04 pH, the numerous pH electrometers now being sold commercially are entirely satisfactory (although one must beware advertising claims of glass electrode pH instruments covering the scale 0–14 pH; see Chapter 7). The majority of these meters contain two or more

---

[23] Fr. Müller and W. Dürichen, *Z. Elektrochem.* **42**, 31 (1936) have given a review of the subject with an extensive bibliography.

vacuum tubes and are built more for ruggedness and stability than for any great sensitivity and extreme accuracy.   For research instruments capable of measuring e.m.f. to 0.1 mv. or better, one-tube circuits employing the General Electric Company's FP–54 tube or other electrometer tubes are most frequently used in America.   In the FP–54 tube the grid current (positive) at a control-grid voltage of -4.0 volts is about 10^{-15} ampere so that even with a glass electrode whose resistance is 1000 megohms, the IR drop across the cell is only 10^{-6} v., a negligible error.   By holding the plate voltage below 8 v., grid current due to ionization of residual gas in the tube is eliminated; by using a relatively low filament power and large open structures in the tube, grid currents due to heating the grid are made negligible; and by placing a space-charge grid, positively charged, between the filament and the control grid the effect of the emission of positive ions by the hot filament is overcome.   Difficulties due to the emission of photo-electrons are reduced by using a thoriated filament in the tube operated at a low temperature, and also by using very low anode (plate) voltages (the latter reduces to an inappreciable value the emission of soft x-rays from the plate which may produce photo-electrons on the grid).

Characteristics of the FP–54 tube and other electrometer tubes are listed in Table 3·2, taken from the review of Müller and Dürichen

TABLE 3·2

CHARACTERISTICS OF ELECTROMETER TUBES

Tube	E_P v.	E_{SG} v.	E_G v.	E_F v.	I_F ma.	I_G amp.	G_m μa./v.	I_P μa.
FP–54 Gen. Elec. Co...	6	4	-4	2.5	110 or 90	$\sim 10^{-15}$	25	40
T 113 A.E.G..........	7	5	-3	3	100	$\sim 10^{-13}$	80	......
T 114 A.E.G..........	6	4	-3	2	80	$\sim 10^{-14}$	30	......
L. St. R. II Strauss....	6	4	-4	2.5	130	$\sim 10^{-14}$	50	......
4060 Philips..........	4	.....	-3	0.56	1100	10^{-14} to 10^{-15}	30	......
D–96475 Western Elec.	4	4	-3	1.0	270	$\sim 10^{-15}$	40	86
Mazda UX–54........	6	4	-4	2.5	100	$\sim 10^{-15}$	25	......
RH–507 Westinghouse	6	.....	-3	2.0	60	$\sim 10^{-13}$	60	200

and from the papers of Cherry,[24] Metcalf and Thompson,[19] and Penick.[25]

[24] R. H. Cherry, *Trans. Electrochem. Soc.* **72**, 33 (1937); **78**, 351 (1940) (Preprint).
[25] D. B. Penick, *Rev. Sci. Instruments*, **6**, 115 (1935).

The subscripts of the symbols of Table 3·2, *P*, *SG*, *G*, and *F* refer to plate, space-charge grid, control grid, and filament, respectively.

Circuits employing these tubes may be roughly divided into two classes, those in which some sort of internal compensation or neutralization of fluctuations in battery changes is attempted and simpler cir-

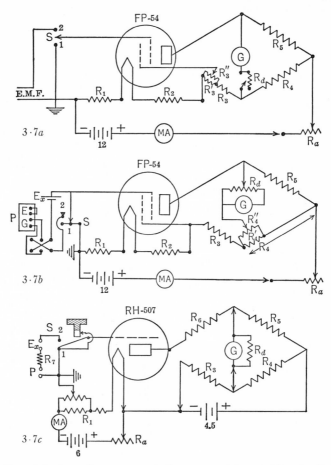

FIGS. 3·7*a*, *b*, *c*. Some representative vacuum-tube amplifier circuits.

cuits in which no attempt at complete elimination of galvanometer drift is made. Let us first consider the latter, of which several circuits are illustrated in Fig. 3·7:

Circuit 7*a* is due to Hill,[26] 7*b* to Briggs,[26] and 7*c*, employing the RH–507 tube, to Cherry.[24] To understand the principles governing

[26] Private communications from Dr. S. E. Hill and Dr. D. R. Briggs.

the specifications of the battery voltages and the various resistances we can imagine the filament-A battery switch closed so that current is flowing through the filament circuit, the magnitude of the filament current being brought to the specified value (see Table 3·2) by means of the variable resistance R_a (20 ohms). The filament current produces a p.d. across R_1 equal to the specified grid biasing voltage -4.0 v. in the case of the FP–54 tube. Since the filament current is about 90 ma, R_1 has the fixed value of 45 ohms, but in circuit 7c R_1 can be varied as conditions require although normally it is given its full value of 50 ohms (to produce the grid biasing voltage of -3.0 v.). Filament current flowing through the resistance R_2 of 17 ohms or R_2 plus a variable amount of R_3'' gives rise to the proper screen-grid voltage of $+4$ v. (we are calculating all voltages with respect to the negative end of the filament taken as zero) since the potential drop across the filament is 2.5 v. The magnitude of resistances R_5 and R_6 must be such that the plate voltage acquires its proper value, $+6.0$ v. in the case of the FP–54 tube; thus the p.d. along R_5 should be 2 volts, which can be obtained in the case of the FP–54 tube, having a plate current of 4.0×10^{-5} amp., by making R_5 equal to 5×10^4 ohms. The resistances R_3 and R_4, one of which must be a variable resistance, are chosen so that the condition of balance of the galvanometer-Wheatstone-bridge circuit, namely,

$$I_5 R_5 = I_4 R_4$$

can be realized. In the case of the FP–54 circuits make R_3 about 22 ohms, and R_4 the same. In the Cherry circuit (Fig. 3·7c), the plate acquires its voltage of 6 volts through the introduction of a 4.5-v. C-battery; $R_5 + R_6$ must be, therefore, about 2500 ohms. R_7, a resistance of 5 megohms, is inserted to prevent polarization of the unknown cell during the e.m.f. measurements.

The fixed resistances of the circuits having unusual values can be made by winding Nichrome wire on Bakelite rods, tying them at the end through a hole drilled in the rod, and soldering the end of the wire to the proper connecting wire. Unless one knows in advance the exact resistance to use, taps should be brought out from each resistance at definite ohmic intervals such as at every 2, 5, or 10 ohms, giving a certain flexibility and possibility of adjustment to the system. Each resistance should be substantially mounted so that vibrations or change in mechanical pressure will not alter the p.d. across the resistance or change the magnitude of contact resistances. The galvanometer should be provided with the proper critical damping

resistance, but the galvanometer shunting circuits within the amplifier
itself (see Eq. 3·4·17) should be taken into consideration in selecting
any additional shunt; otherwise the galvanometer will be overdamped,
reducing the sensitivity.

Operation of the circuits illustrated in Fig. 3·7 is remarkably
simple; with the switch S in position 1, the control grid now being at
earth potential, R_3 or R_4 is varied until the galvanometer deflection
is zero; then the switch S is thrown over to position 2 when the
potentiometer P is varied until the galvanometer coil returns again
to its zero position. If the original adjustment of the Wheatstone-
bridge circuit has not changed, the p.d. reading of the potentiometer
is now equal to the e.m.f. of the unknown cell E_x. Note that the
switches of circuits 7b and 7c "make" before they "break"; that is,
the grid is never left on an open circuit. The vacuum tubes are all
housed in a dehumidified shielded compartment, the grid circuits are
highly insulated and shielded, and the filament current must be
allowed to run for an hour or two before making measurements.
(Some scientists allow their A-battery to discharge continuously
through a "dummy" resistance equal to that of the filament circuit
when the amplifier is not in use, and others allow a small charging
current in excess of the discharging current to flow through the
A-battery during use. These precautions help to reduce galvanometer
drift.)

Details regarding insulation, shielding, and the construction of
switches are given in the next section.

The most serious difficulties encountered in the use of thermionic
amplifiers may be listed as follows:

1. *Leakage currents due to improper insulation of switch S and of the
control-grid circuit.* This source of error may be discovered by measuring the e.m.f. of a standard cell with or without a resistance of
100 megohms or more connected in series. The low resistance e.m.f.
measurement should be made with the potentiometer alone. As a
general precaution this procedure of testing the circuit should be
carried out periodically, particularly if the relative humidity becomes
high as it does in the hot summer months.

2. *Drifting galvanometer zero due to*

  a. Slow changes in battery e.m.f. because of exhaustion of the
     battery or because of temperature changes.
  b. Changes in the circuit resistances because of temperature
     changes.
  c. Slow changes in the characteristics of the tubes.

3. *Fluctuating galvanometer deflections due to*

   a. Improper or insufficient shielding. (Adequate shielding is important in the case of the input circuit, particularly so for circuit 7*c*.)

   b. Poor rheostat contacts.

   c. Mechanical vibrations.

   d. Changes in the emission of the thoriated tungsten filament.

   e. Rapid fluctuations in battery e.m.f. caused by gas formation if Edison storage batteries are used.

With a properly designed and constructed instrument, measurements accurate to 0.1 mv. are consistently and easily made. Electric motors with sparking brushes should be avoided. In the use of the Cherry electrometer in the author's laboratory, it has been found that the behavior of the instrument depends upon the tension on the screws whose heads lie in the top panel; readjustment of these screws is sometimes necessary to restore proper stability of the instrument.

DuBridge and Brown [27] have invented an amplifier circuit in which galvanometer zero drift is reduced to a minimum by internal compensation or "neutralization," a phenomenon brought about by separating the Wheatstone-bridge circuit from the main filament circuit and by balancing the space-charge grid current against the plate current in such a way that slight changes in filament current or filament emission have practically no effect on the galvanometer, both the plate current and space-charge grid current being altered in a constant ratio (see Eqs. 3·5·1 and 3·5·2). The essential features of the DuBridge and Brown circuit are shown in Fig. 3·8*a*. Figure 3·8*b* is a similar circuit due to Barth, [28] while Fig. 3·8*c* represents still another modification due to Penick. [29]

The magnitude of the *A*-battery and resistances chosen depends upon the operating characteristics of the electrometer tube employed, as already explained above, but to obtain neutralization we must choose R_1 and R_2, or R_3 so that

$$\frac{R_4}{R_5} = \frac{I_P}{I_{SG}} \qquad [3·5·1]$$

and

$$\frac{dI_P}{dI_F} = \left(\frac{R_4}{R_5}\right)\left(\frac{dI_{SG}}{dI_F}\right) \qquad [3·5·2]$$

where I_{SG} is the screen-grid current ($I_{SG} > I_P$).

[27] L. A. DuBridge and H. Brown, *Rev. Sci. Instruments*, **4**, 532 (1933).

[28] G. Barth, *Z. Physik.* **87**, 399 (1934).

[29] D. B. Penick, *Rev. Sci. Instruments*, **6**, 115 (1935).

To obtain Eqs. 3·5·1 and 3·5·2 we set E_{ga} equal to zero (the condition at balance of the Wheatstone-bridge circuit), and also dE_{ga}/dI_F zero; in other words no galvanometer deflection for filament-current fluctuations, the property of a neutralized circuit. Fortunately, there is always some value of the filament current I_F corresponding to a definite value of R_2 for which the galvanometer deflection is a minimum, and since it is a rather flat minimum, it is possible to adjust R_2 to give this minimum for the stated filament current of the tube and so neutralize the circuit. DuBridge and Brown's directions for carrying out this adjustment may be quoted as follows:

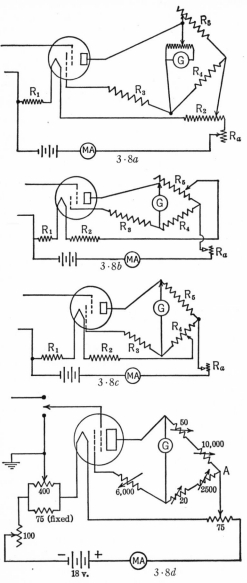

"1. Connect up the circuit, adjusting I_F to approximately the rated value for the tube, and bring the galvanometer approximately to zero by adjustment of R_5. Have the galvanometer connected so that as R_5 is decreased the deflection decreases.

"2. With the Ayrton shunt (of the galvanometer) set at 0.1 or 0.01 slowly vary I_F by changing R_a, in such a direction that the galvanometer deflection is decreased. The galvanometer should then pass through a fairly flat minimum. If it tends to go off the scale before the minimum is reached, bring it back by changing R_5 again.

FIGS. 3·8 a, b, c, d. Some "internally compensated" potentiometer circuits.

"3. If the value of I_F at the minimum differs from the rated value for the tube by more than 3 or 4 per cent, shift the tap on R_2 to a new position and repeat. Two or three trials will usually locate the proper position for this tap.

"4. With the Ayrton shunt at 1.0 make a final adjustment for the minimum by adjusting R_a and finally bring the galvanometer to zero with R_5. The circuit is now ready for operation."

The plate voltage should be at its rated value of 6.0 v.; if it is much less than this, the circuit will lose its sensitivity, but by the additional adjustment of R_1, it is possible to neutralize the circuit and at the same time operate the tube under the stated conditions of Table 3·2.

The stability of the DuBridge and Brown circuit is very good and the input circuit does not have to be shielded to the same extent as do other circuits containing tubes with greater mutual conductances, such as the Cherry circuit. The circuits of Barth and of Penick, Figs. 3·8 b and c, are more flexible than the DuBridge and Brown circuits, since the plate and screen-grid voltages can be independently varied, and are more adaptable to different types of electrometer tubes.

Wyman[30] has also modified the DuBridge and Brown arrangement to include a variable resistance to provide the grid-biasing voltage, see Fig. 3·8d.

"General Radio Co. potentiometers were used for all the resistances except the 100 ohm and 75 ohm fixed vitreous resistances. The sliding contacts of these potentiometers were all equipped with pigtail connections to the center tap. All these resistances, as well as the switches and binding posts for connections with battery, potentiometer, and galvanometer were mounted on a Bakelite sub-panel supported on the heavy aluminum front panel of the box in which the bridge was housed. This aluminum panel was grounded and the Bakelite shaft of each variable resistance and switch was terminated by a brass section where it emerged through a bushing in this panel. This arrangement afforded both a smooth bearing, and, more important, a grounded shield between the knob of each control and its Bakelite shaft. The vacuum tube was mounted in a nearly air-tight grounded brass box fastened to the inner face of the aluminum panel. This box was kept dry with phosphorous pentoxide. The high resistance switch to provide for connecting the control grid of the tube either directly to the bias voltage or to the silver-silver chloride electrode was also contained in this box. This switch had a Pyrex shaft terminated by a brass section which passed through bushings in the wall of the box and in the front panel, to provide a bearing and shield as in the case of the other switches and resistances. The lead from the high resistance switch to the silver-silver chloride electrode emerged through a thick-walled Pyrex tube at one end of the main box. A small Bakelite plate fixed to the inner side of the front panel carried jacks connected with the positive and negative filament

---

[30] Private communication from Dr. J. Wyman, Jr.

terminals, the plate, the bias for the control grid, the space-charge grid, and the point marked A in Fig. 3·8d. This made it easy to measure the operating voltages, even with a low resistance voltmeter. An additional terminal on this plate also made it possible to introduce a microammeter to measure the plate current and determine the tube characteristics. Everything was mounted on the front panel so that by removing this it was easy to get at all the parts. The rest of the box was of bent iron with a removable top. Removal of the top gave sufficient access to the various binding posts and jacks for the normal use of the bridge."

Incidentally, it should be pointed out that because of the low voltage-amplification factor of FP–54 tubes and of electrometer tubes in general (unity or less than unity) one of these tubes cannot be used to amplify the changes in the output voltage of the first, as two tubes would be less sensitive than one; three element tubes such as the 56 or the IJX 112 A tube should be used.[31]   Müller and Dürichen [32] describe a heater-type pentode, two-tube, Wheatstone-bridge arrangement for the amplification of electrometer-tube output voltages.   See Sec. 3·7 for the description of a circuit amplifying the output voltage of an FP–54 tube.

3·6. Insulation, Shielding, and Constructional Details

Before continuing our discussion of thermionic amplifier circuits we wish to devote this section to a consideration of the input circuit and switch, their construction, insulation, and shielding. The lead from the glass electrode to the control grid of the electrometer tube is by far the most important part of the instrument insofar as care in its insulation and shielding is concerned as the high internal resistance of the glass electrode makes necessary a corresponding higher leakage resistance of the input circuit in order to obtain accurate data. In the hot humid weather of summer electrometers which have functioned satisfactorily in winter may be considerably in error, because of the comparatively low resistance of surface films of moisture condensed about the apparatus. Within the last few years several types of synthetic plastics which have excellent electrical properties even under conditions of rather high relative humidity have been developed; furthermore, these plastics have been fabricated into panels, cylindrical rods, tubing, sockets, switches, insulating beads, co-axial cables, etc. These plastics are readily machined, cut or cemented together, and at the present time are causing a rapid change in insulation technique.

---

[31] K. Henney, "Electron Tubes in Industry," McGraw-Hill Book Co., New York, 1934, pp. 88 and 89.

[32] Fr. Müller and W. Dürichen, Z. *Elektrochem.* **41**, 559 (1935).

One such plastic with which the author has had experience is "Amphenol 912,"[33] a polystyrene base insulating material.

The electrometer tube should be supported securely in a socket placed in a brass cylinder, iron box, or other shielded container which can be desiccated by the use of phosphorus pentoxide. In contrast to this technique commonly followed by chemists it is an almost universal procedure among physicists of housing the electrometer vacuum tube and switch in a vacuum-tight brass or soft iron compartment, the switch being operated with the aid of Fulton sylphon bellows, and the whole evacuated during operation. Using an internal magnetically controlled gold-tipped contact switch, Müller and Dürichen[34] have described such a vacuum compartment for an electrometer tube. The input wire which can be shielded by a brass tube is brought in either through quartz, or better through "Amphenol 912" insulation while the base of the electrometer tube can be either Leucite or some other plastic or, as in the case of Müller and Dürichen, Picein cement.

The input circuit switch, S of Figs. 3·7a, b, c, which should be highly insulated has been constructed in a number

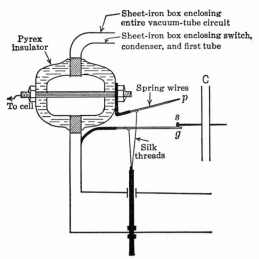

Fig. 3·9. Pyrex insulator and special switch of Ellis and Kiehl (as viewed from top).

of ways, but preferably so that the glass-electrode cell connection to the grid is made before the grid to earth connection is broken, as in Fig. 3·7b. In this way the grid is never on an open circuit, otherwise annoying slight galvanometer deflections might be produced each time the switch is opened or closed. Figure 3·9, which is self-explanatory, illustrates in detail a switch constructed by Ellis and Kiehl,[35] while Mirsky and Anson's[36] simple mercury-cup switch in which contact

[33] Sold in many forms by the American Phenolic Corporation, 1250 Van Buren St., Chicago.

[34] Fr. Müller and W. Dürichen, *Z. Elektrochem.* **41**, 559 (1935).

[35] S. B. Ellis and S. J. Kiehl, *Rev. Sci. Instruments*, **4**, 131 (1933).

[36] A. E. Mirsky and M. L. Anson, *J. Biol. Chem.* **81**, 581 (1929).

at point 7 is made before contact at point 5 is broken when the quartz rod is pushed downwards is shown in Fig. 3·10. Other special electrometer switches have been described by Goodhue,[37] Rosebury,[38] Greville and Maclagan,[39] and DuBois,[40] but the author believes that present day commercial switches with molded Bakelite for insulation are so reliable that the necessity for making individual switches is disappearing.

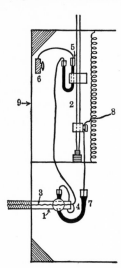

The lead from the input switch to the glass electrode cell should be well insulated and in most instances carefully shielded. An entirely satisfactory commercial insulated bead cable is illustrated in Fig. 3·11. When the electrometer tube has a high mutual conductance, shielding is particularly necessary, but it is advisable for all types of circuits. The shielded parts should include the thermionic tube, the input switch and lead and the glass electrode side of the e.m.f. cell. In regard to the use of the Cherry electrometer, Fig. 3·7c, Professor M. M. Haring[41] writes

FIG. 3·10.   Special switch of Mirsky and Anson.   1,   quartz tube; 2, quartz rod; 3, wire to electrometer; 4, wire to electrometer divides; 5, contact for earthing; 6, to earth; 7, contact to electrode; 8, to glass electrode; 9, shielding.

"Potentiometer, galvanometer and all leads between them and the amplifier are entirely unshielded. The potentiometer operates on the current from Willard low discharge cells. The amplifier case, high resistance lead shield and air thermostat are all interconnected and grounded. A simple U-shaped piece of aluminum sheet is arched over both leads from the measured cell to the amplifier, completely bridging the three-inch gap between the amplifier and thermostat. *This is essential.* Without it even the movement of an arm in a coat sleeve at six feet will cause the galvanometer to go crazy. The leads into the thermostat and

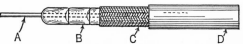

FIG. 3·11. Insulated bead cable. A, copper wire; B, insulating beads of Amphenol plastic; C, braided shield of No. 36 tinned copper wire; D, coating of synthetic resin or rubber.

cell are short pieces of No. 18 bare copper wire. Attachment is made to the

[37] L. D. Goodhue, *Iowa State Coll. J. Sci.* **10**, 7 (1935).

[38] F. Rosebury, *Ind. Eng. Chem., Anal. Ed.* **4**, 398 (1932); **5**, 3 (1933).

[39] G. D. Greville and N. F. Maclagan, *Trans. Faraday Soc.* **27**, 210 (1931).

[40] D. DuBois, *J. Biol. Chem.*, **88**, 729 (1930).

[41] Private communication.

highly insulated input rod by means of a little helix on one end of the wire. For support and insulation, each wire passes through a three-inch length of quartz tube set in a large rubber stopper. The stoppers are inserted in holes in the thermostat wall and are about four inches apart. Aside from this, the leads are air-insulated, throughout ... An induction stirring motor, galvanometer light transformer, relay, rectifying transformer and power line are all within a foot of the amplifier."

The necessity for shielding can be tested by moving the hand or body near the cell or its leads while the e.m.f. of the glass electrode cell is being measured, and noting whether any deflection of the galvanometer is produced, or by rubbing an amberite rod and bringing it near the input leads. Mrs. Kerridge [42] enclosed her electrodes in an earthed cage of wire netting, Stadie [43] placed his entire apparatus on a sheet of grounded galvanized iron and placed a similar sheet under the chair of the operator (galvanometers, ammeters, or voltmeters should not stand on iron, but copper sheets, although for low frequency current shielding iron is necessary). Mirsky and Anson [44] enclosed all their apparatus in an earthed metal box whose door could be left open, and Ellis and Kiehl found it necessary to enclose their cell with sheet metal on all but two sides. In some commercial electrometers the glass-electrode cell is not shielded although the thermionic amplifier is always completely shielded; however, the glass electrode should be shielded inasmuch as the movement of a person near the instrument causes fluctuations in the e.m.f. reading as the author has noticed while trying to use a commercial pH electrometer in a student laboratory.

Kerridge supported her glass electrode on a block of wax, the glass electrode as well as the calomel electrodes being insulated by an amberite rod held in an earthed metal stand. Stadie and Mirsky and Anson supported both their calomel and glass electrodes with silica rods. Ellis and Kiehl placed their glass electrode cell on a small stand having Bakelite legs. They point out that "it is important that cells of high resistance be held in position firmly, without any loose or easily vibrated parts. Otherwise there always seems to be enough vibration present to cause some interference with the measurements and to detract somewhat from the effective sensitivity." The author has usually hung or supported his glass electrode cells in constant-temperature oil baths, the high-resistant oil being a sufficient insulator; water in the bath could not be used. The question of the insulation of the glass

[42] P. T. Kerridge, *Biochem. J.* **19**, 611 (1925).
[43] W. C. Stadie, *J. Biol. Chem.* **83**, 477 (1929).
[44] *Loc. cit.*

stems of the glass electrodes will be considered in the next chapter in connection with the various types of electrodes. We return now to a description of multiple-tube thermionic amplifiers.

3·7. Multiple-Tube Thermionic Amplifiers

All the previous pH meters described in this chapter have involved either an expensive galvanometer, quadrant electrometer, or electrometer tube, or perhaps both an expensive galvanometer and tube. We shall now publish for the first time an interesting, efficient, and remark-

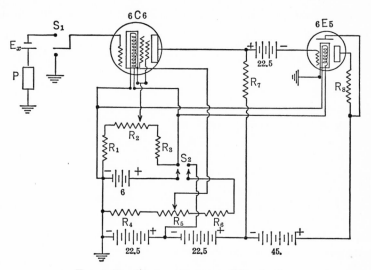

Fig. 3·12.   Electron-beam amplifier circuit.

ably cheap circuit invented by Hill,[45] containing neither an expensive tube, nor a galvanometer, nor even a milliammeter.   It has been used with great success in many different laboratories.   The component parts of the circuit illustrated in Fig. 3·12 can be enumerated as follows: (the suppressor grid is connected to the cathode)

6 C 6   Heater-type, triple-grid, detector-amplifier tube. Grid current about 10^{-12} amp., mutual conductance 20 μa./v. under conditions of use, heater voltage 6.3, heater current 0.3 amp.   Pins 1, 2, 3, 4, 5, 6 and cap connect to the heater, plate, screen grid, suppressor grid, cathode, heater and control grid, respectively.

[45] Private communication from Dr. S. E. Hill.   Electron-ray-tube thermionic amplifiers have been used before, see G. F. Smith and V. R. Sullivan, *J. Soc. Chem. Ind.*, **56**, 104 T (1937).

6 E 5   Electron-ray tube, indicator type with triode unit. Heater voltage 6.3, heater current 0.3 amp., pins, 1, 2, 3, 4, 5 and 6 connect to the heater, plate, grid, target, cathode, and heater, respectively.

S_1 Highly insulated and shielded electrometer switch.

S_2 Double-pole, single-throw switch.

R_1 600 ohms, fixed resistance.

R_2 600 ohms, variable rheostat.

R_3 2500 ohms, fixed resistance.

R_4 10,000 ohms, fixed resistance.

R_5 20,000 ohms, variable rheostat.

R_6 10,000 ohms, fixed resistance.

R_7 5 megohms grid leak (fixed resistance).

R_8 0.5 megohm grid leak.

Metallized filament resistors of low price can be used as the fixed resistances, but the two rheostats should be fairly good ones. Adequate shielding and insulation of the input circuit is most essential, particularly so because of the high mutual conductance and amplification factor of the 6 C 6 tube.

Operation of Hill's amplifier consists in closing the battery switch S_2, opening switch S_1 so that the control grid is "free," adjusting R_5 until the shaded pattern produced by the beam of electrons striking the fluorescent target in the 6 E 5 tube becomes a narrow straight line (which we shall call the electrical zero), closing switch S_1 to connect the control grid to ground, adjusting R_2 to electrical zero, again opening S_1 and again adjusting R_5 to electrical zero, and then repeating the R_2 adjustment with S_1 connected to earth. Repetition of these operations more than twice is not usually necessary; the adjustments bring the voltage on the control grid to earth potential and at the same time provide a grid-biasing voltage of about -1.5 v. with respect to the cathode, very close to the free grid potential. Under these operating conditions, the grid current (theoretically zero with the grid at its free grid voltage) is about 10^{-12} amp., the error arising from this grid current when using a glass electrode having a resistance of 100 megohms is, therefore, only 0.1 mv., a negligible amount. In 1928 Nottingham also suggested operating ordinary amplifying tubes at the free, or nearly free, grid voltage in the case of glass electrode e.m.f. measurements, and his suggestion has been followed by a number of people. Space does not permit the description of their circuits. Usually stability of the circuit is not as good as it is when the control grid is sufficiently negative to produce a low and steady positive control grid current.

After adjustment of rheostats R_2 and R_5 as described above, switch S_1 is now thrown to connect the unknown e.m.f.-potentiometer combination to the grid, and the e.m.f.'s balanced as usual to the electrical zero.   Drift of the electrical zero with time is not serious, and the sensitivity of the apparatus is good enough to measure the e.m.f. to ± 0.5 mv. or ± 0.01 pH unit.

Capacitative coupling or impulse-type pH electrometers have been described first by Morton [46] and later by Ellis and Kiehl [47] and Goodhue [48] and are built and sold by several industrial firms.

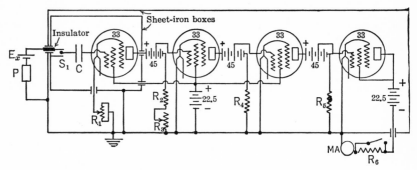

FIG. 3·13.   Impulse-type circuit of Ellis and Kiehl.

Low-cost electron tubes can be used in these amplifiers inasmuch as a condenser, inserted in series in the control-grid circuit, effectually reduces the grid current to a negligible value, but the instruments do not read continuously, alternate charging and discharging of the condenser being required as the unknown e.m.f. is balanced by the potentiometer.   One important advantage to the impulse-type circuit, as

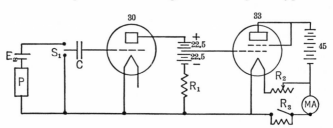

FIG. 3·14.   Impulse-type circuit of Goodhue.

pointed out by Morton, is that drift of electrical zero is of no consequence; one needs to observe only the direction of the deflection of the galvanometer image or milliammeter needle when the tapping key is pressed.   In fact, Morton, one of whose circuits is described in detail in Sec. 13·1 and Fig. 13·3, inserts a condenser in series in the galva-

[46] Morton, *J. Chem. Soc.* **1931**, 2977.
[47] S. B. Ellis and S. J. Kiehl, *Rev. Sci. Instruments*, **4**, 131 (1933).
[48] L. D. Goodhue, *Iowa State Coll. J. Sci.* **10**, 7 (1935).

nometer branch of his end-tube plate circuit so that no current at all flows through the ballistic galvanometer except when the current surges occur. In this way galvanometer drift is completely eliminated. Ellis and Kiehl's and Goodhue's circuits are illustrated in Fig. 3·13 and Fig. 3·14 (filament-heating circuit omitted) while the specifications of the various component parts follow:

	Ellis and Kiehl's Circuit	*Goodhue's Circuit*
S_1	Highly insulated switch	Highly insulated switch
C	Cardwell type 156–B variable air condenser, 0.001 μf. capacity, hard-rubber insulation replaced by amber.	Mica condenser, 0.001 μf. capacity molded in Bakelite
R_1	100-ohm radio potentiometer	150,000 ohms, fixed resistance, 1 watt
R_2	12,500 ohms	2000-ohm wirebound, nontapered, radio potentiometer.
R_3	5000-ohm rhoeostat	5000 ohms, fixed resistance
R_4, R_5	20,000 ohms	
R_6	6000 ohms	
MA	Milliammeter, scale of 0–3 ma.	Milliameter, scale of 0–1 ma.

The grid of the first tube in both circuits is free, while the grids of the second or succeeding tubes are connected to the middle or 22.5 v. tap of a 45-volt B-battery. The operating characteristics of the tubes are not particularly critical, with the exception that the plate current of the second or amplifying tube must be sufficient to bring the milliammeter needle to approximately the middle of its scale.

To make a measurement, one connects switch S_1 to the unknown e.m.f.-potentiometer circuit and notes the direction of the momentary deflection of the milliammeter needle at the instant of making or breaking the contact, the magnitude of the deflection indicates only roughly the degree of unbalance. Thus we are unconcerned with the actual reading of the milliammeter needle; we wish only to know whether the needle deflects on charging and discharging condenser C with the current from the e.m.f.-potentiometer combination. At perfect balance, the condenser C receives no charge and the milliammeter needle reading (which is not zero) remains unchanged on operation of switch S_1. In this way the zero reading of the milliammeter is of no importance and a zero drift introduces no difficulty. The chief precaution to heed in the construction of the amplifier is that condenser C must have an internal resistance high in comparison with the internal grid-to-filament impedance of the first tube, or on opening switch S_1, the grid current, if any, would be cut off, causing the milliammeter needle to deflect.

Finally we wish to point out that many balanced Wheatstone-bridge circuits containing two vacuum tubes each in a separate arm of the Wheatstone bridge have been described,[49] the purpose of the two-tube balancing arrangement being to increase the stability of the circuit and to cut down galvanometer drift. In Chapter 13, Figs. 13·1 and 13·6 and Secs. 13·1 and 13·2, two such circuits are illustrated and discussed. In Fig. 3·15 we have drawn a circuit described by Müller and Dürichen in which it is possible to adjust the operating characteristics of the two tubes until the galvanometer deflections become independent of fluctuations in the filament and plate voltages. The initial adjustment consists in setting R_1 equal to R_2, and changing E_{G_2} until the galvanometer setting is zero. The plate voltage is next altered by a definite amount and the direction and magnitude of the galvanometer deflection noted. A slight change in R_2 is then made, E_{G_2} again varied to bring the galvanometer to zero and again the direction and magni-

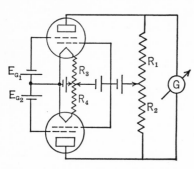

Fig. 3·15. Twin-tube balanced thermionic amplifier.

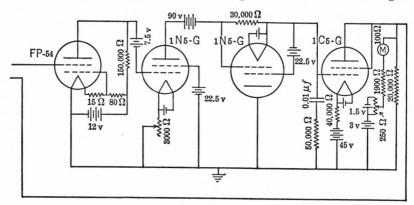

Fig. 3·16. Amplifier circuit of Heidelberg and Rense employing negative feedback.

tude of the galvanometer deflection is noted for the above stated change in plate voltage. If the deflection has decreased, R_2 has been altered

[49] For a review with references see Fr. Müller and W. Dürichen, Z. Elektrochem. **42**, 31 (1936).

in the right direction and the process can be continued until the value of R_2 is such that no galvanometer deflection is observed for a small variation in plate voltage. To neutralize the circuit for variations in filament current the magnitude of resistances R_3 and R_4 is altered until a slight change in filament current produces no galvanometer deflection. Müller and Dürichen state that they have succeeded in constructing a two-tube, Wheatstone-bridge arrangement similar to Fig. 3·7b in which one battery supplies the filament, space-charge grid, and plate voltages for both tubes. In operation during an interval of fifteen minutes the change in plate current was only 1×10^{-10} amp., corresponding to a change of 0.01 mv. in the unknown e.m.f.

Heidelberg and Rense[50] describe a triple stage direct current amplifier employing a negative feedback from the output tube to the input FP–54 tube. Stability of the circuit is exceptionally good, and a sensitive galvanometer is not required; the amplification factor being of the order 10^7 so that a portable Weston microammeter can be used as the null-point indicator. Their circuit is illustrated in Fig. 3·16 which is self-explanatory.

[50] Q. S. Heidelberg and W. A. Rense, *Rev. Sci. Instruments* 11, 386 (1940).

CHAPTER 4

TYPES OF GLASS ELECTRODES AND GLASSES

4·1. Types of Glass for Glass Electrodes

In this chapter we discuss first, the chemical and electrical properties of glass as a function of its composition and second, the different
types of glass electrodes that can be fabricated from the best glass.   In
the following chapter separate reference electrodes such as the "saturated calomel" electrode are described and in Chapter 6 the whole
glass electrode cell, formed by bringing together the glass electrode and
the two reference electrodes, is finally elaborated.

In general, we may say that the criteria by which we judge glasses
for glass electrodes are those originally selected by Hughes,[1] namely,
low electrical resistance of the glass, low errors shown by the glass
electrode in alkaline (and we may now add in acid and non aqueous)
solution, good stability of e.m.f. in the alkaline range, and stable and
low asymmetry potentials of the glass electrode.   Haber and Klemensiewicz[2] obtained their best results with a sodium-rich low-melting
Thuringia glass; high-melting Jena glass electrodes exhibited a scarcely
discernible hydrogen electrode function.

Hughes[3] found ordinary soda-lime glass to be suitable.   Brown[4]
confirmed the observations of Haber and Klemensiewicz that Jena
borosilicate glass acted poorly as a hydrogen electrode, but he also
noticed that this glass acted more like a sodium electrode in alkaline
solutions than did the low-melting Thuringia glass.   When we speak
of the "sodium function" of the glass electrode, or say that the glass
electrode acts "like a sodium electrode" we mean that the e.m.f. developed at the glass surface changes with change of sodium-ion concentration in the solution in the same way that the e.m.f. would change
at the surface of a sodium electrode.

Horovitz (1923) and Schiller[5] (1924) investigated the electrode
functions of five different types of glasses, the compositions, however,

---

[1] W. S. Hughes, *J. Chem. Soc.* **1928**, 491.

[2] F. Haber and Z. Klemensiewicz, *Z. physik. Chem.* **67**, 385 (1909).

[3] W. S. Hughes, *J. Am. Chem. Soc.* **44**, 2860 (1922).

[4] W. E. L. Brown, *J. Sci. Instruments* **2**, 12 (1924).

[5] K. Horovitz, *Z. Physik* **15**, 369 (1923).   H. Schiller, *Ann. Physik* [4] **74**, 105
(1924).

being given only qualitatively in their papers. All the glasses showed the hydrogen-electrode function, but glasses containing sodium acted partially as sodium electrodes, those containing zinc partially as zinc electrodes, etc. Furthermore, the behavior of the glass electrodes was believed by them to depend not only on the composition of the glass, but also on the length of time the glass had stood in contact with various salt solutions. Thus a weak silver-electrode function was developed by allowing the glass electrode to remain for some time in a silver nitrate solution. Glasses that had stood in concentrated sodium chloride solutions were slow in regaining their hydrogen electrode function when replaced in an acid solution. Horovitz [6] and his Vienna co-workers were more interested, however, in demonstrating the different electrode functions and the "mixed-electrode" functions of different glasses than in finding the most suitable glass for pH measurements.

Von Steiger [7] in 1924 used a low-melting Thuringia glass. In 1928 Hughes made the first systematic study of the effect of composition on the properties of the glass electrode.[1] His results, which are shown in Table 4·1 indicate that if the percentage of silica falls much below 72 per cent, the electrical resistance of the glass increases enormously; that if lime (calcium oxide) is replaced by alumina, the conductance is not particularly impaired, but the hydrogen-electrode function decreases badly. (In Table 4·1 the ratio $\Delta Eg/\Delta Eh$ should be unity if the glass electrode acted perfectly as a hydrogen electrode.) The data indicate that a glass similar to No. 793A containing roughly 72% SiO_2, 8% CaO, and 20% Na_2O is best for glass electrode use.

Elder and Wright [8] made a laboratory sample of glass of this composition from fairly pure chemicals, E, and compared its electrical properties with ordinary Corning Soft Glass, CG, with a white flint glass, W, from Wood Bros. Co., England, and with soft glasses from the Kimball Glass Co., K, and the Glasco Products Co., Gl, obtaining the data given in Table 4·2. Evidently the glass recommended by Hughes is better than commercial soft glasses as judged by its low asymmetry potential, although the commercial glasses functioned properly as hydrogen electrodes.

While Elder and Wright were performing their experiments, Mac-Innes and the author [9] also carried out a similar but more extensive

[6] Horovitz, F. Horn, J. Zimmerman, and J. Schneider, *Sitzber. Akad. Wiss. Wien*, **Abt. IIa 134**, 335 (1925).

[7] A. L. von Steiger, *Z. Elektrochem.* **30**, 259 (1924).

[8] L. W. Elder, Jr., and W. H. Wright, *Proc. Natl. Acad. Sci.* **14**, 936 (1928); *J. Am. Chem. Soc.* **51**, 3266 (1929).

[9] D. A. MacInnes and M. Dole, *J. Am. Chem. Soc.* **52**, 29 (1930).

investigation of the properties of the glass electrodes as a function of
its composition.   They made up a variety of glasses which were then
blown into the thin membrane type of electrode described in Sec. 4·5.
The resistances of the different composition glass electrodes having
nearly the same area and thickness (approximately 4 mm. in diameter
and 0.001 mm. thick) were measured using the circuit of Fig. 4·1

TABLE 4·1

ELECTRICAL PROPERTIES OF GLASS AS A FUNCTION OF ITS COMPOSITION
DATA OF HUGHES, 1928

Constituent or Property	Percentage Composition by Weight				
	X-Ray	Soft German	Mon-crieff	No. 793A	No. 444
SiO_2............	66.88	70.62	67.56	71.83	72.19
Al_2O_3..........	4.60	3.23	6.53	0.44	8.96
TiO_2...........	Trace	Trace	Trace	....	....
Fe_2O_3..........	0.08	0.11	0.13	0.04	....
MnO...........	Trace	Trace	0.17	....	....
CaO...........	6.76	7.58	6.54	8.36	0.08
MgO...........	0.81	0.25	....	Trace	....
Na_2O...........	15.48	15.48	15.82	18.83	18.79
K_2O............	5.56	2.62	3.34	....	....
SO_3............	....	....	....	0.22	....
Conductance.....	Very low, useless	Good	Poor	Excellent	Good
$\frac{\Delta E_g}{\Delta E_h}$ (0–10 pH)...	....	0.92	0.88	0.95–0.98	0.24–0.27 (Very variable)
Asymmetry potential........	....	High, slow drift	Very high, slow drift	Very low, soon becomes constant	Fairly low, soon becomes constant
ΔE in N-KOH 16 hours........	....	10–90 mv.	77–90	5–79	121 in 0.3 N. $Ba(OH)_2$

where G is the glass electrode cell, B is a working battery (actually a
dry cell of 1.5 v. was used) and R_R a resistance of 0.5 megohm.   The
IR drop, E_R, was measured by means of a Compton quadrant electrometer.   The open-circuit e.m.f., E_B, could also be measured.   The
resistance of $B + G$ is given by the equation

$$R_G + R_B = R_R \left(\frac{E_B}{E_R} - 1 \right)$$ [4·1·1]

but since R_B is very much smaller than R_G we may neglect it in comparison with R_G and take the entire measured resistance of $B + G$ as

TABLE 4·2

ELECTRICAL PROPERTIES OF GLASS AS A FUNCTION OF ITS COMPOSITION
DATA OF ELDER AND WRIGHT (1928) AND OF ELDER (1929)

Glass	$\Delta E/\Delta pH$ Theoretical = 59.1 mv.	Asymmetry Potential, mv.				
		Electrodes Untreated	Electrodes Annealed	Polarized Negative	Polarized Positive	Thin Membrane
E	60.4 ± 0.6 61.5 ± 1.9	+4.9 ± 1.1	+3.5	+9.8	+3.0	....
CG	58.4 ± 2.6	−41.3 ± 4.0	−105.5	+3.5	−41.0	+1.0
W	51.6 ± 3.0 52.1 ± 3.8	−14.4 ± 3.3	....	....	....	....
K	58.9 ± 2.2	−64.0 ± 6.2	−155.0	....	....	+4.5
Gl	60.3 ± 2.1	−10.3 ± 2.4	−61.5	....	....	....

being equal to that of the glass membrane alone. Resistance measurements were made on all glass membranes as soon as possible after they

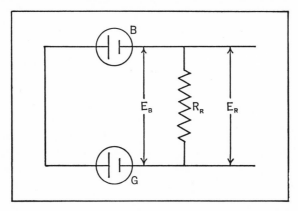

FIG. 4·1. Circuit for measuring resistance of glass electrode.

had been blown and again twenty-four hours later. The asymmetry potential on all electrodes was similarly measured twice to discover a trend, if any.   As a final test of the quality of the glass, MacInnes and Dole measured the error given by the glass electrode in 0.1 N NaOH (the error being the divergence of the glass electrode e.m.f. from the theoretically correct hydrogen electrode value) and the trend of this error with time.

MacInnes and Dole did not study the relation between the composition of the glass electrode and its behavior in acid and nonaqueous solutions because at the time of their work the errors of the glass electrode in acid and nonaqueous solutions had not yet been discovered. Indeed, up to the time of writing this monograph, no author has published any information on this point, but we expect that such an important glass electrode problem will not remain long unsolved.   Below we give some preliminary results obtained by Hubbard, Hamilton, and Finn [10] of the Glass Section of the National Bureau of Standards which indicate that it will be possible to find a better glass for glass electrode work in acid and nonaqueous solutions than is now being used.

MacInnes and Dole's data are collected in Table 4·3 from which may be gleaned the following facts: Pyrex, Jena, potassium, lithium, and magnesium glasses are unsuitable for glass-electrode measurements in contrast to the soda-lime glasses which have the lowest asymmetry potential, the lowest resistance, and the most stable e.m.f.'s in 0.1 N NaOH.   Of the latter glasses, the glass having the composition SiO_2, 72%; Na_2O, 22%; and CaO, 6%; and the glass having the lowest melting point possible for the three-component (CaO - SiO_2 - Na_2O) system according to the ternary-phase diagram of Morey [11] seems to be the best glass for pH determinations.   It has a low electrical resistance, low asymmetry potential and gives the smallest errors and most stable e.m.f. in alkaline solutions.   The Corning Glass Works, Corning, N. Y., manufactures glass of this composition, their number 015, but their product is probably not as good as that made by MacInnes and Dole and occasionally suffers from impurities arising from corrosion of the pots in which it is made [12] or from too prolonged a heat treatment as indicated by the fact that certain batches of their 015 glass have been known to produce inferior glass electrodes. This difficulty is easily remedied by trying a different sample of the 015 glass; we ourselves, have always found the Corning 015 glass to be

[10] D. Hubbard, E. H. Hamilton, and A. N. Finn, *J. Research Natl. Bur. Standards* **22**, 339 (1939).

[11] G. W. Morey, *J. Soc. Glass Tech.* **9**, 232 (1925); "International Critical Tables," McGraw-Hill Book Co., Vol. II, p. 97.

[12] Private communication from E. F. Kelm of the Corning Glass Works, Corning, N. Y.

satisfactory although having a higher electrical resistance than the glass made by MacInnes and Dole. The higher electrical resistance is probably due to the longer heat treatment of the glass necessary to draw it out into tubes.

TABLE 4·3

ELECTRICAL PROPERTIES OF GLASS AS A FUNCTION OF ITS COMPOSITION
DATA OF MACINNES AND DOLE (1930)

Glass	Wt. Percentage				A.P. Millivolts		Resistance Megohms		Initial Error in 0.1 N NaOH
	SiO$_2$	CaO	Li$_2$O	Na$_2$O	1st Day	2nd Day	1st Day	2nd Day	Millivolts
Pyrex...........	....	....	....	....	....	......	Very high	Very high	
Potassium.......	72	6	....	22*	−52	....	High	....	Rapid incr.
Jena thermometer	.....	....	....	.....	−47.0	−42.7	400	....	Rapid incr.
Soft commercial..	.....	....	....	.....	−27.9	− 6.0	72	96	Increase
Soda lime.......	72	8	....	20	+ 4.1	+ 6.1	47	42	Slow incr.
Best soda lime...	72	6	....	22	− 3.8	+ 0.6	12	8	32 (const.)
Soda lime.......	72	4	....	24	− 2.5	....	5	.....	Increase
Soda lime.......	70	6	....	24	− 7.5	− 1.6	7.5	5.8	32 (very slow incr.)
Soda lime.......	74	6	....	20	−14.8	− 4.3	20.3	20.7	Slow incr.
Soda lime.......	74	4	....	22	− 3.3	0	5.4	3.4	Slow incr.
Soda lime.......	70	8	....	22	− 1.6	− 0.9	19.9	22.0	Slow incr.
Lithium.........	72	6	22	....	0	+ 1.1	1.5	0.2	Rapid incr.
Soda-lithium.....	72	6	2	20	....	....	600	.....	Rapid incr.
Soda-lithium.....	72	6	4	18	....	....	High	700	Rapid incr.
Potassium-lithium	72	6	11	11*	....	....	3000	3000	Rapid incr.
Magnesium......	64.5	10†	....	25.5	−12.0	− 7.5	45	75	Rapid incr.

* K$_2$O.
† MgO.

In 1931 Kahler and DeEds studied the asymmetry potentials of the glass electrode as a function of pH by measuring the potential drop across the glass membrane at different pH values of the solution when the solution was the same on both sides of the membrane.[13]   Using a relatively thick bulb made of glass of unknown origin they found that the asymmetry potential increased from −14 mv. at pH 4.5 to −35

[13] H. Kahler and F. DeEds, *J. Am. Chem. Soc.*, **53**, 2998 (1931).

mv. at pH 8.   This means, if we have interpreted their data correctly, that the inside of the bulb in changing its interfacial potentials, has failed to act as nearly like a hydrogen electrode as has the outside of the bulb, or alternately, that the outside surface has suffered too great a change in its interfacial potential, which could be caused by the outside surface failing to develop its positive hydrogen electrode function at pH 8 to the extent that it does at pH 4.5.   The asymmetry potential at pH 4 is larger the thicker the glass membrane.   This would indicate that the asymmetry potential is due in part to "strains" in the glass membrane, or to other inequalities across the membrane such as inequalities of composition which might give rise to an electrical potential difference while the change of asymmetry potential with change of pH indicates that surface inequalities must be taken into consideration.   If the glass membrane was made thinner by dissolving it partially in hydrofluoric acid, the asymmetry potential became smaller [14] while its ability to act like a hydrogen electrode increased.

Haugaard [15] claims that the asymmetry potential is a function of the pH because a convex glass surface in its behavior deviates more from that of the hydrogen electrode than does a concave surface.

Since the Corning 015 glass contains 22% Na_2O, one might expect it to exhibit a considerable sodium-electrode function if the previously mentioned ideas of Horovitz are correct.   Kahler and DeEds found, however, that "only in alkaline solutions does the glass 015 show a significant sodium-electrode function and even then it is far below the hypothetical magnitude."   Horovitz failed to consider that addition of salt might of itself change the pH somewhat; he made no correction for change in the activity coefficient of the hydrogen ion and change in the liquid-junction potential as the salt concentration increased. Kahler and DeEds took both of these effects into account by measuring the pH with the hydrogen electrode.

Further studies during 1931 on the Corning 015 glass were made by MacInnes and Belcher [16] who measured both the alternating-current (a.-c.) and direct-current (d.-c.) resistances of 015 glass electrodes, 4 mm. in diameter and about 0.001 mm. thick, and showed that the a.-c. resistance varied from one to two megohms at 1200 cycles while the d.-c. resistances of the same electrodes varied from 50 to 80 megohms (see Table 4·4).   The a.-c. resistances decreased with rising frequency of the a.-c. while the d.-c. resistances were independent of

[14] For the deleterious effect of hydrofluoric acid on the glass electrode see Sec. 7·3.

[15] G. Haugaard, *Compt. rend. Trav. Lab. Carlsberg, Sér. Chim.* **22**, 199 (1938).

[16] D. A. MacInnes and D. Belcher, *J. Am. Chem. Soc.* **53**, 3315 (1931).

applied voltages; in other words, the d.-c. measurements verified Ohm's law.   Since the d.c. polarizes the glass electrode and produces a back e.m.f. P,

$$I = \frac{E - P}{R} \qquad\qquad [4·1·2]$$

the validity of Ohm's law can only mean that the back e.m.f. is directly proportional to the applied e.m.f.,

$$P = KE \qquad\qquad [4·1·3]$$

Combining Eqs. 4·1·2 and 4·1·3

$$I = \frac{E(1 - K)}{R} \qquad\qquad [4·1·4]$$

in the d.-c. measurement; therefore, the resistance measurement was presumably of $R/1\text{-}K$ instead of R.

TABLE 4·4

ELECTRICAL PROPERTIES OF CORNING 015 GLASS; RESISTANCES IN MEGOHMS
DATA OF MacINNES AND BELCHER, 1931

Elec-trode No.	Apparent Resistance		Electrode No. 6		Electrode No. 7		
	a.c.	d.c.	Frequency	Apparent Resistance	Applied e.m.f. Volts	I × 10⁹	Apparent Resistance
1	1.28	54.5	0	81.0	0.126	1.02	123
2	1.32	51.0	1020	2.55	0.252	2.17	121
3	3.96	129.0	1470	2.05	0.377	3.12	121
4	1.69	52.5	2050	1.86	0.629	5.15	122
5	2.84	102.0	3380	1.27	0.879	7.26	121

MacInnes and Belcher believe that the a.-c. resistance, although including capacitative reactance, represents more nearly the true electrical resistance of the glass, but since Ohm's law is valid for the d.-c. resistance, they concluded that it is better to adhere to the d.-c. rather than the a.-c. method of measurement.   We might also point out that the d.-c. resistance is the resistance that is of importance in e.m.f. measurements, which is what we are chiefly concerned with in this book.   MacInnes and Belcher's data are collected in Table 4·4. The temperature is 25° C.

In 1932 the Russian chemists, Sokolov and Passinski [17] compared a lithium, a sodium, and a potassium glass with respect to their behavior in alkaline aqueous solutions obtaining extremely interesting results of which the most important for practical purposes are their data, illustrated in Fig. 4·2, obtained with a glass electrode made from a glass having the composition SiO_2, 80%; CaO, 10%; and Li_2O, 10%.

In the case of this lithium glass electrode there is a linear relationship between e.m.f. and pH up to a pH of nearly 13 when any of the alkali hydroxides, except lithium hydroxide, are used as bases. This means that the glass electrode acts as a perfect hydrogen electrode up to this pH which is rather astonishing since with the Corning 015 glass

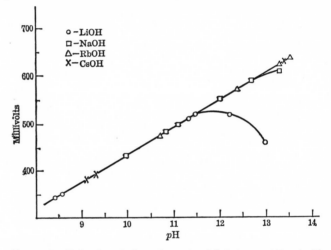

FIG. 4·2.   Behavior of glass electrode of Sokolov and Passinski.

the e.m.f.-pH curve begins to depart from linearity at a pH of 9.   Unfortunately Gabbard and the author [18] were unable to confirm their results; in fact, they were unable to make reliable measurements at any pH using lithium glass electrodes having the composition stated by Sokolov and Passinski.   The electrical resistance of the lithium glass electrodes was extremely high, the asymmetry potentials large and fluctuating and the change of e.m.f. with change of pH considerably smaller than that of a perfect hydrogen electrode.   (See, however, the remarks about lithium glass electrodes in Sec. 7·3.)

In 1934 Lengyel and Blum [19] carried out a thorough and extensive study of the electrical properties of glass electrodes as the composition

[17] S. I. Sokolov and A. H. Passinski, *Z. physik. Chem.* **160A**, 366 (1932).

[18] J. L. Gabbard and M. Dole, *Trans. Electrochem. Soc.* **72**, 129 (1937).

[19] B. Lengyel and E. Blum, *Trans. Faraday Soc.* **30**, 461 (1934).

of the glass was varied in a systematic and judicious manner.   They pointed out that glasses in general could be divided into two groups; glasses of the type studied by the author and co-workers which Lengyel and Blum designate by the symbol D_l, and which act well as hydrogen electrodes over a wide pH range and glasses of the type D which act poorly as hydrogen electrodes, but exhibit a fairly well developed sodium electrode function even at intermediate pH values.   Figure 4·3 taken from their paper illustrates this difference in behavior, the glass electrode of the D_l glass (nearly identical with Corning 015) giving an e.m.f. directly proportional to the pH up to a pH of 9 and having only a weak sodium electrode function in solutions of higher

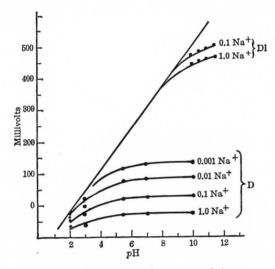

Fig. 4·3.   Comparison of two types of glasses.

pH; and glass electrodes of the D class giving potentials practically independent of the pH from pH 4 and above, and exhibiting a very pronounced sodium electrode function except in acid solutions.   Lengyel and Blum varied the composition of glasses of type D_l in two ways, first, by varying the soda-lime ratio holding the mole-percentage of silica constant, and second, by varying both the proportion of silica and of the basic oxides.   Glasses of the type D were varied by introducing other acid oxides in the place of silica as well as by varying the soda-lime ratio.   The compositions in mole per cent of the fifteen glasses studied by them are given in Table 4·5.

The striking fact about the data of Table 4·5 is that there is apparently no relation between the composition of the glass and its specific conductance, κ, nor between the composition and the Q values of the table.

TABLE 4·5

COMPOSITION AND ELECTRICAL PROPERTIES OF GLASSES STUDIED BY LENGYEL AND BLUM, 1934

Composition in mole per cent, glasses of type D_l

Glass	Acid Oxides			Basic Oxides				κ_{298} Ohms^{-1} Cm.$^{-1}$	A	Q Cal.
	SiO$_2$	Al$_2$O$_3$	B$_2$O$_3$	Na$_2$O	CaO	K$_2$O	Sum of Basic Oxides			
D_g	71.5	.....	.....	28.5	.....	.....	28.5			
D_h	71.5	.....	.....	25	3	.....	28	4.0×10^{-11}	32	16,200
D_l	71.5	.....	.....	21	8	.....	29	1.0×10^{-12}	170	19,300
D_i	71.5	.....	.....	14	14	.....	28	3.2×10^{-17}	16	21,000
D_f	76	.....	.....	24	.....	.....	24			
D_c	64	.....	.....	.....	19	16	35			
D_v	60	.....	.....	24	16	.....	40	2.5×10^{-13}	100	20,100

Glasses of Type D

D_r	58	.....	14	14	14	.....	28	3.2×10^{-16}	60	23,000
D_m	72	.....	14	14	.....	.....	14	6.3×10^{-14}	63	20,700
D_u	61.5	11	.....	24	3	.....	27	6.3×10^{-10}	158	16,500
D_a	75	3	11	11	.....	.....	11	1.5×10^{-13}	6	17,700
D*	.....	.....	.....	5 Wt. %	.....	.....	.....	2.8×10^{-15}	4	20,600

* High melting Jena glass.

Transition Glasses

D_p	67	.....	4	22	7	.....	29	5.6×10^{-13}	56	19,200
D_s	69	.....	7	23	.....	.....	23			

These Q values were obtained by measuring the conductance of the glass as a function of temperature from room temperature to 500°C., and calculating Q from the equation

$$\kappa = Ae^{-Q/RT}$$

[4·1·5]

Taking logarithms of this equation, we obtain

$$2.3 \log \kappa = 2.3 \log A - \frac{Q}{RT} \qquad [4\cdot1\cdot6]$$

By plotting $2.3 \log \kappa$ against $1/T$ a straight line results having a slope $-Q/R$, and an intercept on the ordinate equal to $2.3 \log A$ (when $1/T$ equals zero). The quantity Q may be considered to be an "activation energy" for the conducting ion in the glass, the energy required for the ion to surmount the "potential hill" between locations of equilibrium in the glass structure.

But when we study the electromotive behavior of Lengyel and Blum's glass electrodes, we find immediately a pronounced and systematic variation which is a function of the composition. This difference has already been shown graphically in Fig. 4·3 for two of the glasses and in Table 4·5 the complete set of data is given. All the glasses show about the same behavior in solutions of pure hydrochloric acid; the glasses which have the same mole per cent of silica D_g, D_h, D_l, D_i function alike, except the glass D_g which contains only soda as the basic oxide. This glass, and the similarly constituted glass D_f, act as hydrogen electrodes but show a lower e.m.f. over the whole pH range and are more sensitive to sodium-ion concentration. If the silica content is lowered as in glasses D_c and D_v, not much difference is noted, but if the silica content is lowered and at the same time other acidic oxides such as the oxides of aluminum or boron introduced, as in glasses D_r, D_m, D_u, D_a, and D, the electromotive behavior of the glass electrode becomes entirely different, the hydrogen electrode function disappears at pH 4 or 5 and the glass electrode acts like a sodium electrode.

Lengyel and Blum point out that this is probably owing to the change in the vitreous framework of the glass. According to the work of Zachariasen [20] glass has a definite but irregular crystalline structure, a structure which is determined by the network of silicate ions. A change in the type of basic oxide present does not alter the silicate structure, but if other acid oxides are added, the atomic arrangement in the glass changes and the electromotive properties become quite different. Since, however, the Q values of Table 4·5 and the specific conductance of the glasses are in no way related to the composition, Lengyel and Blum are forced to the conclusion that the surface properties of glass are of greatest importance to the electromotive behavior, that these surface properties are a function of the composition, and that the internal structure of the glass is immaterial.

[20] W. H. Zachariasen, *J. Am. Chem. Soc.* **54**, 3841 (1932).

TABLE 4·6

ELECTROMOTIVE BEHAVIOR OF GLASS ELECTRODES AS A FUNCTION OF COMPOSITION AT ROOM TEMPERATURE

DATA OF LENGYEL AND BLUM, 1934

E.M.F. in millivolts; glasses of type D_l

Glass	c HCl or Na^+	E.M.F. in HCl	E.M.F. in Na^+ Solutions pH							
			1	3	5.5	6.0	8.0	8.9	10.0	10.5
D_g	1.0	.....	−105	−23	....	147	....	....	....	....
	0.1	−83	−83	+26	....	151	....	314	....	....
	0.01	−26	−81	....	....	179	....	....	....	427
	0.001	+35	.....	....	....	....	....	....	....	....
D_h	1.0	.....	.....	....	....	212	....	....	410	....
	0.1	−83	.....	....	....	214	....	....	423	....
	0.01	−33	.....	....	....	222	....	....	417	....
	0.001	+30	.....	....	....	215	....	....	....	....
D_l	1.0	.....	.....	....	....	197	....	....	428	....
	0.1	−83	.....	....	....	197	....	....	432	....
	0.01	−30	.....	....	....	202	310	....	423	455
	0.001	+25	.....	....	....	205	....	....	....	....
D_i	1.0	.....	.....	33	....	180	....	....	....	....
	0.1	−83	.....	41	....	180	....	....	420	....
	0.01	−26	.....	32	....	190	300	....	....	....
	0.001	+30	.....	....	....	....	....	....	....	....
D_f	1.0	.....	−96	....	....	129	....	....	340	....
	0.1	−83	−83	....	....	130	....	....	350	....
	0.01	−30	−83	....	....	138	....	....	360	....
	0.001	+29	.....	....	....	139	....	....	....	....
D_c	1.0	.....	.....	....	....	184	....	....	424	....
	0.1	−83	.....	....	....	181	....	....	444	....
	0.01	−29	.....	....	....	188	....	....	414	....
	0.001	+31	.....	....	....	....	....	....	....	....
D_v	1.0	.....	.....	....	....	190	....	....	....	....
	0.1	−83	.....	....	....	192	....	....	422	....
	0.01	−30	.....	....	....	....	316	....	....	....
	0.001	.....	.....	....	....	....	....	....	....	....

TABLE 4·6—*Continued*

ELECTROMOTIVE BEHAVIOR OF GLASS ELECTRODES AS A FUNCTION OF COMPOSITION
AT ROOM TEMPERATURE

DATA OF LENGYEL AND BLUM, 1934

E.M.F. in millivolts; glasses of type D_l

Glass	c HCl or Na$^+$	E.M.F. in HCl	E.M.F. in Na$^+$ Solutions							
			pH							
			1	3	5.5	6.0	8.0	8.9	10.0	10.5
Transition Glasses										
D_p	1.0	.....	.....	....	....	199	....	....	390	....
	0.1	−83	.....	....	....	201	....	....	394	....
	0.01	−29	.....	....	....	....	....	....	....	....
	0.001	+27	.....	....	....	....	....	....	....	....
D_s	1.0	.....	.....	....	....	142	....	....	272	....
	0.1	−83	.....	....	....	177	....	....	313	....
	0.01	−37	.....	....	....	192	....	....	348	....
	0.001	+28	.....	....	....	....	....	....	....	....
Glasses of Type D										
D_r	1.0	.....	.....	....	....	−103	....	....	−100	....
	0.1	−83	.....	....	....	−50	....	....	−48	....
	0.01	−30	.....	.....	....	+1	....	....	....	....
	0.001	+21	.....	.....	....	+51	....	....	+52	....
D_m	1.0	.....	.....	....	....	−97	....	....	−97	....
	0.1	−83	.....	....	....	−50	....	....	−47	....
	0.01	−23	.....	....	....	+3	....	....	+6	....
	0.001	+33	.....	....	....	+55	....	....	....	....
D_u	1.0	.....	.....	....	....	−24	....	....	−24	....
	0.1	−83	.....	....	....	+30	....	....	+27	....
	0.01	−31	.....	....	....	+81	....	....	+79	....
	0.001	+27	.....	....	....	+130	....	....	....	....
D_a	1.0	.....	.....	....	−125	−110	....	....	−98	....
	0.1	−83	.....	....	−66	−48	....	....	−52	....
	0.01	−29	.....	....	−14	+5	....	....	+12	....
	0.001	+34	.....	....	+36	....	....	....	....	....
D	1.0	.....	.....	....	−29	....	....	....	−27	....
	0.1	−83	.....	....	+22	+30	....	....	+31	....
	0.01	−28	.....	....	+77	+80	....	....	+86	....
	0.001	+23	.....	....	+125	+125	....	....	+144	....

Chemists at the National Technical Laboratories [21] have developed a special glass more resistant chemically than Corning 015 for use at high temperatures. A special glass suitable particularly for the high pH range at room temperature is also announced by them. Schwabe and Herdey [22] find that a glass more electrically conductive than Corning 015 exhibits greater voltage errors.

Passinski [20] states that a calcium-free glass of low electrical resistance, having the composition Na_2O 28%, MgO 8%, and SiO_2 64% may be used for glass electrode pH measurements with satisfactory results.

Up to this point we have said nothing about the water content of the glass, not because the subject is of no importance, but because no one has published any quantitative data for the water content and its relation to the electrical properties of glass. Probably the conductance measurements of Lengyel and Blum are to be interpreted largely on the basis of the water content, inasmuch as qualitative experiments to be described in the next section show a very definite and important connection between water content, electrical resistance, and electromotive behavior.

We end this section with the conclusion that at the time of writing of this monograph the best glass for glass electrode work except in the range of high temperature and high pH is the Corning 015 glass, glass having the composition SiO_2 72%, Na_2O 22%, CaO 6%.

4·2. Water Content of Glass.   Durability and Treatment of the Glass Surface

The water content of glass both on the surface and in the body of the glass is of the utmost importance in determining the electrical characteristics of glass. Haber and Klemensiewicz [24] steamed out their glass bulbs which were 0.06 to 0.1 mm. thick for one hour and then soaked them in water until used. They found that if the bulbs dried out in air, irregular results were obtained; for example, a sodium rich, SiO_2 poor glass gave ΔE 0.6 v. between an acid and base solution; after drying, the ΔE varied between 0.3 and 0.5 v. Jena glass showed ΔE equal to zero (no hydrogen electrode function), but after treating with superheated water at 250°C. in an autoclave until the glass looked like "frosted" glass, ΔE rose to 0.3 v. In other words, by forcing water into the glass a hydrogen electrode function could be developed.

[21] Private communication from Dr. A. O. Beckman.

[22] K. Schwabe and O. Herdey, Jr., *Zellstoff u. Papier* **19**, 530 (1939).

[23] A. Passinski, *Zavodskaya Lab.* **8**, 869 (1939).

[24] F. Haber and Z. Klemensiewicz, *Z. physik. Chem.* **67**, 385 (1909).

Hughes [25] states that annealing glass reduces its electrical conductance, drives off surface water, and if dried at high temperature, the hydrogen electrode function may disappear completely. (Rebbeck and Ferguson [26] have demonstrated that sorbed water has no effect on conductance of soft soda-lime glass.) Elder [27] annealed his glass electrodes for 15 to 20 hours at 120°C. to reduce the asymmetry potential on the plausible assumption that if the asymmetry potential is caused by strains in the glass, annealing the glass should relieve the strains and eliminate the asymmetry potential. Much to his surprise he found that the asymmetry potential increased on annealing, see Table 4·2. This was probably caused by the glass becoming dehydrated unsymmetrically.

MacInnes and the author [28] discovered that adding a small amount of lithium oxide to the Corning 015 glass increased the resistance of the electrode from 12 megohms to 600 or over, and if the sodium oxide in the glass was completely replaced by lithium oxide, the resistance became lower than the resistance of the original Corning 015 glass (see Table 4·3). Furthermore, the resistance of this lithium glass decreased rapidly on standing, the glass took on a "milky" appearance and on further standing the very thin membrane disintegrated completely. These results are undoubtedly to be explained on the basis of the water content of the glass; if we assume that the electrical conductance of the soft soda-lime glasses is primarily a function of the water content, adding 2 to 4 per cent of lithium oxide would increase the resistance because the lithium oxide, being very hygroscopic, would combine with the small amount of water present and prevent it from taking part in the conduction process. If a large quantity of lithium oxide is added, 22 per cent, the glass is so hygroscopic that it deliquesces, the resistance drops off, and the glass practically dissolves. MacInnes and Belcher [29] studied the increase in resistance of the membrane type glass electrode with and without drying. An electrode having initially a resistance of 32 megohms developed a resistance of 40,000 megohms on heating to 50°C. in vacuum over phosphorus pentoxide. For treatment at 25°C. see the data of Table 4·7.

MacInnes and Belcher's dried membranes slowly returned to their original resistance after immersion in water. Their results showing that the resistances of the glass electrode increased on standing over

[25] W. S. Hughes, *J. Chem. Soc.* **1928**, 491.
[26] J. W. Rebbeck and J. B. Ferguson, *J. Am. Chem. Soc.* **46**, 1991 (1924).
[27] L. W. Elder, Jr., *J. Am. Chem. Soc.* **51**, 3266 (1929).
[28] D. A. MacInnes and M. Dole, *J. Am. Chem. Soc.* **52**, 29 (1930).
[29] D. A. MacInnes and D. Belcher, *J. Am. Chem. Soc.* **53**, 3315 (1931).

water are interesting because the usual type of experiments in which the glass electrode stands immersed in water proves that the resistance decreases on standing.   This decrease may be due to the gradual solution of the glass in the water with a consequent thinning of the membrane.   Laug [30] demonstrated that short periods of drying were without effect on the asymmetry potential and measured the rate at 38°C. at which an electrode regains its normal condition when reimmersed in water after prolonged drying.   These measurements, made on an electrode of average resistance, are illustrated in Fig. 4·4.   (0.0617 is the theoretically correct slope at 38°; see Appendix III).   The time to

TABLE 4·7

D.-C. RESISTANCES OF GLASS ELECTRODES IN MEGOHMS AT 25°C. WITH AND WITHOUT DRYING

DATA OF MacINNES AND BELCHER, 1931

Electrode Number	Initial Resistance	After 10 Days Over P_2O_5	Electrode Number	Initial Resistance	Over Water for 10 Days
1	28	113	1	22	30
2	28	60	2	28	38
3	36	118	3	42	56
4	27	99	4	41	51
5	24	93	....	....	....
6	41	110	....	....	....
Average Increase		230%	....	....	34%

reach equilibrium at room temperature might be somewhat longer than the three hours found by Laug for 38°.

Yoshimura [31] has recently published some new measurements on the change in the electrical properties of glass electrodes on standing in water and on the effect of drying separately both surfaces of the glass electrode. His conclusions are that the asymmetry potential of glass electrodes, the errors in alkaline solution, and the relative rate of corrosion decline on standing in water although the ability to act as a hydrogen electrode improves with time.   The asymmetry potential is made more negative by drying the outer surface of a glass electrode and more positive by drying the inner surface; in both cases the ability of either surface to act as a hydrogen electrode becomes less on drying,

[30] E. P. Laug, J. Am. Chem. Soc. **56**, 1034 (1934).
[31] H. Yoshimura, Bull. Chem. Soc. Japan, **12**, 359 (1937).

i. e., dE/dpH becomes less on drying.   On reimmersion in water these trends are reversed.

Not only can the glass-electrode functions become impaired by exposure of the surface to a vacuum or by drying in hot air, but irregular results are also obtained if the glass electrode is immersed in an anhydrous, nonaqueous medium like alcohol.   Private communications from two sources [32] indicate that too prolonged contact of the glass surface with 80 per cent alcohol or with other anhydrous (or nearly so) media, causes a deterioration of the glass in two ways, a change in the asymmetry potential and a decrease in the hydrogen-electrode function, i.e., a decrease in dE/dpH.   Reinstatement of the glass electrode in water will usually cause the electrode to recover its normal functions.

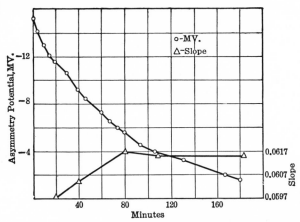

FIG. 4·4.   Rate at which the asymmetry potential and hydrogen-electrode function of glass electrode changes with time.

Powney and Jordan [33] noted the deleterious effect of hot alkaline solutions on glass electrodes stating, "The glass electrode gave reproducible results when working in alkaline solutions for the first few days of use, but the e.m.f. produced then increased slowly and more frequent calibration each day became necessary. Electrodes finally gave a very high and nonreproducible e.m.f., the attainment of this state being accelerated by working in strongly alkaline solutions at high temperatures.   Such electrodes could not be reconditioned by soaking in chromic acid and had to be rejected."

Watson [34] reports difficulties with glass electrodes cleaned with

[32] From Dr. J. M. Lupton of the DuPont Experimental Station, Wilmington, Del., and from Dr. R. F. Dillon of G. D. Searle & Co., Chicago, Ill.

[33] J. Powney and D. O. Jordan, *J. Soc. Chem. Ind.* **56**, 133 (1937).

[34] F. J. Watson, *Chem. Eng. Mining Rev.* **20**, 59 (1927).

cleaning solution (concentrated sulfuric acid and potassium dichromate), but Kerridge [35] cleaned her freshly blown electrodes with cleaning solution, steamed them out for two hours, and soaked them in water for twenty-four hours before use, obtaining good results. Dr. R. L. Slobod, working in the author's laboratory has observed that a Pyrex glass float when cleaned in chromic acid cleaning solution becomes slightly heavier, and only by standing in water for 48 hours does the float regain its normal density. Evidently chromic acid is strongly adsorbed by glass. No such effect was observed when the float was cleaned with a hot mixture of concentrated nitric and sulfuric acids, and the author recommends this mixture for the cleaning of glass electrodes.

The chemical stability of the glass, the rate at which it can be attacked and the rate at which the glass gives off alkali to the solution are important practical factors, particularly in the measurement of the pH of unbuffered solutions or of small quantities of solutions; and may be of importance theoretically. MacInnes and the author [36] remark that water dissolves from the Corning 015 glass about 7×10^{-10} equivalent of base in twenty-four hours per sq. mm. of surface, at 25°C. (or 0.2 mg. Na_2O per sq. dm.). Lengyel and Blum [37] measured the milligrams of sodium oxide dissolved per sq. dm. of glass surface when the glass was immersed in water at 80°C. for three hours, obtaining the results of Table 4·8.

TABLE 4·8

SOLUBILITY OF GLASS AS A FUNCTION OF COMPOSITION

DATA OF LENGYEL AND BLUM, 1934

Glass Symbol (see Table 4·5)	D_g	D_h	D_l	D_i	D_f	D_r	D_m	D_u	D
Solubility mg. Na_2O/dm^2..........	10.0	3.1	5.6	0.6	4.8	1.1	1.0	0.6	0.2

Ellis and Kiehl [38] found that the Corning 015 glass increased the pH of distilled water in which it was immersed so rapidly even when the distilled water flowed by the electrode, that they had to use ordinary commercial soft glass to measure its pH (see Sec. 10·1). Yoshi-

[35] P. M. T. Kerridge, *J. Sci. Instruments* **3**, 404 (1926).
[36] D. A. MacInnes and M. Dole, *J. Am. Chem. Soc.* **52**, 29 (1930).
[37] B. Lengyel and E. Blum, *Trans. Faraday Soc.* **30**, 461 (1934).
[38] S. B. Ellis and S. J. Kiehl, *J. Am. Chem. Soc.* **57**, 2139 (1935).

mura [39] studied the rate of solution of base as a function of age of the glass electrode by measuring the time of fading of a 0.0001 N hydrochloric acid solution containing 0.001% methyl red when rotated at 50°C. in the bulb of a glass electrode. His data indicate that as the electrode gets older, it gives off base less rapidly. Haugaard [40] has studied the action of water and 0.1 N hydrochloric acid on glass powder at 60° C. for 66 days finding that the drop of acidity of the solution was approximately equivalent chemically to the increase in "water of constitution" of the glass; in other words, hydrogen ions of the solution exchanged with nearly all the sodium ions in the glass (the glass powder was made from thin films of glass).

Recently some important work on the durability of glass electrodes has been done by Hubbard, Hamilton, and Finn.[41] Their method of measuring the rate of attack of Corning 015 and other glasses consisted in making an optical flat of the glass under investigation, partially immersing the flat in the selected acid or basic solution, covering the solution with a paraffin oil to retard evaporation, heating the solution to 50°C. for forty-eight hours, or at other temperatures for various lengths of time, then after washing and drying the flat, covering it with another optical flat

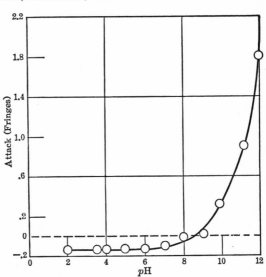

FIG. 4·5. Attack of Corning 015 glass in universal buffer for 6 hours at 80°C. A negative attack represents swelling.

and measuring the degree of attack of the glass by noticing the shift in the fringes of a Pulfrich interferometer at the line of demarcation between the glass surface which had been exposed to the solution

[39] H. Yoshimura, *Bull. Chem. Soc. Japan*, **12**, 359 (1937).

[40] G. Haugaard, *Nature* **140**, 66 (1937); *Glastech. Ber.* **17**, 104 (1939); *J. Phys. Chem.* **45**, 148 (1941).

[41] D. Hubbard, E. H. Hamilton, and A. N. Finn, *J. Research Natl. Bur. Standards*, **22**, 339 (1939); *Tech. News Bull. Natl. Bur. Standards*, **221**, 88 (1935).

and the unattacked glass surface which had been above the solution in the reaction vessel.　Figure 4·5 illustrates the attack of Corning 015 glass by the Britton-Robinson [42] universal buffer solutions for six hours at 80°C.　The remarkable fact about these results is that the durability of the glass becomes less (attack greater) just at the pH where the hydrogen electrode function begins to break down, and as the pH increases the attack increases in a manner quite similar to the way in which the error of the glass electrode (that is, error as a hydrogen electrode) increases.　Figure 4·6 represents the attack in very acid solutions in which just the opposite effect is noted; the swelling of the glass begins to decrease at the pH where the hydrogen electrode function of the glass again begins to break down.　In the case of a glass which behaves perfectly as a hydrogen electrode even in the "super-acid" range where the pH is -1, there is no detectable attack, see Fig. 4·7.　Finally in Fig. 4·8 data are tabulated and represented graphically for the electromotive behavior and attack of a glass electrode in ammonia solutions; here we have the interesting example of a solution which causes no alkali error of the electrode, but which as a matter of fact produces an error in the opposite direction, the slope dE/dpH increasing instead of decreasing.　This error has the same sign as the error in very acid solutions and we find here again that the durability of the glass improves; thus once more obtaining a correlation between hydrogen-electrode function and durability.

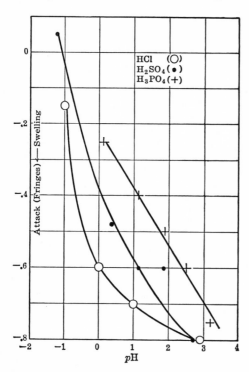

FIG. 4·6.　Swelling of Corning 015 glass in concentrated acids for 48 hours at 80°C.

The significance of these important results will be considered in

[42] H. T. S. Britton, "Hydrogen Ions," Second Edition, Chapman and Hall, London, 1932, p. 225.

Chapter 16 on the theory of the glass electrode.   We pass now to methods of making glass electrodes.

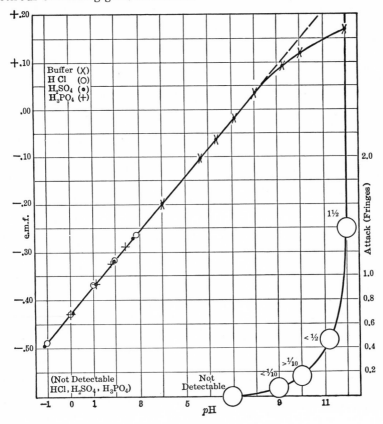

FIG. 4·7.   Electrode prepared from glass A.

4·3. Bulb Types of Glass Electrodes

Of the various shapes and types of glass electrodes that have been invented, the bulb type is the most important from the standpoint of practical use, convenience in handling and ease of construction; the thin membrane type has certain theoretical advantages while capillary glass electrodes are not only rugged but useful in micro-*p*H determinations.

Haber and Klemensiewicz,[43] the first to blow a glass electrode, made the bulb type illustrated in Fig. 2·2.   The Morton [44] glass elec-

[43] F. Haber and Z. Klemensiewicz, *Z. physik. Chem.* **67**, 385 (1909).
[44] C. Morton, *J. Sci. Instruments* **7**, 187 (1930).

trode used extensively in Great Britain, is similar to the Haber electrode in shape, but contains a sealed-in quinhydrone electrode.   (For reference electrodes see the next chapter).

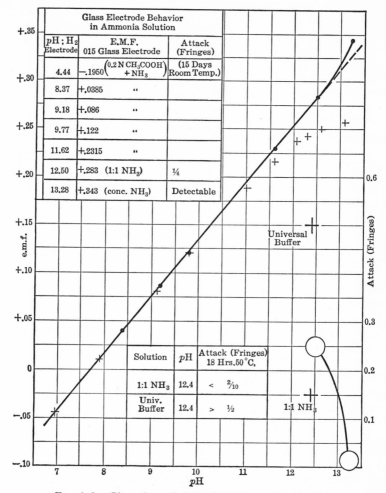

FIG. 4·8.   Glass electrode behavior in ammonia solution.

Harrison[45] blows his Haber type electrodes with a glass guard ring about them for mechanical protection.   Other methods of increasing the mechanical strength of Haber type electrodes involve coating the inner glass surface with a low-melting alloy[46] or filling the electrode

[45] G. B. Harrison, *J. Chem. Soc.* **1930**, 1528.
[46] P. A. Kryukov and A. A. Kryukov, *Russ.* 51,509 (1937); L. Kratz, *Kolloid-Z.* **86**, 51 (1939).

with viscous organic substances that solidify without a sudden increase of volume after an inner metallic coating has been applied.[47]

Mrs. Kerridge [48] invented the cup type illustrated in Fig. 2·5. Mirsky and Anson [49] give the following directions for blowing this form of glass electrode.

"Glass tubing having walls of medium thickness and an inside diameter of $\frac{3}{8}$ inch is used. A small bulb is blown at one end with walls thick enough to be strong. By directing a fine small flame at a point on the bulb and then sucking at the open end of the tube a small cup is formed depressed below the surface of the bulb. The cup should contain about 0.5 to 1.0 cc. and should be made quickly and without annealing."

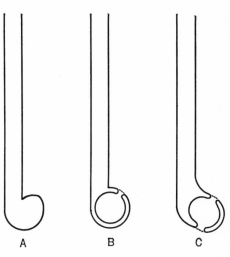

Figure 4·9 illustrates a serviceable low-resistant type of glass electrode described by Cameron.[50]

"A bulb of fairly heavy wall is blown from one-cm. diameter Corning 015 glass. This bulb is blown at an angle of 45° to the tube and is about two cm. in diameter. A small needle flame is then directed against the bulb near the stem, and when a small spot of the glass is hot, the bulb is removed from the flame and sucked in, thus forming a bulb within a bulb, as shown in *B*. The sucking is best done through a rubber tube in order to observe the formation of the inner bulb. The bulb is allowed to cool somewhat and a spot on the bottom, diametrically opposite the top opening is heated with a tiny gas flame. A flame about one cm. long, burning on the end of a drawn-out glass capillary, is suitable for this operation. A small bulb is sucked in until it touches the inner bulb and forms a flat membrane. Without further suction, the flame is directed at the center of this membrane until the glass melts through and the hole opens out."

Fig. 4·9. Thin-wall bulb electrode invented by Cameron.

It is not necessary to anneal the electrodes, the resistance is low, from 1 to 10 megohms, and the electrodes are not as easily broken as

[47] *Jenaer Glaswerk Schott & Gen.; Brit.* 495,303 (1938); 509,555 (1939).

[48] P. M. T. Kerridge, *Biochem. J.* 19, 611 (1925).

[49] A. E. Mirsky and M. L. Anson, *J. Biol. Chem.* 81, 581 (1929).

[50] A. E. Cameron, *Ind. Eng. Chem., Anal. Ed.* 9, 436 (1937).

the ordinary bulb type.   When filled with liquid, severe jolts are likely to break the electrodes and they are not applicable to liquids of high viscosity.   The inner membrane should not be so thin that the glass "clicks" when sucked in, or that spots of color show on the glass.

Commercial glass electrodes supplied in certain pH electrometers are made by sealing a bulb of Corning 015 glass on to a more resistant (chemically and electrically) soft glass.   The Corning company recommend their normal soft glass, No. 881, for this purpose.[51]   These electrodes are made by sealing a piece of the 015 glass tubing onto the soft glass and then blowing the 015 glass out into the shape of a bulb, the seal between the two types of glass being just at the top of the bulb.

A "tube" or "pipet" type of glass electrode having some unique features and invented by Briggs [52] is shown in Fig. 4·10.

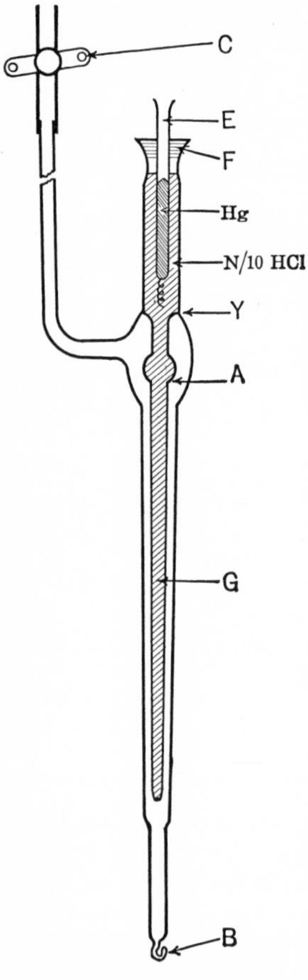

"The electrode glass is in the form of a capillary closed at the lower end and sealed to ordinary soft glass at A.   This in turn is sealed to the pipet at Y. A silver-silver chloride half cell E is sealed with de Khotinsky cement F into the chamber G continuous with the inside of the capillary of electrode glass after a solution of 0.1 N hydrochloric acid has been placed therein.   The solution upon which the pH is to be measured is sucked up in the pipet and held there by a small clamp C acting on a short length of rubber tubing at top of pipet. The tip of the pipet B is then placed in saturated potassium chloride solution in a beaker continuous with the salt bridge leading to calomel half cell; connections to the electrical measuring system are made through the mercury in the glass tube which is in electrical contact with the silver-silver chloride electrode.   The walls of the capillary of Corning 015 glass are of the order of 0.2 to 0.4 mm. in thickness.   The length of the capillary may be as short as 0.5 cm.   The electrode glass should be completely covered by the liquid the pH of which is being determined."

FIG. 4·10.   Briggs pipet-type glass electrode.

[51] Private communication from Frederick Kraissl of the Corning Glass Works.
[52] Private communication from Dr. D. R. Briggs of the Univ. of Minnesota.

The Briggs electrode can be designed to use very small quantities of liquid, it can be incorporated into systems for continuous flow of liquid around it, or into systems for measuring the *p*H of blood or of other liquids which must be kept out of contact with air, etc.

4·4. Insulation of Glass Electrode Stems

Before considering other types of glass electrodes we shall discuss the difficulties due to electrical leakage, methods of supporting the glass electrode on insulated holders, methods of painting the glass stem with nonconducting material, and the depth to which the glass electrode should be immersed. We are indebted to Kahler and DeEds [53] and to Morton [54] for making experimental studies of these questions.[55]

A schematic diagram illustrating shunt resistances across the glass electrode cell and parallel e.m.f.'s is shown in Fig. 4·11 where E is the actually measured e.m.f., E_g is the true e.m.f. of the glass electrode, e an extraneous parallel e.m.f., R the resistance of the glass electrode, and r the resistance of any leakage or shunting circuit. The cells represented in the figure are the whole galvanic combination; that is, both glass electrode and calomel reference electrode, not just the glass electrode half cell. The glass electrode has such an enormous resistance,

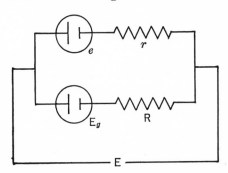

FIG. 4·11.   Diagram illustrating leakage resistances and film e.m.f.'s of glass electrode.

however, in comparison with both the calomel and silver-silver chloride electrodes that the following remarks may be attributed to the glass electrode alone.

For the case when e is equal to zero, which was true in Morton's experiments, we can write down the following easily derived equations (as given by Morton).

$$\frac{E_g}{E} = \frac{R + r}{r} \qquad\qquad [4·4·1]$$

[53] H. Kahler and F. DeEds, *J. Am. Chem. Soc.* **53**, 2998 (1931).
[54] C. Morton, *J. Chem. Soc.* **1934**, 256.
[55] See also I. H. Yoshimura, *J. Biochem. Japan*, **23**, 91 (1936).

$$\text{Percentage error in e.m.f. reading} = \frac{100(E_g - E)}{E_g} = \frac{100R}{(R + r)} \quad [4\cdot4\cdot2]$$

$$\text{Apparent efficiency in per cent} = \frac{100E}{E_g} = \frac{100r}{R + r} \quad [4\cdot4\cdot3]$$

$$\text{Slope of experimental calibration curve} = \frac{dE}{dp\text{H}}$$

$$= 0.0001983T \frac{r}{(R + r)} \quad [4\cdot4\cdot4]$$

where T is the absolute temperature.

$$\text{Experimental asymmetry potential} = E_g - E = \frac{RE_g}{(R + r)} \quad [4\cdot4\cdot5]$$

For the extreme case when the external shunting resistance is equal to the internal resistance of the glass electrode ($R = r$) the slope of the calibration curve is reduced to one-half its correct value and the apparent efficiency of the glass electrode becomes only 50 per cent. If the impedance (effective resistance) of the input circuit of the vacuum-tube amplifier is as low as 10,000 megohms, the error for a glass electrode of 100 megohms resistance is 1 per cent. This effect serves as a possible explanation of the abnormal observations of Britton and Robinson.[56]

Table 4·9 contains the experimental data obtained by Morton to test the validity of Eqs. 4·4·4 and 4·4·3. He shunted his glass-electrode cell with various resistances (input impedance was 10^{14} ohms) and then measured the e.m.f. of the glass electrode in 0.05 c potassium acid phthalate (solution a) and in a borax buffer (solution b). The theoretically perfect change in e.m.f. should be 302 mv.

The data of Table 4·9 indicate the correctness of Morton's analysis and prove that the external shunting resistance, r, must be one thousand times the resistance of the glass electrode, R, for the error to be as small as 0.1 per cent. Kahler and DeEds also pointed out in 1931 that the stem of a glass electrode should have an external surface resistance of 10^{11} ohms if the membrane resistance was 10^8 ohms.

Kahler and DeEds studied the dependence of the measured e.m.f. on the geometry of the two wetted surfaces, on the depth of immersion, on the time necessary to reach equilibrium and on the chemical composition of the film covering the outside surface of the glass. Their conclusions may be summarized as follows.

[56] H. T. S. Britton and R. A. Robinson, *Trans. Faraday Soc.* 28, 531 (1932).

1. The measured potential E in terms of E_g, e, R and r, is given by the equation

$$E = \frac{E_g r + eR}{R + r} \qquad [4·4·6]$$

2. When a tube-type glass electrode is filled on the inside to a depth of 19 cm. and immersed on the outside to a depth of 5.5 cm., the e.m.f. of the membrane is only 217.8 mv. when the theoretical e.m.f. is 246.3 mv. This error of 28.5 mv. is a function of the resistance of the

TABLE 4·9

BEHAVIOR OF GLASS ELECTRODE AS A FUNCTION OF SHUNT OR LEAKAGE RESISTANCE

DATA OF MORTON, 1934

Resistances in megohms; e.m.f. in millivolts; $R = 86$ megohms at 18°C.

Shunt resistance r.....	164	287	435	737	1580	7400	∞
E (solution a).........	145	171	185	203	210	221	223
E (solution b).........	−52	−61	−66	−69	−73	−77	−78
ΔE.................	197	232	251	272	283	298	301
Slope $\Delta E / \Delta p\mathrm{H}$.......	37.4	44.1	47.6	51.6	53.7	56.5	57.1
Measured efficiency %.	64.8	76.3	82.5	89.4	93.1	98.0	99
Efficiency calculated by Eq. 4·4·3.........	65.6	76.9	83.5	89.3	94.8	98.9	100

glass wall, see Eq. 4·4·6. If the inside and outside depths are the same, both either 5.5 cm. or 19.0 cm., the thoretical e.m.f. is observed.

3. If the entire outside surface is coated with a nonconducting film, such as stearic acid or paraffin wax, the inside of the glass electrode acts like a perfect hydrogen electrode, but the potential of the outside surface is independent of the pH.

4. The spurious effects are due to a conducting film on the surface of the glass above the outside solution which produces its own potential (in Fig. 4·11 this e.m.f. is denoted by e) as can be proved in two ways; painting the dry surface of the electrode with paraffin wax over the upper part of its exterior and immersing the electrode up to this coat eliminates the errors and causes the glass electrode to act perfectly regardless of the depth of immersion. If the dry surface above

the highest point of immersion is painted with hydrochloric acid, the hydrochloric acid wiped off and the electrode re-immersed up to this point, an error of 70 mv. results.

5. Errors due to the "deviation film" can be eliminated by making r sufficiently large and R sufficiently small (see Eq. 4·4·6).

It is common practice to paint the upper exterior and interior surfaces of glass electrodes with paraffin wax, or to seal them into non-conducting supports. When electrodes are made of Corning 015 glass, the errors due to shunting electrical leaks or to deviation films are negligibly small; yet the possibility of the existence of these difficulties must not be lost sight of and the exterior surfaces of the electrodes should not be allowed to become covered with conducting contaminations.

A general rule regarding depth of immersion is to immerse the glass electrode until all the 015 glass is covered or until all the thin wall part of the 015 glass is covered.

Varney [57] blows his Haber electrode with a double shank to increase the surface leakage path.

For additional material on glass shank leakage difficulties under conditions of high relative humidity see Sec. 10·3.

4·5. Capillary and Thin-Membrane Types of Glass Electrodes

In 1929 MacInnes and the author [58] made for the first time glass electrodes having walls only 0.001 mm. thick and so thin that red and green interference colors could be seen. This membrane type of glass electrode, illustrated in Fig. 4·12, is made by sealing the thin membrane of Corning 015 or other glass onto an ordinary soft glass stem.

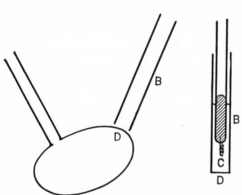

FIG. 4·12.   Method of constructing MacInnes and Dole thin-membrane electrode.

"A bulb, D, is blown on the end of a tube of suitable glass until portions of the resulting film show interference colors. The end of the supporting tube, B, is then heated to a low red heat, the correct

[57] P. L. Varney, *Science*, **82**, 396 (1935).

[58] D. A. MacInnes and M. Dole, *Ind. Eng. Chem., Anal. Ed.* **1**, 57 (1929); *J. Am. Chem. Soc.* **52**, 29 (1930).

temperature being found by experiment (slightly below red heat—M.D.). The heated tube is then placed against the thin bulb. If the conditions are right, the film of glass will fuse onto the tube."

A single large bubble of Corning 015 glass should be used to make only one electrode; the glass should not be reheated and reworked in the flame, but a new portion of the original glass stock used for each electrode.

An improved method of constructing the thin membrane electrode has been invented by Bedford, Keller, and Gabbard:[59]

"By careful suction applied by the mouth to a rubber tube attached to the electrode tube, the glass electrode is gently drawn against and fused onto the hot end of the electrode tube held just above it, thus producing an electrode which, because its inner surface is convex, is consequently stronger than those with plane surfaces obtained by the methods previously described."

A number of electrodes can be made from one bubble of gas.

The seal between the thin membrane and the glass shank is tested for minute leaks by measuring the resistances of each electrode after the electrodes have been numbered and after the inside and outside upper surfaces of the electrodes have been covered with paraffin wax. Electrodes 4 or 5 mm. in diameter and having resistances less than 1 megohm should be discarded. These thin glass electrodes of Mac-Innes and Dole are easily broken by shock although they are strong enough to withstand a considerable pressure applied gradually; their other disadvantage is that it requires a certain technique to make them, but that is easily acquired after a little practice. The electrode is partly filled with 0.1 N hydrochloric acid or a buffer solution containing chloride ions and the silver-silver chloride electrode C inserted to make contact with the mercury from which connection to the e.m.f. potentiometer is easily made.

The advantages of the MacInnes and Dole electrode are: first, a number of glass electrodes can be made and compared, all having nearly the same thickness and electrical resistance. This advantage is quite important in any theoretical study of the properties of the glass electrode where uniformity and reproducibility of behavior are essential. Second, the MacInnes and Dole electrode consists of a restricted area of the special 015 glass fused onto a tube of thick, relatively high electrically resistant soft glass; this means that the r of Eqs. 4·4·3 and 4·4·6 will be much greater than R with the result that the leakage and deviation film errors of the glass electrode are reduced

[59] M. H. Bedford, W. H. Keller, and J. L. Gabbard, *J. Am. Chem. Soc.* **55**, 3953 (1933).

to a minimum.   No change of e.m.f. with depth of immersion can be detected.   Third, it is possible to make these electrodes out of small solid pieces of glass by melting these pieces into the end of a tube of Pyrex glass or other hard glass, by blowing out the thin bubble while the special glass is still hot, and then by sealing the thin membrane onto the holding tube.   Glass electrodes have been made in this way out of a lithium glass which is extremely fluid when molten, so fluid that it would be difficult to make any other type of electrode.   Fourth, asymmetry potentials are practically negligible, and electrical resistances are not too high, varying from 10 to 50 megohms, depending on the glass.

Païc [60] has succeeded in constructing a thin membrane-type glass electrode with the membrane held within a glass tube rather than on

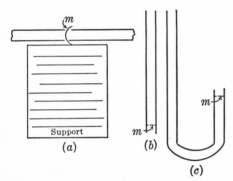

its end, see Fig. 4·13b and c. (m denotes the thin membrane.) This electrode is blown according to the following instructions of Païc (author's translation):

"One prepares first a thin membrane showing interference colors by blowing a bulb at the end of a tube of Corning 015 glass, after the manner of MacInnes and

FIG. 4·13.   Method of constructing thin-membrane electrode of Païc.

Dole.   The membrane is next detached from the tube and placed on a support behind the flame about 10 cm. above the table.   Two tubes of Corning 015 glass are then taken and heated simultaneously at the ends until the onset of softening when they are united with the membrane in between as illustrated in Fig. 4·13a.   The membrane, m, is perfectly fused between the two tubes.   The excess part of the membrane is quickly nipped off with pincers and the joint is annealed in a luminous flame up to the softening point.   After a slow cooling the joint is found to hold perfectly; a file scratch about 1 or 2 cm. from the membrane is made and a red-hot point of glass applied to produce an even cutting of the glass tube.   The electrode is then ready."

Electrodes of this type, which are not as fragile as those of MacInnes and Dole, can be used for micro-pH determinations, see Sec. 14·2, or for differential or direct potentiometric titrations, see Secs. 15·1 and 15·2.

[60] M. Païc, *J. chim. phys.* **35**, 327 (1938).

Mouquin and Garman [61] have also invented a protected thin-membrane glass electrode which has all the advantages of the Mac-Innes and Dole electrode with the additional benefits of greater durability, longer life, and considerably lower electrical resistance. Their electrode, illustrated in Fig. 4·14, is made of 5- to 10-mm. bore Corning 015 glass according to the following instructions:

"Starting with two pieces of tubing about 10 cm. long, a small, sturdy bulb is blown at one end of each tube (bulbs should be about twice the diameter of the tube bore). The two tubes are inserted in a two-hole stopper, which is mounted on a blowing tube, as shown in Figure 4·14a, making it easy to blow equally into both tubes. The two tubes are then heated as uniformly as possible, allowing them to touch and fuse together at one point. A final blow will cause the point of contact to expand into a thin plane membrane (Fig. 4·14b) so thin that a few faintly colored interference rings should appear near the center of the membrane. If a gray or black spot appears, the blowing has been too prolonged; on the other hand, if the exterior hemispheres expand excessively, the pressure has been applied too suddenly; in either case the electrode will be excessively fragile.

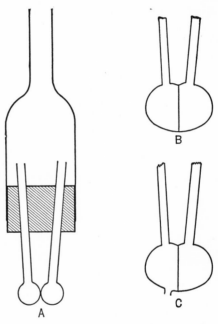

Fig. 4·14.   Mouquin and Garman glass electrode.

"A small hole near the bottom of one of the hemispheres (not too near the membrane) is necessary for drainage (Fig. 4·14c). It is made while the glass is still hot and before removing from the mounting, by using a narrow pointed flame and blowing gently as the glass softens in the flame.

"Several other precautions may prove useful. Since the No. 015 glass tends to crystallize, only fresh tubing should be used and the number of reheatings kept to a minimum. If, on cooling, the electrodes tend to crack into two halves, the tubes should be mounted in the blower at a greater angle to each other. This will place the tubes farther away from the membrane. Finally, the outside of the electrodes may be given a light coat of paraffin wax to prevent creeping of solutions."

[61] H. Mouquin and R. L. Garman, *Ind. Eng. Chem., Anal. Ed.* 9, 287 (1937); see also M. L. Nichols and J. M. Schempf, *ibid.*, 10, 286 (1938).

Mouquin and Garman state that a precision better than one millivolt or 0.02 pH unit is easily obtainable with electrodes having a resistance of 10^5 ohms used in conjunction with a Leeds and Northrup enclosed lamp and scale portable galvanometer.

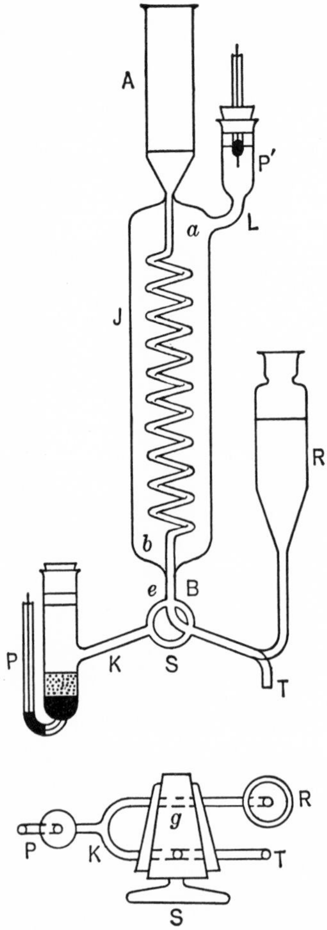

In 1931 Youden and Dobroscky [62] published an account of their experiences in making pH measurements using a capillary type of electrode.

MacInnes and Belcher [63] incorporated the capillary idea into a spiral glass electrode, Fig. 4·15. The spiral is made of Corning 015 glass and is sealed both at the top and bottom by means of Corning Seal Glass H to Jena thermometer glass; the resistance of different electrodes varied from 19 to 30 megohms. Volume of unknown solution required was about 7 cc. and the initial asymmetry potential of 100 mv. declined slowly on standing. In Fig. 4·15 P' is a reference silver-silver chloride electrode and P is the reference saturated potassium chloride calomel electrode. The special five-way stopcock at S allows the solution to wash out at T, or to make liquid connection with the saturated potassium chloride at K, or to rinse the stopcock with the potassium chloride solution from its reservoir at R.

Michaelis [64] has improved the MacInnes and Belcher electrode by constructing the spiral of thinner glass and having the spiral in the shape of a wavy vertical line rather than in spiral form.

FIG. 4·15.   MacInnes and Belcher glass electrode.

Electrical resistance is low enough to make e.m.f. readings with a galvanometer as indicating device. More recently it is becoming

[62] W. J. Youden and I. D. Dobroscky, *Contribution from Boyce Thompson Institute,* **3**, 347 (1931).

[63] D. A. MacInnes and D. Belcher, *Ind. Eng. Chem., Anal. Ed.* **5**, 199 (1933).

[64] L. Michaelis, *Science,* **83**, 213 (1936); see also P. J. Hartsuch, *J. Infectious Diseases,* **59**, 183 (1936).

the custom to make the inner capillary tube perfectly straight. Johnson [65] makes a low-resistance glass electrode by cementing together at the top a bundle of Corning 015 glass tubes of 1-mm. bore and 0.05- to 0.1-mm.-wall thickness, each sealed at its lower end.   A buffer solution is placed inside each tube and the bundle of tubes held in a glass apparatus in such a way that the solution whose pH is to be measured bathes the outer walls of the thin capillary tubes.   Resistance is 1–2 megohms.

[65] W. C. Johnson, *Chemistry & Industry* **58**, 573 (1939).

CHAPTER 5

REFERENCE ELECTRODES FOR GLASS ELECTRODE CELLS

In this chapter detailed directions are given for the construction and use of reference electrodes for glass electrode cells while methods of building both the glass and reference electrodes into different types of complete cells are described in the following chapter.

5·1. Internal Electrodes for Glass Electrodes. The Silver Chloride Electrode

In order to measure the e.m.f. developed across the glass-electrode membrane, it is necessary to insert into the solution inside the glass electrode some other electrode through which metallic connection may be made to the e.m.f. measuring system. For practical considerations it is of the utmost importance that the potential developed at the inner wall of the glass electrode and at the surface of the inner electrode remain as constant as possible with time, for the calculation of the pH from the measured e.m.f. requires a knowledge of these inner potentials and although the glass electrode may be standardized to find these e.m.f.'s, nevertheless, too rapid fluctuations would make the glass electrode almost worthless as a useful instrument and too wide fluctuations might go beyond the limit of the correcting range of the measuring instrument (this has often happened in some of the earlier commercial outfits).

Morton [1] seals into his glass electrode a bright platinum electrode which dips into a buffer solution saturated with quinhydrone. This arrangement has the advantage of giving at constant temperature an inner e.m.f. independent of the pH of the buffer solution (providing it is within the pH range 1 to 6), because the inner surface of the glass electrode changes its potential at the same rate as the quinhydrone electrode with change of pH. Unfortunately, the quinhydrone itself is not perfectly stable over long periods of time, particularly at higher

---

[1] C. Morton, *J. Chem. Soc.* **1932**, 2469.

temperatures, yet this combination is quite satisfactory. (See Sec. 2·2 for a more extensive discussion of the quinhydrone electrode.)

Parsy [2] obtained fairly constant e.m.f. readings with a glass electrode containing a bright platinum electrode immersed in a two per cent solution of $PtCl_4$ having a pH of 2.00; variations less than 1 mv. over a period of one or two months were noted.

Most workers make use of the silver-silver chloride electrode as the inner electrode. A number of these electrodes can be rather easily made at a time, the electrodes compared among themselves, and the erratic ones rejected. Some different recipes for making these electrodes follow: (All these electrodes must be constructed on soft glass tubes small enough to fit inside the glass electrodes.)

Method of Jones and Hartmann [3]

"A platinum wire about 0.1 mm. in diameter and 1.5 to 2 cm. long is half coiled into a spiral and the straight half sealed into a soft glass tube in such a way that the part of the wire inside the tube can make contact with mercury poured into the tube. The platinum wire is carefully cleaned either by heating in the flame during the sealing-in process (not afterwards, because of the danger of cracking the seal) or by cleaning in warm cleaning solution, or nitric acid. It is next washed and then silver-plated from a silver cyanide bath using a current of 0.002 amp. until a thick coat is obtained. After washing and removing the mercury from inside the tube, the spiral is covered with a mass of purified silver oxide paste and the latter reduced to metallic silver by heating to about 325°C. preferably in an electric oven. This forms a large surface of spongy silver which is quite adherent to the silver coated wire. Usually commercial silver oxide is used, but for the highest accuracy silver oxide may be made by precipitating it from silver nitrate using barium hydroxide (carbonate-free) and washing with distilled water until a sample of the precipitate no longer shows the presence of barium when tested with nitric and sulfuric acids.

"The electrode, after filling with a little mercury, can now be made the anode in a 0.1 N sodium chloride solution and chloride-plated for several hours using a current of 0.001 amp. for each electrode (four or more electrodes should be made at a time) until the silver is completely covered with a brownish purple layer of silver chloride. During this electroplating process the silver anode should be separated from the platinum wire cathode by a salt bridge to prevent contamination of the anode solution by the products of electrolysis at the cathode. The electrodes can next be placed in the solution in which they are to be used and should be short-circuited together for twenty-four hours after which time their e.m.f.'s with respect to one another can be measured and the abnormal electrodes rejected. The good electrodes should agree to 0.01 mv. and if properly treated, will give a constant e.m.f. for an indefinite length of time."

[2] G. Parsy, *J. Intern. Soc. Leather Trades Chem.* **20**, 188 (1936).

[3] Grinnell Jones and M. L. Hartmann, *J. Am. Chem. Soc.* **37**, 752 (1915).

These electrodes are small, compact, readily moved from one glass electrode to another, not easily broken, and can be sealed into the stem of glass electrodes to make a very permanent arrangement.

Method of Carmody [4]

"1. Clean platinum gauze electrodes by boiling in concentrated nitric acid for a few minutes.

"2. Electrolyze as cathodes in an H-cell from a solution of potassium silver cyanide that has been prepared free from excess potassium cyanide and purified by recrystallization. The electrolysis is carried on for eight hours, a current of eight milliamperes per electrode being used.

"3. Wash in running water for five days.

"4. Electrolyze as anodes in dilute hydrochloric acid for one hour. A current of 3 milliamperes per electrode is employed.

"5. Keep in distilled water and protect from contact with direct or diffused sunlight."

The above procedure produces *white* silver chloride electrodes; but occasionally brown electrodes result which give potentials 0.2 to 0.3 mv. higher than the white electrodes. These white electrodes remain constant in potential only if kept in water or dilute hydrochloric acid from which oxygen has been removed; in acid solutions containing oxygen their potential declines. Brown's [5] silver chloride electrodes were prepared by electrolysis on platinum wire, were purplish-brown in color and were unaffected in their electrochemical behavior by sunlight. Shedlovsky and MacInnes [6] seal hollow truncated cones of platinum foil into the bottom of glass tubes so that the outer surfaces of the cones are sealed into the inside surface glass and make contact with platinum wires sealed through into mercury cups in a small side arm. Solution flows through a smaller opening in the bottom to make contact with the external liquid. They reported: "The chief advantage of electrodes of this design is that they are completely protected from mechanical disturbance of their active surfaces. This we have found to be essential if the reproducibility is to reach 0.01 mv. or better." They washed the plated silver with strong ammonia before chloridizing to assure the removal of the last possible trace of silver cyanide.

Neither Brown nor Shedlovsky and MacInnes were able to obtain white electrodes and it is our opinion that for glass electrode work the detailed precautions of either Carmody or Brown are not necessary;

[4] W. R. Carmody, *J. Am. Chem. Soc.* 51, 2901 (1929); 54, 188 (1932).

[5] A. S. Brown, *J. Am. Chem. Soc.* 56, 646 (1934).

[6] T. Shedlovsky and D. A. MacInnes, *J. Am. Chem. Soc.* 58, 1970 (1936).

neither of these authors compares his results with the spongy type electrode which we feel is entirely satisfactory. As a matter of fact merely coating a silver wire with silver chloride by electrolysis can give an electrode sufficiently reliable for use in many instances where extreme precision is not required. Brown's electrode as adapted by Shedlovsky and MacInnes is probably best when accurate measurements in very dilute solutions are desired (in this case exclude oxygen!).

In certain instances the calomel electrode has been used inside the glass electrode, but this electrode cannot be prepared as conveniently as the silver chloride electrode in a compact, easily movable form; yet it is widely used, however, as the reference electrode in glass electrode circuits. For this reason a detailed description of the "saturated calomel" electrode is given in the next section.

Thompson [7] eliminates the inside solution and inner electrode entirely, connecting the inside glass surface to mercury, thus making a "metal-connected" glass electrode. He also silvered the outside of Corning 015 glass test tubes having walls 0.5 mm. thick and copper plated the silver deposit. This type of metal-connected electrode gave better results than the mercury-filled tubes. When the metal layer is on the outside, the unknown solution under investigation is poured into the test tube, making a "containing" type glass electrode. Thompson determined by calibration the constant of his e.m.f. system necessary to calculate the pH over a period of days and found that the metal-glass connection gave a fairly stable e.m.f.; a change in e.m.f. equivalent to 0.01 pH unit per day rarely occurred, and one electrode used for over a year showed practically no change for the last four months of its use. Parsy,[8] however, found that a glass electrode with internal coating of metallic silver might have errors ranging from 0.08 to 0.35 pH units.

5·2. The Calomel Reference Electrode

Of the various possible reference electrodes the only one which we shall consider is the so-called "saturated calomel electrode" since this electrode composed of mercury, mercurous chloride, and saturated potassium chloride is almost universally accepted as the standard (except for the most accurate work); thus in 1920 Fales and Mudge [9] conclude, "the saturated potassium chloride cell is the best cell for use

[7] M. R. Thompson, *J. Research Natl. Bur. Standards*, **9**, 833 (1932).

[8] G. Parsy, *Le Cuir Tech.* **26**, 152 (1937); see also O. J. Stewart and W. L. Carruth, *Ind. Eng. Chem., Anal. Ed.* **9**, 581 (1937).

[9] H. A. Fales and W. A. Mudge, *J. Am. Chem. Soc.* **42**, 2434 (1920).

in conjunction with a saturated salt bridge, because it has a very small temperature coefficient, is easily reproducible, can safely be used at temperatures 5° to 60°, and can be relied upon for its constancy of value over long periods of time."

Good results can be obtained with these electrodes when they are made by the very simple process of placing mercury in the bottom of a tube in contact with a sealed-in platinum wire which leads to a mercury cup for electrical connection, grinding commercial calomel (mercurous chloride) in a mortar with some mercury and saturated potassium chloride solution, and pouring this paste over the mercury. Finally the cell is filled with the saturated potassium chloride solution. Since the glass electrode has to be standardized because of its variable asymmetry potential, it is only necessary for the calomel electrode to be as constant in its e.m.f. as the glass electrode; small variations in the absolute e.m.f. of the calomel electrode are not objectionable in actual glass electrode technique.

However, there are many times when the calomel electrode must give the correct e.m.f. for standardization of buffer solutions; for example, with the hydrogen electrode it is essential that the reference electrode e.m.f. is known with considerable precision. For this reason we shall review a few of the detailed directions for making the saturated calomel electrode as given in the literature.

Method of Ellis [10]

"The mercury for use in the cells was purified by first electrolyzing it as the anode in a 2% solution of nitric acid, stirring both the mercury and the solution well, and using a current density of 0.005 ampere per sq. dm., in the manner recommended by Wolff and Waters.[11] Electrolysis was continued for thirty hours, but six hours before its completion the mercury had ceased to tail. After this process the mercury was dried and twice distilled at a pressure of 30 mm. in a current of air. At the end of the second distillation no visible residue was left in the distilling flask. The mercury thus prepared preserved a mirror surface indefinitely.

"The calomel first used in making the calomel electrodes was Kahlbaum's best product; but it did not give reproducible results. Calomel prepared by precipitation from a mercurous nitrate solution made by dissolving pure mercury in pure nitric acid was then tried. This also proved unsatisfactory, although great care was taken in its preparation. Finally, satisfactory calomel was secured by an electrolytic process analogous to that suggested by Wolff and Waters for the preparation of mercurous sulfate for standard Weston cells. Pure mercury, placed in a large clean beaker, was covered with 1 N hydrochloric acid. Both

[10] J. H. Ellis, *J. Am. Chem. Soc.* **38**, 740 (1916).
[11] Wolff and Waters, *Bull. Natl. Bur. Standards* **3**, 625 (1907).

the acid and mercury were kept well stirred by a glass stirrer. The mercury was made the anode, and the cathode consisted of a piece of clean platinum foil contained in another beaker filled with hydrochloric acid and connected with the first beaker by a siphon tube. On passage of the current, the mercury surface became covered with a thin film of calomel; and, as this was swept away by the stirrer, it was re-formed continually. Various rates of stirring and various current densities ranging from 2 amp. to 0.2 amp. per sq. dm. were used, without affecting the electromotive properties of the product. The product was always of a moderately dark gray color, due to the presence of a large amount of finely divided mercury in the form of globules of diameter 0.3 mm. and less. Under the microscope, however, the calomel particles were visible as a perfectly white, amorphous, flocculent substance. Stirring was always continued for four hours after the electrolysis was terminated, in order to enable the precipitated calomel to come into equilibrium with the solution. The calomel prepared in this manner was transferred to a clean bottle and preserved under the mother liquor of the electrolysis."

Method of Gerke [12]

"Chemically precipitated calomel was made by the addition of dilute hydrochloric acid to dilute mercurous nitrate in nitric acid solution in equilibrium with mercury. The mercurous chloride was washed by decantation at least six times with M potassium chloride solution and was shaken with mercury to insure the following equilibrium:

$$Hg_2^{++} + 2Cl^- \rightleftarrows Hg + HgCl_2$$

"Such calomel, whether or not washed with M potassium chloride solution after shaking with mercury, gives within 0.0002 volt the same potential as calomel prepared by electrolysis of hydrochloric acid using a mercury anode, while calomel which has not been equilibrated with mercury may differ from the equilibrated variety as much as 0.001 volt.

"It was observed that calomel in potassium chloride solutions on long standing is alkaline to phenolphthalein. This development of alkalinity may be ascribed to slow oxidation of the mercury by atmospheric oxygen, according to the following reaction:

$$2Hg + \tfrac{1}{2}O_2 + 2Cl^- + H_2O \rightleftarrows Hg_2Cl_2 + 2OH^-$$

which involves the removal of chloride ion in dilute solutions of potassium chloride, and thus causes discrepancies in the potential of the calomel electrode."

Randall and Young [13] proved that oxygen can change the e.m.f. of the calomel electrode by 1 to 3 mv. in the presence of acid, but that air does not seriously affect the potential of the Hg|HgCl electrode in neutral chloride solutions. Probably in the case of the saturated calomel electrode this effect of oxidation is not serious since any slight

[12] R. H. Gerke, *J. Am. Chem. Soc.* **44**, 1684 (1922).
[13] M. Randall and L. E. Young, *J. Am. Chem. Soc.* **50**, 989 (1928).

removal of chloride ion by the above reaction over a long period of time would produce an inappreciable change in the large chloride-ion concentration.

Method of Scatchard [14]

"The potassium chloride for the salt bridge was Kahlbaum's c.p. material recrystallized once from distilled water. For use in the electrode vessel this was further crystallized twice from distilled water. The mercury was purified by passing eight or ten times in a fine spray through a 1.5 meter column containing a dilute nitric acid solution of mercurous nitrate and was then distilled twice in a current of air under reduced pressure (see Hulett [15]). The calomel was prepared electrolytically from this mercury and molar hydrochloric acid (see Ellis[10]), and the resulting mercury-calomel paste was shaken several times with fresh portions of a saturated solution of potassium chloride. A solution saturated with both calomel and potassium chloride was prepared by long agitation of the purified paste with a saturated solution of potassium chloride. Two calomel electrodes prepared in this way never differed by 0.1 mv. and generally agreed to 0.05 mv."

It is advisable to cover the calomel with a few crystals of potassium chloride so that the solution in contact with the calomel will always remain saturated with respect to the potassium chloride.[16] It is unnecessary to saturate the potassium chloride solution with calomel before admitting to the cell according to Wingfield and Acree. Temperature control of the calomel electrode is quite important. This question will be more fully discussed in Chapter 9. Care should be taken not to shake or to disturb the calomel electrode immediately before measuring its e.m.f.

Hitchcock and Taylor [17] found that several different saturated calomel half cells varied as much as a millivolt from each other at 38°C., so that they were compelled to test them daily against the hydrogen electrode in 0.1 N hydrochloric acid at 38°.

Rothschild [18] has studied the effect of anodic polarization currents on the potential of the saturated calomel electrode with the conclusion that "the maximum current density which an anodic calomel electrode will sustain over reasonable periods of time (5 hr.) without polarization is 15 μa. per cm.^{2}" The calomel electrode is much more resistant to cathodic polarization.

[14] G. Scatchard, *J. Am. Chem. Soc.* **47**, 696 (1925).

[15] G. A. Hulett, *Z. physik. Chem.* **33**, 611 (1900).

[16] B. Wingfield and S. F. Acree, *J. Research Natl. Bureau Standards* **19**, 163 (1937).

[17] D. I. Hitchcock and A. C. Taylor, *J. Am. Chem. Soc.* **60**, 2710 (1938).

[18] Lord Rothschild, *Proc. Roy. Soc.* **125B**, 283 (1938).

CHAPTER 6

CELL ASSEMBLIES AND LIQUID-JUNCTION POTENTIALS

When a reference electrode half cell and a glass electrode half cell are united to make a complete electrochemical cell, a union which is necessary for the determination of pH, it is inevitable that two liquids usually differing in composition and concentration meet at a liquid junction, and produce a liquid-junction potential which is always a part of the measured e.m.f. Before describing cell assemblies we shall consider the theory of liquid junctions and their potentials.

Phase-boundary potentials existing at the junction of two immiscible liquids are usually of much greater magnitude than liquid-junction potentials between two miscible liquids, and prevent us from obtaining an accurate measure of the hydrogen-ion activity in nonaqueous solutions with reference to that of some standard aqueous solution. But it is interesting to examine briefly the theoretical obstacles in the path of our attempts to surmount these uncertainties which fundamentally are based on our inability to determine single or individual electrode potentials. We might almost say that we have one equation with two unknowns and hence the solution is impossible.

6·1. The Theory of the Liquid-Junction Potential

Consider the cell 6·1·A

$$\text{Pt, H}_2 \mid \text{HCl (c)} \parallel \text{HCl (c + dc)} \mid \text{H}_2\text{, Pt} \qquad [6\cdot1\cdot\text{A}]$$
$$L$$

if the potential existing at each platinum electrode (the single electrode potential) could be determined, the sum of the two electrode potentials could be subtracted from the total e.m.f. giving as the difference the liquid-junction potential of the junction, L, but it is impossible to find these single electrode potentials.

Consider the phase boundary cell 6·1·B

$$\text{Pt, H}_2 \mid \text{HCl in water} \mid \text{HCl in benzene} \mid \text{H}_2\text{, Pt} \qquad [6\cdot1\cdot\text{B}]$$
$$P$$

On shaking up the two solutions the hydrochloric acid will distribute itself between the two mutually saturated solvents until equilibrium is attained when the measured e.m.f. of the cell will become zero as can be easily demonstrated by a few simple arguments. The sum of the potentials existing at the two electrode-solution interfaces would then be equal to the phase boundary potential at the junction P, and if we could determine the individual or single electrode potentials, the phase boundary potential could be found, but it is impossible to do this. This experimental impossibility is based on the fact that there is no experiment by which we can measure the difference in electric potential existing between two phases, or between two points in different media, in different thermodynamic environments.

At equilibrium the so-called electrochemical potential, $\bar{\mu}_i$, of an ion defined by the equation

$$\bar{\mu}_i = \mu_i + \epsilon_i \psi \qquad [6\cdot1\cdot1]$$

is the same throughout a heterogeneous system. μ_i is the ionic chemical potential or the "partial molal free energy," ϵ_i the ionic charge, and ψ the electrostatic potential of the homogeneous medium. This is true if certain requirements are fulfilled such as constancy of temperature and pressure and absence of mechanical restrictions to the motion of the ion, so that we can write

$$\bar{\mu}_i' = \bar{\mu}_i'' \qquad [6\cdot1\cdot2]$$

or

$$\mu_i' + \epsilon_i \psi' = \mu_i'' + \epsilon_i \psi'' \qquad [6\cdot1\cdot3]$$

where the single and double primes refer to different phases. In other words, when an ion is transferred at equilibrium from one phase to another the total work of transfer, both electrical and chemical which is

$$(\mu_i' + \epsilon_i \psi') - (\mu_i'' + \epsilon_i \psi''),$$

has to be equal to zero; hence Eq. $6\cdot1\cdot3$. As an example of two phases in equilibrium we can imagine an aqueous solution of copper ions in contact with a copper electrode, the copper metal to be considered as a crystal lattice of positive ions immersed in a cloud of comparatively free electrons.

The electric potential difference between the two phases is given by the expression

$$\psi'' - \psi' = \frac{1}{\epsilon_i}(\mu_i' - \mu_i''), \qquad [6\cdot1\cdot4]$$

but since we need to know $\psi'' - \psi'$ to compute $(\mu_i' - \mu_i'')$, and *vice versa*, we cannot solve the problem of the single electrode potential. When we transfer an ion between two phases, we do both chemical and electrical work, but it is impossible to partition experimentally the total work into these individual contributions. We are reduced, therefore, to somewhat questionable calculations in our attempt to estimate liquid-junction potentials.

The general thermodynamic equation for the change in chemical potential of the reaction occurring at any liquid junction during the passage of one faraday of electricity across the junction is

$$\Delta\mu = \sum_i \int_{\prime}^{\prime\prime} \frac{t_i}{z_i} d\mu_i \qquad [6\cdot1\cdot5]$$

where $\sum_i$ signifies a summation taken over all ionic and molecular species transferred, t_i is the transference number and z_i the valence of the ith ion. If there is a change in chemical potential of the solvent across the junction, the contribution to the change in free energy due to the transference of the molecules by the ions can be formally taken into account when we sum over all ionic and molecular species by letting the factor t_i/z_i represent the number of moles of solvent transferred by the ith ion per Faraday of electricity passed, and $d\mu_i$ represent the change in chemical potential of the solvent. The derivation of Eq. 6·1·5 is given in the Appendix to this chapter. Equation 6·1·5 is not of much help, however, since we do not know how the μ_i vary with the concentration and are therefore unable to integrate it. We have to turn to methods involving approximations.

In making the assumptions that

(1) the solvent is the same throughout the junction;
(2) the mobility of the ions is constant throughout the junction;
(3) the laws of ideal solutions are obeyed;
(4) the junction between the two solutions is formed as follows: ions may diffuse freely between the parallel planes A and B, but to the left of A and the right of B the concentrations of the original solutions remain unaltered,

Planck[1] was able to derive a transcendental equation for the potential of a liquid junction formed in the above described manner between solutions containing ions of the same numerical valence. This equation will not be reproduced here since it is generally inapplicable to the usual type of e.m.f. cell with liquid junction (because very few

---

[1] M. Planck, *Wied. Ann.* **39**, 161 (1890); **40**, 561 (1890). For a general solution see H. Pleijel, *Z. physik. Chem.* **72**, 1 (1910). Planck's equation is given and discussed by Guggenheim, *J. Am. Chem. Soc.* **52**, 1315 (1930), and by Dole, "Experimental and Theoretical Electrochemistry," McGraw-Hill Book Co., New York, 1935.

investigators have studied liquid junctions of the Planck type) and since in several simplifying and special situations it reduces to the more general Henderson [2] liquid-junction potential equation which is

$$E_l = \frac{RT}{F} \frac{(U_2 - V_2) - (U_1 - V_1)}{(\overline{U}_2 + \overline{V}_2) - (\overline{U}_1 + \overline{V}_1)} \, ln \, \frac{\overline{U}_1 + \overline{V}_1}{\overline{U}_2 + \overline{V}_2} \qquad [6·1·6]$$

where

$$\overline{U}_2 = \underset{+}{\Sigma} u_i'' z_i c_i'' \qquad \qquad \overline{V}_2 = \underset{-}{\Sigma} v_i'' z_i c_i''$$

$$\overline{U}_1 = \underset{+}{\Sigma} u_i' z_i c_i' \qquad \qquad \overline{V}_1 = \underset{-}{\Sigma} v_i' z_i c_i'$$

$$U_2 = \underset{+}{\Sigma} u_i'' c_i'' \qquad \qquad V_2 = \underset{-}{\Sigma_i} v c_i''$$

$$U_1 = \underset{+}{\Sigma} u_i' c_i' \qquad \qquad V_1 = \underset{-}{\Sigma} v_i' c_i'$$

($\underset{+}{\Sigma}$ and $\underset{-}{\Sigma}$ signify summations over all positive and negative ions and u and v are the mobilities of the positive and negative ions). Henderson [2] based his theoretical derivation on the assumption that the liquid junction is such that the solution at any point in the transition layer could be formed by mixing together definite quantities of the two end solutions. This method of bringing the two cell solutions into contact with one another results in the transition layer being called a "continuous-mixture boundary" in contrast to the Planck type of "constrained diffusion junction." Assumptions 1, 2, and 3 of Planck mentioned above were also made by Henderson.[3,4]

A third type of junction, known as the "free diffusion junction," in which the boundary between the two solutions meeting in a cylindrical tube is initially sharp has been discussed theoretically by Taylor [5] and both theoretically and experimentally by Guggenheim.[6]

The mathematical treatment is especially difficult, but enough progress has been made for the conclusion to be drawn that if there is cylindrical symmetry, "that is, if the gradients of the concentrations and of the electric potential are throughout parallel to a fixed straight line, it appears that the potential difference between the ends (of the transition layer) is independent of the time, at least after a sufficient time (30 to 40 minutes) has elapsed for the effect of the initial devia-

[2] P. Henderson, *Z. physik. Chem.* **59**, 118 (1907); **63**, 325 (1908).

[3] L. G. Sillen, *Physik. Z.* **40**, 466 (1939) has recently discussed the Planck and Henderson equations and has derived the Planck equation in modern form.

[4] F. O. Koenig, *J. Phys. Chem.* **44**, 101 (1940), also has made a detailed mathematical study of the theory of liquid-junction potentials.

[5] P. B. Taylor, *J. Phys. Chem.* **31**, 1478 (1927).

[6] E. A. Guggenheim, *J. Am. Chem. Soc.* **52**, 1315 (1930).

tions from 'sharpness' to have died out." For the case of hydrochloric acid against potassium chloride of the same concentration, Taylor calculates that the difference in e.m.f. between the "free-diffusion junction" and the "continuous-mixture layer" is only 0.3 to 0.4 mv.

A fourth type of junction is the so-called "flowing junction" in which the two end solutions flow together and meet in a fairly sharp contact layer. The flowing junction has never been treated theoretically as such, but is considered by most of the workers in the field to be a "continuous-mixture boundary" to which the Henderson equation may be applied. It is assumed that under conditions of continuous flow the ionic constituents of the solutions do not have enough time to diffuse physically, but mix only mechanically. The excellent work of Ferguson, Van Lente, and Hitchens [7] indicates that at high rates of flow the transition layer becomes somewhat mixed, probably the flow is turbulent and cylindrical symmetry is lacking; at medium rates the layer is very thin; and at slow rates of flow it becomes diffuse. The type of boundary, therefore, depends upon the rate of flow, but over the range of rates for which the e.m.f. is constant, the boundary is probably a continuous-mixture junction.

We can also have the "free-diffusion junction" with agar-agar, the junction formed by free diffusion through the narrow channels between a glass stopper and its sheath, and finally the most common type of junction, that of indefinite type in which the saturated potassium chloride solution of the salt bridge comes into contact with the test solution at the open tip of a capillary tube. It is impossible to treat junctions of uncertain geometry in any exact theoretical way. To estimate the errors introduced into pH measurements through fluctuating and irreproducible liquid contact potentials, we must turn to experimental studies of the different types of boundaries.

In the simple cases where the two end solutions contain only one and the same solute, or contain a common ion at the same concentration of the two solutes, both the Henderson and Planck equations as well as the experimental data demonstrate that the liquid-junction potential is independent of the method of forming the junction. However, pH measurements are almost never made under these simple conditions, so that the problem remains a serious one.

6·2. Experimental Studies of the Liquid-Junction Potential

Among the many experimental studies of liquid junction potentials, it will be sufficient here to consider only the accurate and illuminating

[7] A. L. Ferguson, K. Van Lente, and R. Hitchens, *J. Am. Chem. Soc.* **54**, 1285 (1932).

work of Guggenheim and of Ferguson, Van Lente, and Hitchens.[8] In Fig. 6·1 is illustrated the type of 0.1 N potassium chloride calomel cell used by Guggenheim in his study of continuous-mixture, constrained-diffusion, free-diffusion, and sharp but indefinite junction potentials. The large reservoir E contains excess 0.1 N potassium chloride which can be used to flush out the tube FCB. The joint C allows the tube B to be removed for separate cleansing and the opening D is a trap for air bubbles should any collect. The cock A can be connected to a reservoir to allow liquid to be sucked up into the side tube B.

The continuous-mixture junction is theoretically unstable, being disturbed by diffusion, but the instability can be minimized by making the mixture layer extend over the greater length of the tube B. The "free-diffusion" junction was made very simply by filling an additional vertical tube H with potassium chloride of concentration c up to and including the stopcock which was then closed, and above the stopcock with 0.1 N hydrochloric acid. Each end of H was connected by rubber tubing to the bottom end of the tube B on the calomel half cells containing 0.1 N acid and 0.1 N potassium chloride solution, respectively (actually an additional T-tube and reservoir not shown in Fig. 6·1 were included in each half of the apparatus). After temperature and pressure equilibrium had been attained, cock G (whose internal bore was of the same size as the tube H) was then carefully opened, allowing the two solutions to meet in sharp contact. For the agar-agar junction a U-tube 22 cms. in height and of 5-mm. bore was half filled with a hot solution of 1 N potassium chloride containing 3 per cent agar-agar. After cooling and formation of the gel, the upper halves of the U-tube were filled with 0.1 N potassium chloride and 0.1 N hydro-

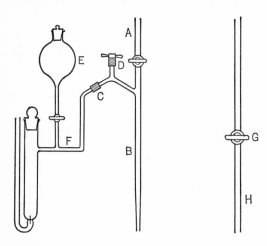

FIG. 6·1.   Calomel electrode half cell used by Guggenheim (1930).

[8] E. A. Guggenheim, *J. Am. Chem. Soc.* **52**, 1315 (1930); A. L. Ferguson, K. Van Lente, and R. Hitchens, *J. Am. Chem. Soc.* **54**, 1285 (1932).

chloric acid, respectively, which could be easily connected to the calomel half cells through solution-filled rubber tubes.

Sharp junctions of indefinite type were made simply by dipping the
side tubes of the electrode vessels into a U-tube containing the bridge
solution. "Constrained-diffusion junctions" were made by replacing
the cock G of tube H, Fig. 6·1, with a collodion membrane. During
measurements of the potential across the collodion membrane, the
two solutions were slowly flowed over each surface of the membrane at
the equal rate of one to one-tenth drop per second.

Data obtained by Guggenheim indicate that the most erratic and
less reproducible results are obtained in the case of the indefinite type
of liquid junction, probably because of lack of cylindrical symmetry;
that agar-agar junctions and indefinite junctions formed in side tubes
are superior to the completely indefinite type; that the carefully made
continuous-mixture and
free-diffusion junctions
are more constant and
more reproducible than
any of the other types
studied; that the root
mean square deviation is
independent of the abso-
lute magnitude of the
liquid-junction potential;
and finally and most im-
portant, that the liquid-

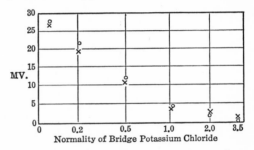

FIG. 6·2. Liquid-junction potential as a function of salt bridge concentration.

junction potential declines with rise of concentration of the bridge
potassium chloride. (See Fig. 6·2.)

The sharp indefinite junction potentials may be in error by as much
as 3 to 5 mv. or nearly 0.1 pH unit; it is advisable therefore in all pH
work to form the liquid junctions definitely and under conditions of
cylindrical symmetry. The ground-glass stopper or cotton-plug type
of junction is to be avoided if accurate data are desired.

We come now to a consideration of the flowing liquid junction first
invented by Lamb and Larson [9] and later by MacInnes and Yeh;[10] see
also Scatchard.[11] Ferguson, Van Lente, and Hitchens have made a
direct comparison of static and flowing junctions. A three-way stopcock which enabled these authors to make a sharp static junction at
its lower edge as well as to use it in preparing a flowing junction is

[9] A. B. Lamb and A. T. Larson, *J. Am. Chem. Soc.* **42**, 229 (1920).

[10] D. A. MacInnes and Y. L. Yeh, *ibid.*, **43**, 2563 (1921).

[11] G. Scatchard, *ibid.*, **47**, 696 (1925).

shown in Fig. 6·3. The bore of the stopcock was the same as that of the tubes leading to it. The rate of flow was controlled by the stop-cock in the exit tube; the small projection within the stopcock and opposite to the outlet prevented the two solutions from mixing when the junction is flowing. The data of Ferguson, Van Lente, and Hitchens are best given in the form of an illustration, Fig. 6·4. For the cells

$$Hg \mid HgCl \mid Sat.\ KCl \parallel 0.1\ N\ HCl \mid AgCl \mid Ag \qquad [6·2·A]$$

and

$$Hg \mid HgCl \mid Sat.\ KCl \parallel 0.01\ N\ HCl \mid AgCl \mid Ag \qquad [6·2·B]$$

the e.m.f. increases with the increase of flow up to a maximum and

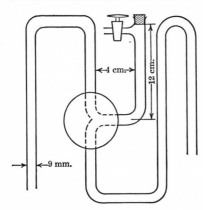

then declines to a nearly constant value until the rate of flow becomes so large that the potential again falls. Identical data at each rate of flow are obtained on changing the rate in either direction. The more dilute solution junction po-tential is less reproducible, and its e.m.f. increases on stirring in con-trast to the potential of cell 6·2·A which decreased 1.5 mv. when the junction was stirred. Note that the flowing junction potential is less than the static. Scatchard also observed in the case of the junction

FIG. 6·3. Three-way stopcock for liquid-junction formation. Ferguson, Van Lente, and Hitchens (1932).

$$1\ N\ HCl \parallel Sat.\ KCl$$

that the potential of the cell rose as much as 3.5 mv. when the flow was stopped.

We have said nothing about temperature control, but it is obvious that fluctuations of temperature will produce even greater uncertain-ties in the liquid-junction potential.

Concluding this discussion of liquid junctions, we recommend that wherever and whenever possible, the liquid junction be formed in a definite, cylindrically symmetrical way. Flowing junctions will prob-ably be avoided because of the volume of solution needed in the meas-urements, but there is no reason for not forming junctions in tubes half-filled with agar-agar, or by turning stopcocks so as to make a sharp junction in a cylindrical tube, or by sucking the junction up into a side tube, as in Clark's method (see Sec. 2·1). Finally, we should point out that the uncertainties involved in the liquid-junction potential between the saturated potassium chloride solution and a buffer solution of intermediate pH value are considerably less than when the

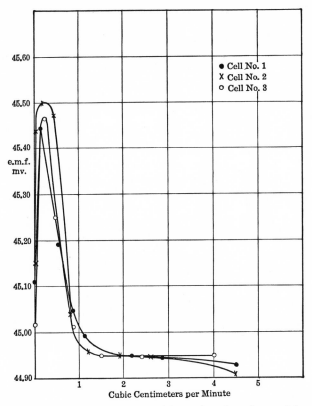

FIG. 6·4. Liquid-junction potential as a function of rate of flow.

test solution is a pure acid, yet they may be significant. Thus, a change in potential of 0.4 mv. is noted, for example, if the junction

$$0.1 \ N \ \text{KF} \ \| \ \text{Sat. KCl}$$

is first made inside a tube, and then made at the end of the tube. This represents an uncertainty of slightly less than 0.01 pH unit.

If the liquid junction is always formed in a cylindrically symmetrical tube, fluctuations in its potential would be less than 0.01 pH.

6·3. Liquid Junctions in Glass Electrode Cells and Cell Assemblies

MacInnes and co-workers [12,13] have always been most careful in their manner of forming liquid junctions. This is demonstrated in the description of the glass electrode micro-pH cell given in Sec. 14·2 and Fig. 14·1, and in the description of the MacInnes and Belcher glass electrode, Sec. 4·5. We shall give here a more detailed explanation of the use of the special stopcock shown in Fig. 4·15 than is given on page 96. With the cock in the position indicated in the drawing, the test sample is poured in at A until the spiral tube is filled and a small amount of the sample has fallen from the reject tube T. The cock is then turned through an angle of 120° in a clockwise direction so that saturated potassium chloride solution from the reservoir R can flow through the stopcock around through the connecting tube K and out at T, thus sweeping the stopcock free of the test sample. Another 120° turn of the stopcock again in a clockwise direction connects the spiral tube a containing the test sample with the salt bridge K, thus making a sharp, reproducible junction which has the proper symmetry characteristics.

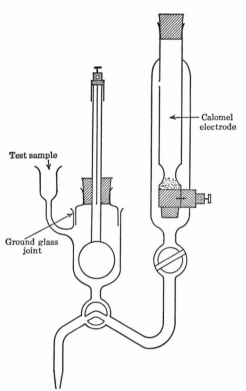

FIG. 6·5.   Glass electrode cell assembly of Morton (1930).

In their experiments measuring the pH of a bacterial suspension over a long period of time, Longsworth and MacInnes [14] inserted into the tip of the salt-bridge tube containing 3.5 N potassium chloride a

[12] D. A MacInnes and M. Dole, *J. Gen. Physiol.* **12**, 805 (1929).
[13] D. A. MacInnes and D. Belcher, *Ind. Eng. Chem., Anal. Ed.* **5**, 199 (1933).
[14] L. G. Longsworth and D. A. MacInnes, *J. Bact.* **29**, 601 (1935).

porous plug made "from a sintered mixture of 30 per cent alundum powder and 70 per cent finely ground Pyrex. With a head of about 15 cm. of the potassium chloride solution a few drops a day will pass through the plug." Such a junction is not as reproducible as the ones described above, but was required by the conditions of the experiment.

Figure 6·5 illustrates a glass electrode-saturated calomel electrode system devised by Morton [15] which is self-explanatory, while in Fig. 6·6 we find a cell for glass electrodes recently invented by Highberger.[16] Stopcock B in Highberger's apparatus is so designed that both the cell and the salt bridge can be flushed out without disturbing each other. Only the outside edges of stopcock B are greased and reservoirs D and E are closed with stoppers when not in use.

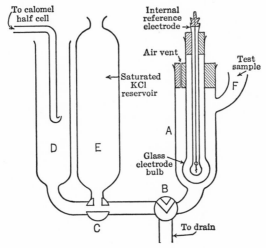

FIG. 6·6.   Glass electrode cell assembly of Highberger (1936).

Blair [17] has invented a calomel cell and salt bridge arrangement which is particularly useful when liquid junctions of the salt bridge solution with opaque or turbid liquids have to be made, or when the experiments have a prolonged duration. Used in his studies of the pH of certain foods (see Sec. 12·1) Blair followed a definite procedure in making his liquid junctions so that a stable and reproducible potential would be developed. Instead of forming the liquid junction in A by suction at B, see Fig. 6·7, it was formed "by drawing out a standard number of drops of saturated KCl at the tip C. In this way the junc-

[15] C. Morton, *J. Sci. Instruments*, **7**, 187 (1930).

[16] J. H. Highberger, *J. Am. Leather Chem. Assoc.* **31**, 32 (1936).

[17] J. S. Blair, *Trans. Electrochem. Soc.* **74**, 567 (1938).

tion may be formed in the middle of the bulb even when the solution is opaque as is always the case in a quinhydrone cell."

Figure 6·8 illustrates a water-jacketed glass electrode cell designed by Wyman,[18] the water at constant temperature being circulated about the cell by means of a small aquarium pump.

"The glass electrodes consisted simply of suitable lengths of special Corning glass tubing the walls of the middle portions of which were blown thin, but not

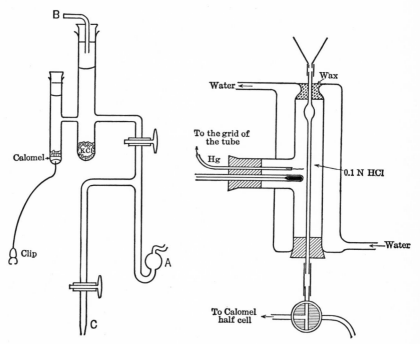

FIG. 6·7.   Blair's calomel elec-   FIG. 6·8.   Wyman's glass electrode cell.
trode and salt bridge (1938).

so thin as to make them unduly fragile.   They were mounted in a special glass vessel which provided both for an outside solution of 0.1 N HCl and for a jacket of circulating water to maintain the desired temperature.   Paraffin or beeswax was used to seal the upper end of the glass electrode into the vessel, the molten wax being flowed over the 0.1 N HCl solution surrounding the electrode and allowed to harden.   The lower end of the electrode was held in a rubber stopper. The silver-silver chloride electrode which made contact with the 0.1 N HCl entered from the side through a rubber stopper which also admitted a thermometer

---

[18] J. Wyman, Jr., Private communication.

to record the temperature of the water-jacketed portion of the system.   Since the silver-silver chloride electrode was connected to the grid of the vacuum tube of the bridge circuit, it was essential that the electrical resistance between it (or the 0.1 N HCl) and ground be much greater than that through the walls of the glass electrode itself.   No trouble was found in satisfying this condition although the walls of the electrode were not made particularly thin.   The water to and from the jacket passed through sections of grounded copper tubing.   This completely excluded electrical disturbances arising in the constant temperature bath from which the water was drawn; and, if anything, the system was more stable electrically as a result of the grounded circulating water.   The upper end of the glass electrode was connected with a funnel and the lower end with one arm of a three-way stopcock.   The electrode was filled either by driving the liquid up from below through the open arm of this stopcock or by pouring it into the funnel at the top. In the former event the funnel served conveniently to catch the overflow.   The liquid junction was made in the arm of the stopcock leading to the calomel half cell."

DuBois [19] makes a calomel electrode out of a leveling bulb, and ZoBell and Rittenberg [20] prepare an asbestos potassium chloride bridge according to the following directions: "Small threads of asbestos are freed of mineral impurities by bleaching in dilute HCl and water.   Then each thread is heated to incandescence in a gas flame, after which it is sealed through the end of a glass tube of the desired length and diameter."   The asbestos thread can be made so tiny that less than 0.01 cc. of the bridge solution leaks through per hour.   (See Fig. 12·3).

Commercial pH electrometers make use of ground-glass stoppers or plugs at the end of the salt bridge, rubber tubes containing the salt bridge leading to the cup for the test sample, or simply glass tubes containing the unknown liquid which dip into saturated potassium chloride reservoirs.   Although these methods of forming the liquid junction are convenient and inexpensive, they differ in their reliability and are not so good as the methods of forming liquid junctions of symmetrical character within cylindrical tubes.   The ground-glass stopper or plug type is difficult to clean while lack of temperature control often causes crystalline potassium chloride to precipitate in the rubber tubes, thereby causing electrical errors to appear in the pH measurements.   The deposition of the solid chloride in any type of salt bridge should be avoided at all costs; it is important to examine the salt bridge frequently for these crystals.   In the rubber-tube salt bridge one can feel the crystals on pinching the rubber tube between

[19] D. DuBois, *Science* **76**, 441 (1932);   *J. Biol. Chem.* **88**, 729 (1930).
[20] C. E. ZoBell and S. C. Rittenberg, *Science* **86**, 502 (1937).

the fingers; washing and rinsing of the rubber tube immediately restores the apparatus to proper working condition.

Acree and co-workers [21] have made an extensive study of different solutions to be used as the salt bridge with the conclusion that saturated potassium chloride is the best bridge liquid. This is the recommendation made by many other workers so that it is fairly evident that standard practice should include the use of saturated potassium chloride as the salt bridge. The chief purpose of the salt bridge is to reduce the troublesome liquid-junction potential to as low a value as possible, and to make it convenient to reproduce accurately the liquid-junction potential. From Eq. 6·1·6 it can be seen that the closer the mobilities of the positive and negative ions of the more concentrated solution of the two forming the junction, the less the liquid-junction potential will be, and the more concentrated the solution on the one side, the less the liquid-junction potential. Potassium chloride is a good solute to use in regard to both of these points because the transference number of the potassium ion in aqueous solutions of potassium chloride is nearly one-half (0.4857 at 3.0 N) [22] and falls only slightly with increase of concentration. The salt is also quite soluble; in saturated solution at 25°C. the concentration is 4.1 N. In Fig. 6·2 it is also demonstrated that the higher the salt concentration of the bridge solution, the less the liquid-junction potential. Saturated potassium chloride solutions tend to creep over the surface of glass, depositing potassium chloride crystals as the solvent evaporates, but this difficulty can be easily overcome by painting the glass and other surfaces with a film of paraffin.

All glass-electrode cells should be securely mounted on vibration-free supports which are at the same time well insulated; quartz rods or Bakelite frames have been used for cells immersed in air baths while grounded metal frames or holders serve as satisfactory supports for glass-electrode cells in constant temperature oil baths. Rosebury's [23] shielded and thermally insulated, constant-temperature air bath for glass electrodes is illustrated in Fig. 6·9 which is self-explanatory. The dotted lines with arrow points show the direction of air currents within the chamber.

We conclude this section with a few remarks concerning the type of liquid junction or of phase boundary to use in the case of pH measurements of nonaqueous solutions. Here the liquid-junction potential

---

[21] For a review of the subject see G. M. Kline, M. R. Meacham, and S. F. Acree, *J. Research Natl. Bur. Standards* **8**, 101 (1932).

[22] D. A. MacInnes and M. Dole, *J. Am. Chem. Soc.* **53**, 1357 (1931).

[23] F. Rosebury, *Ind. Eng. Chem., Anal. Ed.* **4**, 398 (1932).

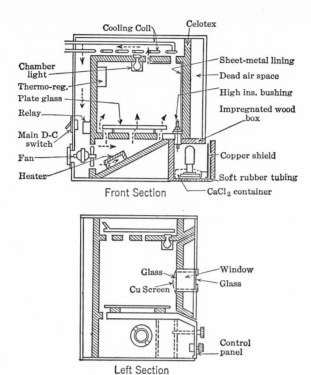

Front Section

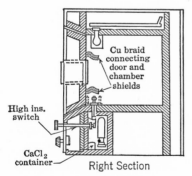

Left Section

Right Section

FIG. 6·9.   Constant-temperature air chamber of Rosebury
(1932).

difficulty is not only tremendously magnified, potentials as great as 0.1 v. or higher,[24] but no extensive studies have been made of the best way to reduce them, nor has any standard practice been developed. Furthermore, the theoretical aspects of the phase boundary potential are more dubious and uncertain than are those of the ordinary liquid-junction potentials; for all these reasons pH measurements of non-aqueous solutions can be given little significance. Yet they may have relative or empirical usefulness, and if so, the phase boundaries should be made in a carefully stated manner so that they may be reproduced by other workers. In Sec. 17·6, the problem of the pH of nonaqueous solutions is considered in detail and recommendations given and in Sec. 17·7 the significance of such measurements is discussed.

APPENDIX TO CHAPTER 6

6·4. Derivation of Eq. 6·1·5 [25]

Suppose solutions 1 and 2, Fig. 6·10, of infinite volume are separated by a layer from x_1 to x_2 in which the composition changes in some continuous but unspecified manner from the composition of solution 1 to that of solution 2. Let us denote the chemical potential and transference number of ionic species i in 1 by $\mu_i^{(1)}$ and $t_i^{(1)}$, respectively, with a similar notation for the corresponding quantities in solution 2. Let z_i be the valence of ionic species i (negative for negative ions).

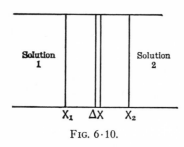

FIG. 6·10.

If we let $\psi^{(1)}$ and $\psi^{(2)}$ be the electrostatic potential in the homogeneous phases 1 and 2, we have for the passage of one faraday of positive electricity from left to right

$$\psi^{(2)} - \psi^{(1)} = -\frac{1}{F}\Delta G \qquad [6\cdot4\cdot1]$$

where F is the faraday and ΔG is the total increase in the Gibbs free energy of the system (Eq. 6·4·1 is equivalent to Eq. 6·1·4) when the process takes place reversibly. ΔG may be separated into three parts, namely, the increase $\Delta G^{(1)}$ in 1, the increase $\Delta G^{(l)}$ in the transition layer and $\Delta G^{(2)}$, the increase in G in 2.

[24] See the review of the subject of phase boundary potentials in the author's "Theoretical and Experimental Electrochemistry," McGraw-Hill Book Co., New York, 1935. Chapter XXII.

[25] The author is indebted to Dr. Richard M. Roberts for this particular discussion.

With the passage of a faraday of positive electricity from 1 to 2, solution 1 gains $-\dfrac{t_i^{(1)}}{z_i}$ moles of the ith ion, and solution 2 gains $\dfrac{t_i^{(2)}}{z_i}$ moles of the same ion; hence

$$\Delta G^{(1)} = -\sum_{i=1}^{r} \frac{t_i^{(1)}}{z_i}\,\mu_i^{(1)} \qquad\qquad [6\cdot4\cdot2]$$

$$\Delta G^{(2)} = \sum_{i=1}^{r} \frac{t_i^{(2)}}{z_i}\,\mu_i^{(2)} \qquad\qquad [6\cdot4\cdot3]$$

on summing over all ionic species r.

To compute $\Delta G^{(l)}$, the increase in free energy in the transition layer, we divide the layer from x_1 to x_2 into laminae of width Δx. Let us consider any selected lamina, such as the jth lamina where $t_i^{(j)}$ and $t_i^{(j)} + \Delta t_i^{(j)}$ are the transference numbers of the ith ion at the left and right faces of the lamina, respectively. Let $\mu_i^{(j)}$ be the average chemical potential of the ith ion in the jth lamina. On passing a faraday of positive electricity from left to right through the lamina, $\dfrac{t_i^{(j)}}{z_i}$ moles of the ith ion will enter through the left face, and $\dfrac{t_i^{(j)} + \Delta t_i^{(j)}}{z_i}$ will leave through the right, giving a net increase of $\dfrac{-\Delta t_i^{(j)}}{z_i}$ moles of the ith ion in the jth lamina. Thus the increase of the Gibbs free energy in this lamina will be, on summing over all ionic species

$$\Delta G^{(j)} = -\sum_{i=1}^{r} \frac{\Delta t_i^{(j)}}{z_i}\,\mu_i^{(j)} \qquad\qquad [6\cdot4\cdot4]$$

If the layer from x_1 to x_2 has been divided into p laminae, then the total increase of the Gibbs free energy for the layer, $\Delta G^{(l)}$, will be

$$\Delta G^{(l)} = \sum_{j=1}^{p} \Delta G^{(j)} = -\sum_{j=1}^{p}\sum_{i=1}^{r} \frac{\Delta t_i^{(j)}}{z_i}\,\mu_i^{(j)} \qquad\qquad [6\cdot4\cdot5]$$

If we make Δx vanishingly small, we may assume that the sum over j can be replaced by an integral, and we have

$$\Delta G^{(l)} = -\sum_{i=1}^{r} \int_{1}^{2} \frac{\mu_i}{z_i}\,dt_i \qquad\qquad [6\cdot4\cdot6]$$

where the limits of integration are the values of the argument in solutions 1 and 2.

We now integrate by parts

$$\int_1^2 \frac{\mu_i}{z_i} dt_i = \frac{\mu_i^{(2)} t_i^{(2)}}{z_i} - \frac{\mu_i^{(1)} t_i^{(1)}}{z_i} - \int_1^2 \frac{t_i}{z_i} d\mu_i \qquad [6\cdot4\cdot7]$$

On substituting Eq. $6\cdot4\cdot7$ into Eq. $6\cdot4\cdot6$ and remembering that

$$\Delta G = \Delta G^{(1)} + \Delta G^{(2)} + \Delta G^{(l)}$$

we have

$$\Delta G = \sum_{i=1}^r \int_1^2 \frac{t_i}{z_i} d\mu_i \qquad [6\cdot4\cdot8]$$

the desired relationship, Eq. $6\cdot1\cdot5$. From Eq. $6\cdot4\cdot1$, $\psi^{(2)} - \psi^{(1)}$, the liquid junction potential, E_l is given for the general case by the equation

$$E_l = -\frac{1}{F} \sum_{i=1}^r \int_1^2 \frac{t_i}{z_i} d\mu_i \qquad [6\cdot4\cdot9]$$

while for the simple system of potassium chloride being the sole solute in the two solutions

$$E_l = -\frac{1}{F} \left[\int_1^2 t_+ d\mu_+ - \int_1^2 t_- d\mu_- \right]$$

or since

$$t_+ + t_- = 1$$

and

$$\mu_+ + \mu_- = \mu_{KCl},$$

it is true that

$$E_l = \frac{1}{F} \left(\mu_-^{(2)} - \mu_-^{(1)} \right) - \frac{1}{F} \int_1^2 t_+ d\mu_{KCl} \qquad [6\cdot4\cdot10]$$

Although t_+ and μ_{KCl} are known as functions of concentration, so that the integral can be evaluated, we have no way of measuring either $\mu_-^{(2)}$ or $\mu_-^{(1)}$. This treatment demonstrates the connection between single-electrode potentials and liquid-junction potentials; if we could measure single-electrode potentials, we could compute $\mu_-^{(2)} - \mu_-^{(1)}$ and so find E_l, but to obtain the latter we must be able to measure in some way $\mu_-^{(2)} - \mu_-^{(1)}$ which we cannot do unless we know E_l. Thus we are led by our reasoning into a vicious circle.

CHAPTER 7

LIMITATIONS OF THE GLASS ELECTRODE IN ALKALINE
pH RANGE

7·1. Introduction

In Sec. 2·4 we have recounted the historical development of the discoveries concerning the errors of the glass electrode in alkaline solution and in Sec. 4·1 we have given some data for the effect of composition of glass on the alkaline behavior. In this chapter we shall discuss chiefly the alkaline solution potentials exhibited by Corning 015 glass electrodes. In 1931 the first study of the glass electrode was made in which the concentration of sodium, lithium, potassium, or other positive ions was maintained constant as the pH was raised.[1] From a theoretical point of view, it would be necessary or advisable to maintain not the concentration but the activity (concentration × activity coefficient) of these ions constant with change of pH; there is no precise method of doing this. However, a close approximation to the ideal thermodynamic requirement can be obtained by changing the hydrogen-ion activity many-fold merely by adding a few drops of base. Under these circumstances the activity of the sodium or other positive ion remains practically constant, at least if the pH does not become too far removed from the end point of the acid being titrated. Gardiner and Sanders,[2] Dole and Wiener,[3] Gabbard and Dole,[4] Jordan,[5] and Dole and Roberts [6] also followed this procedure of maintaining all positive ion concentrations other than the hydrogen-ion concentration constant, and thus obtained significant data.

Before describing experimental methods, we should first ask ourselves if the glass electrode gives reproducible and reversible potentials in alkaline solution—do we always get the same e.m.f. under identical conditions and do the potentials follow along the same e.m.f.-pH curve as we first raise and then lower the pH? The answer to both of

[1] M. Dole, *J. Am. Chem. Soc.* **53**, 4260 (1931).

[2] W. C. Gardiner and H. L. Sanders, *Ind. Eng. Chem., Anal. Ed.* **9**, 274 (1937).

[3] M. Dole and B. Z. Wiener, *Trans. Electrochem. Soc.* **72**, 107 (1937).

[4] J. L. Gabbard and M. Dole, *ibid.* **72**, 129 (1937).

[5] D. O. Jordan, *Trans. Faraday Soc.* **34**, 1305 (1938).

[6] M. Dole, R. M. Roberts, and C. E. Holley, Jr., *J. Am. Chem. Soc.* **63**, 725 (1941).

these questions is in the affirmative provided that the glass electrode is studied in the scientifically exact manner described above, the sodium-ion concentration of the solution is not greater than one normal, and the temperature is not too high or the time of contact too long. Statements in the literature to the effect that the glass electrode potentials are not reproducible in alkaline solution are usually based on erroneous experimental methods.

Gardiner and Sanders [2] obtained checking and reproducible results in 5.0 M sodium ion solutions at 30°C., but they did not reverse the direction of measurement so that we do not know whether the glass-electrode surface is temporarily altered in such strong salt solutions or whether on being replaced in acid solution the glass electrode would give immediately the correct results. In this connection it is interesting to note that Powney and Jordan [7] state "The glass electrode gave reproducible results when working in alkaline solutions for the first few days of use, but the e.m.f. produced then increased slowly and more frequent calibration each day became necessary. Electrodes finally gave a very high and nonreproducible e.m.f., the attainment of this state being accelerated by working in strongly alkaline solutions at high temperatures. Such electrodes could not be reconditioned by soaking in chromic acid, and had to be rejected."

7·2. An Experimental Method of Measuring Glass Electrode Error

In order to determine the extent to which the glass electrode behaves as a perfect hydrogen electrode and gives potentials from which correct pH values can be calculated, it is necessary to compare the glass and hydrogen electrodes in the same solution and at the same time. This procedure, first devised by Hughes,[8] was adopted by the author because it eliminates any liquid-junction potential and temperature-fluctuation uncertainties in so far as a comparison of the two electrodes is concerned. A hydrogen-glass-electrode comparison cell similar to one used by Dole and Wiener is illustrated in Fig. 7·1 where the e.m.f. developed between either of the glass electrodes G and either of the hydrogen electrodes H can be measured. At the same time the pH of the solution can be measured by measuring the difference in e.m.f. between the hydrogen and saturated potassium chloride calomel electrodes. In Fig. 7·1 S is the salt bridge leading to the calomel electrode; the three-way stopcock A allows either the cell to be emptied, the salt bridge on either side of the stopcock to be flushed

[7] J. Powney and D. O. Jordan, *J. Soc. Chem. Ind.* **56**, 133T (1937).
[8] W. S. Hughes, *J. Am. Chem. Soc.* **44**, 2860 (1922).

out, or the liquid junction to be made within the bore of the stopcock. The stopcock is ungreased in order that, when closed, its electrical resistance will not be too great. The buret B with reservoir C and hydrogen outlet E was adapted from the design of MacInnes and Cowperthwaite;[9] by proper manipulation of the stopcock F oxygen could be swept out of the buret and titrating solution before the titrating solution was run into the buret.

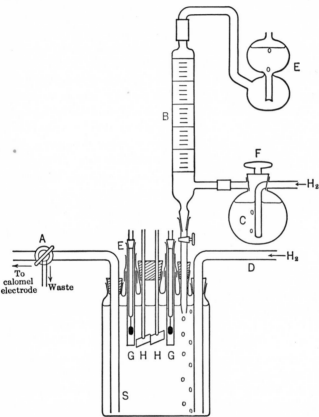

F IG. 7·1.   Hydrogen-glass-electrode comparison cell.   Hydrogen gas outlet not indicated.

The e.m.f. cells measured by the author at 25°C. (see Chapter 9 for a discussion of the temperature effects) were the two hydrogen electrode-calomel electrode cells

Pt, H_2 (1 atm.) | Buffer Solution ‖ Sat. KCl | HgCl | Hg   [7·2·A]

[9] D. A. MacInnes and I. W. Cowperthwaite, *J. Am. Chem. Soc.* **53**, 555 (1931).

from whose average e.m.f., the pH was calculated by the equation (the constant in this equation would now be different—see Appendix IV).

$$p\mathrm{H} = \frac{E - 0.2458}{0.05915} \qquad [7·2·1]$$

and the two glass electrode-calomel electrode cells

$$\overline{\mathrm{Ag} \mid \mathrm{AgCl} \mid 0.1 \ N \ \mathrm{HCl} \mid \mathrm{Glass}} \begin{array}{c} \mathrm{Buffer} \\ \mathrm{Solution} \end{array} \Bigg\| \begin{array}{c} \mathrm{Sat.} \\ \mathrm{KCl} \end{array} \Bigg| \mathrm{HgCl} \mid \mathrm{Hg} \qquad [7·2·\mathrm{B}]$$

By subtracting the e.m.f. of cell 7·2·B from that of 7·2·A the e.m.f. of the glass electrode-hydrogen electrode cell

$$\mathrm{Pt, \ H_2 \ (1 \ atm.)} \Bigg| \begin{array}{c} \mathrm{Buffer} \\ \mathrm{Solution} \end{array} \overline{\mathrm{Glass} \mid 0.1 \ N \ \mathrm{HCl} \mid \mathrm{AgCl} \mid \mathrm{Ag}} \qquad [7·2·\mathrm{C}]$$

was obtained. Occasionally the e.m.f. of cell 7·2·C was measured directly as a check, but usually the glass electrode and. hydrogen electrode potentials were measured with reference to the calomel electrode potential in order to discover any trend of the observed e.m.f. with time. The potential of the hydrogen electrode was much more sluggish than that of the glass electrode, so that as soon as the solution was completely stirred by the hydrogen gas and as soon as the platinum electrodes had become stable in their potentials, the e.m.f. of the various cell combinations could be read. It is only in basic solutions containing a very high concentration of sodium ions that the glass electrode potentials show any drift.[10,11]

The measured e.m.f. of cell 7·2·C contains no liquid-junction potential.

To illustrate, some data obtained in a single typical experiment are given in Table 7·1.

In the experiment of Table 7·1 a buffer solution was made 0.9 N in sodium acetate and 0.05 M in disodium phosphate, and the pH lowered by adding a few drops of concentrated acid. To vary the pH oxygen-free 1.0 N sodium hydroxide was added and after the measurement at the pH 11.836 had been taken, oxygen-free acid was again added and the pH lowered to 6.09. For both the glass electrodes, numbers C–71 and C–73, the e.m.f. of cell 7·2·C returned to its previous value, thus indicating the reproducibility and reversibility of the glass electrode. Other unpublished data supporting this conclusion have also been obtained.

[10] D. A. MacInnes and M. Dole, *J. Am. Chem. Soc.* 52, 29 (1930).
[11] W. C. Gardiner and H. L. Sanders, *Ind. Eng. Chem., Anal. Ed.* 9, 274 (1937).

If the glass electrode always acted as a perfect hydrogen electrode, the e.m.f. of cell 7·2·C would be constant and independent of the pH of the buffer solution. An examination of Table 7·1 shows that this is true between pH 6.49 and 7.49, but that at pH 9.34 and above the value of cell 7·2·C becomes larger than 0.3371 and 0.3380, the correct values for electrodes C–71 and C–73, respectively (actually the correct value should have been 0.3524 v., but was not because of asymmetry potentials and because exactly 0.1 N hydrochloric acid was not used as the solution inside the glass electrode). If we subtract from the measured value of cell 7·2·C its theoretical value, that is, 0.3371 v. for

TABLE 7·1

E.M.F. OF CELLS 7·2·A, 7·2·B, 7·2·C, AND 7·2·D IN VOLTS AT 25°C.

1 N NaOH added to 0.9 N NaAc, 0.05 M Na$_2$HPO$_4$

pH	Cell 7·2·A		Cell 7·2·B		Cell 7·2·C		Cell 7·2·D	
	H$_2$–1	H$_2$–2	C–71	C–73	C–71	C–73	C–71	C–73
					Against	H$_2$–2	ΔE	ΔE
6.485	0.6291	0.6293	0.2924	0.2916	0.3370	0.3378	0.0	0.0
7.493	0.6886	0.6890	0.3516	0.3510	0.3374	0.3380	0.0	0.0
9.341	0.7979	0.7983	0.4567	0.4563	0.3416	0.3420	0.0045	0.0040
9.779	0.8240	0.8242	0.4793	0.4787	0.3449	0.3455	0.0078	0.0075
10.435	0.8628	0.8630	0.5103	0.5095	0.3527	0.3535	0.0156	0.0155
11.047	0.8991	0.8992	0.5344	0.5338	0.3648	0.3654	0.0277	0.0274
11.836	0.9459	0.9459	0.5582	0.5574	0.3877	0.3885	0.0506	0.0505
6.088	0.6065	0.6065	0.2692	0.2684	0.3371	0.3381	0.0	0.0

the cell containing glass electrode C–71 and 0.3380 v. for the cell containing C–73, we obtain the e.m.f. of cell 7·2·D.

| Ag | AgCl | 0.1 N HCl | Perfect Glass Electrode | Buffer Solution | Actual Glass Electrode | 0.1 N HCl | AgCl | Ag | [7·2·D] |

The e.m.f. of cell 7·2·D should always be zero if the glass electrode acted as a perfect hydrogen electrode, but since it does not, the e.m.f. of cell 7·2·D will have a finite value in certain solutions which we shall call "the error of the glass electrode" and shall designate by ΔE. Values of ΔE are given in Table 7·1 in the right-hand columns where the agreement between the two membrane-type glass electrodes can be seen.

Before concluding this section it should be pointed out that the author selected the theoretical value of cell 7·2·C, 0.3371 v. for glass electrode C–71 and 0.3380 v. for glass electrode C–73, by observing the e.m.f. of cell 7·2·C over the range where the e.m.f. is independent of pH. This is a dangerous procedure since there may be a constant error entering into the e.m.f. of cell 7·2·C in which case it would not be observed in this method. It is better to make up cell 7·2·C using a hydrochloric acid solution of known concentration inside the glass electrode so that the e.m.f. of the cell is known in advance of the measurements.

In Table 7·2 we have collected some of the measured values of ΔE.

TABLE 7·2

ERRORS OF THE GLASS ELECTRODE AT 25° IN ALKALINE SOLUTIONS

DATA OF DOLE (1931) IN MILLIVOLTS
DATA OF DOLE AND WIENER (1937) IN PARENTHESES

pH	0·1 N Li$^+$	1·0 N Li$^+$	0·1 N Na$^+$	1·0 N Na$^+$	0·1 N K$^+$	1·0 N K$^+$	1·0 N Ba^{++}
9.0	. . . .	. . . .	(1.0)	(3.0)	. . . . .	. . . . .	. . . .
9.5	0.5 (0.5)	0 (1.0)	1.6 (2.0)	5.0 (5.0)	0.8	. . . . .	. . . .
10.0	1.5 (1.0)	1.2 (1.5)	3.4 (3.2)	9.8 (9.2)	1.5	1.8	0.5
10.5	3.0 (2.0)	4.6 (4.2)	6.0 (6.0)	17.2 (14.8)	2.5	3.3	0.8
11.0	5.3 (3.5)	10.6 (9.0)	10.8 (10.0)	27.2 (22.1)	3.6	5.2	1.1
11.5	8.6 (6.0)	20.2 (17.2)	16.4 (15.8)	42.0 (31.6)	4.9	7.2	1.4
12.0	(12.8)	33.3 (29.0)	24.3 (25.0)	59.2 (45.0)	6.2	9.6	1.7
12.5	(19.0)	(49.5)	. . . .	(64.5)	. . . . .	12.0	2.1
13.0	. . . .	(71.0)	. . . .	(90.0)	. . . . .	14.6	. . . .

7·3. Errors of the Glass Electrode in Alkaline Solutions

The errors of the glass electrode as measured by the previously described method vary with a number of factors so that it is impossible to state the extent to which pH measurements with the glass electrode will be in error unless the temperature, type of glass, pH, and positive ion composition and concentration of the solution are known. In this chapter we shall restrict our remarks chiefly to Corning 015 glass at or near 25°C. Under these conditions the glass electrode error seems to depend only on the type of positive ions present, the concentration of these ions, the temperature, and the pH.

In Fig. 7·2 the errors of the glass electrode (the e.m.f. of cell 7·2·D) in sodium-ion solutions of different concentrations are plotted as a function of the pH; rise of sodium-ion concentration and rise of pH produce an increase in the error. In Fig. 7·3 we have illustrated the difference in the behavior of the glass electrode in solutions containing different types of positive ions all at unit concentration, the data of different investigators being plotted so that the reproduc-

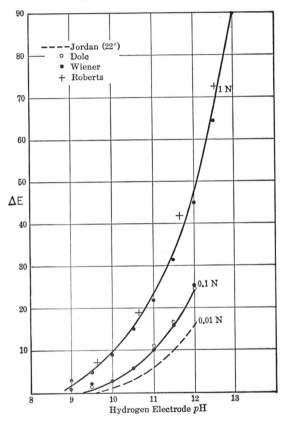

FIG. 7·2.   Glass electrode errors (millivolts) at 25°C. in sodium salt solutions.

ibility of the glass electrode in alkaline solutions can be visualized. The original study by the author [12] of the errors in 1 N Na$^+$ solutions did not yield data in agreement with the later work of Dole and Wiener [13] and Dole and Roberts,[14] possibly because the sample of

[12] M. Dole, *J. Am. Chem. Soc.* **53**, 4260 (1931).

[13] M. Dole and B. Z. Wiener, *Trans. Electrochem. Soc.* **72**, 107 (1937).

[14] M. Dole, R. M. Roberts, and C. E. Holley, Jr., *J. Am.Chem. Soc.* **63**, 725 (1941).

Corning 015 glass was not a particularly good one. All other repetitions of the early work, however, have satisfactorily verified the first measurements.

The work of Jordan and of the author clearly demonstrates that the errors of the glass electrode in solutions containing only divalent cations are very much less than in solutions of lithium or sodium salts, but we are somewhat at a loss to understand why Jordan's results for

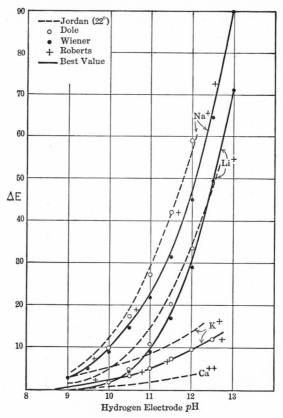

FIG. 7·3. Glass electrode errors (millivolts) in 1 M salt solution at 25°C.

strontium solutions show considerably greater glass electrode errors than do those for the calcium or barium solutions.

In 1932 the author [15] measured the errors of the glass electrode in 0.5 N sodium acetate and found them to be identical with the errors of the glass electrode in a mixture containing 0.5 N sodium acetate and 0.5 N barium acetate.

[15] M. Dole, *J. Phys. Chem.* **36**, 1570 (1932).

For a study of the glass electrode in lime liquors containing sodium chloride and sodium sulfide see Sec. 12·2.

The data obtained by Hill[16] given in Fig. 7·4 are interesting as they indicate that the error of the glass electrode in ammonia solutions is very much less than in basic solutions containing sodium ions. In fact, from the experiments of Hubbard, Hamilton, and Finn,[28] illustrated in Fig. 4·8 it would appear that the glass electrode functions without error in aqueous ammonia solutions, the deviations, if any, being in the opposite direction to those hitherto discussed in this chapter. However, in this connection there is some doubt concerning the exact validity of the hydrogen electrode potentials in the concentrated ammonia solutions so that the data of Hubbard, Hamilton, and Finn are possibly open to question.

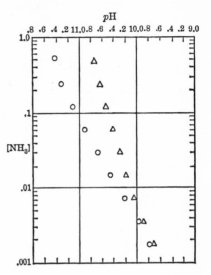

FIG. 7·4. Comparison of pH as measured by the glass electrode in aqueous ammonia (o) and in aqueous ammonia which is 0.5 M in sodium chloride (Δ).

MacInnes and the author[17] similarly found very little glass electrode error in a 0.1 N solution of the strong base tetramethylammonium hydroxide.

Although all of the early data indicated that the type of negative ion such as the acetate, phosphate, and chloride ions existing in the alkaline solutions was without influence on the alkaline errors of the glass electrode, the author in collaboration with Roberts[18] reexamined this question particularly in regard to the fluoride ion, the smallest of all negative ions (excepting the hydroxyl ion). It was found that the fluoride ion as such produced no variation in the glass-electrode behavior, but that the alkaline errors of the glass electrode greatly increased if the glass surface was first immersed in solutions containing hydrofluoric acid, the effect being greater the lower the pH of the fluoride solution. Figure 7·5 illustrates the measurements on one normal

[16] S. E. Hill, *J. Gen. Physiol.* **12**, 813 (1929).

[17] D. A. MacInnes and M. Dole, *J. Am. Chem. Soc.* **52**, 29 (1930).

[18] M. Dole and R. M. Roberts, unpublished data; Dole, Roberts, and Holley, *J. Am. Chem. Soc.* **63**, 725 (1941).

potassium fluoride solution, the values of ΔE being the error of the electrode at the pH 12.2 as a function (abscissa) of the pH of the potassium fluoride at the start of the experiment.

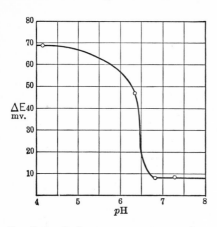

FIG. 7·5. Ordinates represent error in a solution 0.985 N in KF and 0.015 N in KAc at the pH 12·2. Abscissas represent pH of the 1 N K$^+$ solution in which glass electrode was immersed before making the measurement at the pH 12·2.

Because the errors of the glass electrode due to the sodium ion are so pronounced, Urban and Steiner [19] found that they could analyze mixtures of sodium and potassium ions for their sodium-ion content by means of the glass electrode. The average error was 3.6 per cent. (A commercial soft glass was used; perhaps the accuracy in analyzing for sodium could be increased by using a glass more sensitive to sodium-ion concentration such as glasses of the type D studied by Lengyel and Blum.)[20]

Dr. Beckman [21] of the National Technical Laboratories announces a new type of glass which exhibits alkaline errors much smaller than that of Corning 015 glass when made into glass elec-

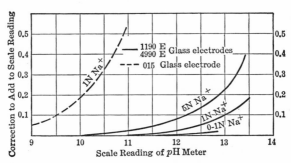

FIG. 7·6. Sodium-ion corrections of 1190–E and 4990–E glass electrodes at 25°C.

trodes, see Fig. 7·6. These electrodes, their numbers 1190–E and

[19] F. Urban and A. Steiner, *J. Phys. Chem.* **35**, 3058 (1931).
[20] B. Lengyel and E. Blum, *Trans. Faraday Soc.* **30**, 461 (1934).
[21] Private communication.

4990–E, are not recommended for use at tempratures above room temperature or for ordinary pH measurements below a pH of 9.0, but they do make possible a more accurate measurement of pH in strongly alkaline solutions. Electrodes made of this new glass behave in the following way:

"*a*. When placed in a highly alkaline solution (e.g., 1 N NaOH) the electrode does not instantly assume equilibrium but may indicate a gradually increasing pH for ten minutes or more.

"*b*. The asymmetry potential (zero correction) tends to change when the electrode is immersed in solutions of high pH. This change is in the direction of giving lower pH readings. In combination with the sluggishness noted in (*a*), this effect will usually give a time curve of pH readings reaching a maximum in approximately five minutes followed by slowly decreasing pH readings.

"*c*. As the electrode ages both of the phenomena noted above take place more slowly; that is, the response to pH changes becomes more sluggish and the change of asymmetry potential takes place more slowly. In acid solution (e.g., 0.1 N HCl) aging takes place relatively fast and is appreciable after a few days of continuous immersion. Above a pH of 10.0, aging takes place very slowly if at all.

"These phenomena cause a small uncertainty in the results of a pH measurement. However, this difficulty is pronounced only in extremely alkaline solutions and in most cases results reproducible to better than 0.1 pH unit may be obtained by making frequent buffer calibration of the electrode in the usual manner. For the best results under severe conditions, the following procedure is recommended:

"1. When in intermittent use, store the glass electrode in a buffer solution of pH 10. New glass electrodes should be soaked in pH 10 buffer for at least several hours before being placed in service.

"2. After prolonged service, the response of the glass electrode may become excessively sluggish due to aging effects. To restore it to its original condition, prepare a solution containing 20% of ammonium bifluoride in a waxed paper cup or paraffined beaker. Immerse the bulb portion in this solution for three minutes and then allow it to soak overnight in pH 10.00 buffer. This procedure should be used only when necessary as the bifluoride solution has an etching action on the glass."

For pH measurements the following instructions are given.

"1. Put the pH meter in operation in accordance with instructions supplied with the meter.

"2. Immerse the electrodes in pH 10 buffer solution, set the temperature compensator to the solution temperature and, after allowing a moment for equilibrium to take place, set the Zero Adjustor so that the meter indicates the pH of the buffer solution.

"3. Rinse the electrodes with distilled water, flush the calomel electrode and immerse the electrodes in the test sample. Set the temperature compensator to the sample temperature and note the pH reading at convenient intervals; for example, one minute, three minutes and five minutes after immersion.   If appreciable upward drift in the readings occurs at the end of five minutes, the readings should be extended to ten minutes or more.   For most purposes, the maximum pH reading may be taken as the correct reading for the sample.

"For maximum accuracy, the buffer standardization should be repeated immediately after taking the final reading on the test sample.   Clean the electrodes, immerse in pH 10 buffer and allow about one-half minute for equilibrium to be attained.   If the pH reading does not agree exactly with the buffer pH, subtract the reading from the buffer pH and add the difference to the final pH reading of the test sample.

"4. If the pH and sodium ion concentration are high, a correction estimated from Fig. 7·6 must be added to the observed pH readings to obtain the true pH of the test sample."

An example of some actual data obtained according to the above instructions follows.

"A meter using a new ⅍ 4990–E glass electrode was adjusted to read pH 10.00 at 25°C. in the buffer solution.   The electrodes were then immersed in an approximately 1.0 N sodium hydroxide solution at a temperature of 25°C.   The following scale readings were obtained:

Time—minutes:	1	3	5	8	10
Scale reading:	13.50	13.52	13.52	13.51	13.50

"The electrodes were then returned to the pH 10.00 buffer, whereupon a reading of 9.95 was obtained.   The corrected scale reading was computed as follows:

$$(10.00 - 9.95) + 13.50 = 13.55$$

From the chart, at a scale reading of 13.55 and sodium ion concentration of 1.0 N, the sodium ion error is seen to be 0.19 pH unit, giving a true pH for the solution of

$$13.55 + 0.19 = 13.74$$

The hydrogen electrode gave pH 13.75 for this solution, in good agreement with the glass electrode value."

Passinski [22] writing from Moscow states "In his report delivered at the All-Union Conference on Analytical Chemistry, which was held toward the end of 1939, B. Nikolsky (Leningrad) mentioned Evseyevich's latest experiments.   Evseyevich, after making a systematic study of Li-glass electrodes, came to the conclusion that they were very stable, gave reproducible potentials and could be used to make measurements in the alkaline region, which our data confirm.   This work will be published soon."   It may be inferred from these remarks that Beckman's new glass may possibly be a lithium-containing glass.

[22] Private communication.

7·4. Methods of Avoiding Alkaline Errors

We shall now consider the difficult problem of avoiding or diminishing the alkaline error of Corning 015 glass electrodes which must be attempted if the new Beckman glass is unavailable and if high pH measurements must be made using Corning 015 glass. If sodium or lithium hydroxides or ions could be avoided or eliminated from the solution, the errors would be very much reduced as a study of Fig. 7·3 easily proves; other bases that could be substituted to very great advantage are the alkaline earth hydroxides such as barium hydroxide; the weak base, ammonium hydroxide, or strong bases having large positive ions such as tetramethylammonium hydroxide. However, these are all more or less expensive and very little used in practice so that this recommendation is not a particularly happy solution of the problem. Furthermore, sodium ions must not be present if these bases are to be used, which constitutes a serious limitation to this plan of reducing the alkaline solution errors.

Apparently the only method of accurately determining the pH in sodium solutions in the alkaline range in the case of Corning 015 glass electrodes is to measure the pH and then to apply a correction, *provided the total sodium-ion concentration of the solution is known.* If lithium or potassium ions are present, they should also be taken into consideration in calculating the correction to be applied. In Appendix V a graph is given showing the correct pH as a function of the pH as observed with the glass electrode, and as a function of the concentration of the sodium ion. As the pH becomes higher and the concentration of the sodium ion becomes greater, the calculated pH values become less certain, but the graph gives one the possibility of measuring pH up to a pH of 12 in the presence of 1 N sodium ions with an error of ± 0.1 or ± 0.2 pH unit while if no correction were made the glass electrode would be in error by approximately a whole pH unit under these conditions.

Another possibility also involving a knowledge of the total sodium-ion concentration in the solution is to standardize the glass electrode in buffers having as close as practical the pH and sodium-ion concentration of the unknown solution.[23] This procedure reduces the error to a large extent, but it does not eliminate it completely, for if the pH of the test sample is not exactly equal to that of the standardizing buffer solutions, the change in e.m.f. will not give the entire difference

---

[23] The Hartman-Leddon Company, 6003 Girard Ave., Philadelphia, Pa., is prepared to supply alkaline buffers of known pH and of different sodium chloride concentrations.

in pH because the rate of increase of e.m.f. of the glass electrode with increase in pH is much less in alkaline solutions than in regions where the glass electrode functions without error.   As a pronounced example of this, the author [24] found that in 3.5 N sodium acetate solutions between the pH limits 11.69 and 12.35, the change in glass electrode e.m.f. was 73 per cent less than the theoretical amount.   At the pH 11.69 the glass electrode was in error by 1.13 pH units; if the glass electrode had been standardized at the pH 11.69 in 3.5 N sodium acetate solution, the error reduced to zero, and then used to measure the pH of the solution at the true pH of 12.35, the glass electrode would have been in error by 73 per cent of (12.35–11.69) or 0.48 pH units. If the glass electrode had not been standardized at the pH 11.69, it would have been 1.6 pH units in error at the pH 12.35.   Thus this standardizing method reduces the error from 1.6 to 0.48, but does not eliminate it completely.   In fact, as illustrated by the above calculation, this method is open to serious question.   A still better method would be to standardize the glass electrode in buffer solutions of known sodium-ion concentration having pH values both higher and lower than that of the unknown, and to interpolate these results to obtain the correct pH from the e.m.f. reading of the unknown.   Thus suppose we have the following results obtained in 3.5 N sodium acetate solutions.

True pH	11.17	11.69	12.35
pH given by glass electrode......	10.35	10.56	10.74
Error in pH reading............	0.82	1.13	1.61

If we make a linear interpolation of the error of the solutions of pH 11.17 and 12.35 to find the correction to be applied to the glass electrode at the pH 11.69, we obtain 1.25 as the correction and 11.81 as the corrected pH reading of the glass electrode.   Thus, this treatment reduces the alkaline error from 1.13 to 0.12 pH units.   It should be emphasized, however, that the sodium-ion concentration was the same in all the solutions of the above example.

Instead of computing the sodium error by interpolation or estimating it graphically, it is possible to calculate it using the relation suggested by Jordan,[25]

$$\log \Delta E = A \ pH' + B \log m - C \qquad [7·4·1]$$

[24] M. Dole, *J. Am. Chem. Soc.* **53**, 4260 (1931).
[25] D. O. Jordan, *Trans. Faraday Soc.* **34**, 1305 (1938).

where pH' is the uncorrected pH as measured with the glass electrode and ΔE is the glass electrode error in millivolt. The empirical constants of the equation have the values given in Table 7·3.

TABLE 7·3

CONSTANTS OF EQUATION 7·4·1

Temperature 22°

Cation	A	B	C	Lithium Concentration	A	D
Sodium...	0.540	0.46	4.20	0.01	0.321	3.335
Potassium	0.218	0.23	1.43	0.04	0.321	2.925
Strontium	0.275	0.50	1.98	0.1	0.321	2.710
Calcium..	0.397	0.38	4.10	0.4	0.467	4.010
Barium...	0.257	0.30	2.59	1.0	0.563	4.890

By means of Eq. 7·4·1 we calculated the errors of the glass electrode as determined by Jordan which are illustrated in Figs. 7·2 and 7·3. In Sec. 12·2 we also give some corrections of the glass electrode in sodium sulfide solutions as calculated from Eq. 7·4·1 with the conclusion that if the pH becomes so high and the sodium-ion concentration so great that the glass-electrode e.m.f. is insensitive to real changes in pH, Eq. 7·4·1 is inapplicable and there is no way in which the glass electrode can be of service in determining the pH of alkaline solutions. The pH limit seems to be 12.5 if the experimental work cited in Sec. 12·2 is correct.

For other mathematical relations between ΔE and pH see Chapter 16.

As we conclude this section, we note that the glass electrode can be used to measure variations in pH in alkaline solutions or to bring the pH of these solutions always to the same value without knowing the exact pH; in other words, it can be used for comparison or control purposes. Care should be taken, however, that the sodium-ion concentration is the same in all the solutions compared, or the comparison or control measurements will be meaningless in the high pH region.

7·5. Qualitative Explanation of Alkaline Errors

In Chapter 16 the theory of the glass electrode is discussed extensively and chiefly from a mathematical point of view. Here we shall explain the alkaline errors qualitatively by saying that they must be due to the sodium ions or positive ions other than the hydrogen ion taking part in the glass electrode reaction. When current flows through the glass electrode membrane (as an infinitesimal current must flow in making glass-electrode measurements even when the most sensitive and refined pH electrometers are used), the glass electrode will act as a perfect hydrogen electrode, provided only hydrogen or hydroxyl ions pass from the solution into the glass or vice versa.[26] If, however, sodium or other positive ions also pass into the glass (or out of it if the current is reversed), then we can deduce from the principles of thermodynamics that the glass electrode will no longer be a pure hydrogen electrode but will have a "mixed-electrode" function and will exhibit what we have called here the errors of the glass electrode. If a glass could be invented into or out of which sodium ions would not migrate in an electric field, electrodes of this glass would have no sodium errors.

Several years ago Quittner [27] carried out electrolysis experiments obtaining results which confirm the general picture of the glass electrode behavior outlined above (see Sec. 16·2). In acid solutions the current across the water-glass boundary seemed to be carried entirely by hydrogen ions, but in basic solutions he found that it was the sodium ion that migrated into the glass.

Hubbard, Hamilton, and Finn [28] suggest a relation between glass electrode errors and chemical durability of the glass; this hypothesis will be considered in detail in Chapter 16.

[26] M. Dole, *J. Am. Chem. Soc.* **53**, 4260 (1931).
[27] F. Quittner, *Ann. Physik.* [4] **85**, 745 (1928).
[28] D. Hubbard, E. H. Hamilton, and A. N. Finn, *J. Research Natl. Bur. Standards,* **22**, 339 (1939).

CHAPTER 8

LIMITATIONS OF THE GLASS ELECTRODE IN ACID AND NONAQUEOUS SOLUTIONS

8·1. Introduction

In the month of September, 1931, papers by MacInnes and Belcher[1] and by Buchböck[2] were published containing data which proved that in concentrated acid solutions (above 1 N) the glass electrode does not act like a perfect hydrogen electrode and cannot be used to measure the pH accurately if the pH becomes too low. In 1932 the author[3] showed that similar errors occurred when one tries to measure the pH of nonaqueous solutions and strong salt solutions. These results of MacInnes and Belcher and of Dole were all obtained with the Corning 015 glass so that in this chapter we shall restrict our discussion chiefly to this type of glass and to room temperature (25°C.)

As far as could be discovered by orienting experiments, the acid errors of the glass electrode did not depend directly upon the type or concentration of either positive or negative ions so that it was unnecessary to employ the technique of maintaining either the positive or negative ion-concentration constant.

In acid and nonaqueous solutions the e.m.f. of the cell

$$\text{Pt, H}_2 \text{ (1 atm.)} \left| \begin{array}{c} \text{Acid or Non-} \\ \text{aqueous Solution} \end{array} \right| \text{Glass} \left| \begin{array}{c} 0.1\ N \\ \text{HCl} \end{array} \right| \text{AgCl} \left| \text{Ag} \right. \quad [8\cdot1\cdot\text{A}]$$

becomes less than its constant theoretical value of 0.3524 v.; the e.m.f. of the cell

$$\text{Ag} \left| \text{AgCl} \right| \begin{array}{c} 0.1\ N \\ \text{HCl} \end{array} \left| \begin{array}{c} \text{Perfect} \\ \text{Glass} \\ \text{Electrode} \end{array} \right| \begin{array}{c} \text{Buffer} \\ \text{Solu-} \\ \text{tion} \end{array} \left| \begin{array}{c} \text{Actual} \\ \text{Glass} \\ \text{Electrode} \end{array} \right| \begin{array}{c} 0.1\ N \\ \text{HCl} \end{array} \left| \text{AgCl} \right| \text{Ag} \quad [8\cdot1\cdot\text{B}]$$

is, therefore, negative in very acid and nonaqueous solutions and the glass electrode error is negative. This behavior is just the opposite of

---

[1] D. A. MacInnes and D. Belcher, *J. Am. Chem. Soc.* **53**, 3315 (1931).

[2] G. Buchböck, *Z. physik. Chem.* **156A**, 232 (1931).

[3] M. Dole, *J. Am. Chem. Soc.* **54**, 2120, 3095 (1932).

the behavior of the glass electrode in basic solutions where the e.m.f. of cell 8·1·A becomes greater than its constant theoretical value and the e.m.f. of cell 8·1·B is positive. Thus the glass-electrode potential fails to follow the platinum-hydrogen-electrode potential either as the pH becomes very high or as the pH becomes very low; the total e.m.f. across the glass membrane cannot, therefore, become as great as it would if each surface of the glass acted as a perfect hydrogen electrode.

8·2. Experimental Data in Acid and Nonaqueous Solutions

MacInnes and Belcher found qualitatively (data published in graphical form only) that the glass electrode gives the largest negative error in phosphoric acid solutions, and smallest in hydrochloric acid at

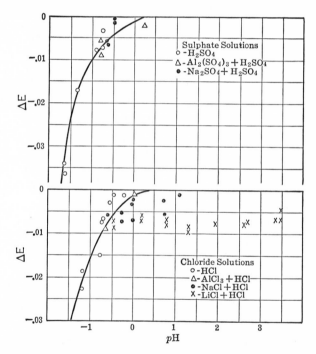

FIG. 8·1.   Acid errors of the glass electrode.

any definite pH. From these results they concluded that the negative errors in acid solutions depend on the negative ions, but this conclusion is untenable for the following reasons.[4] Increasing the negative

[4] M. Dole, *J. Am. Chem. Soc.* **54**, 2120, 3095 (1932).

ion concentration by adding a large quantity of neutral salt has little effect on increasing the error unless the salt concentration becomes very high.   In basic solutions the positive error is enormously reduced if univalent sodium ions are replaced by divalent barium ions, but in acid solutions the negative errors for hydrochloric and sulfuric acids are only slightly different.   The negative errors can be produced by adding alcohol to the aqueous solution without appreciable change in negative ion concentration.

The author's data for hydrochloric and sulfuric acid solutions are plotted in Fig. 8·1 and for alcoholic solutions in Fig. 8·2.   A surprising result was the constant error observed in 4.4 N lithium chloride solution as the pH was decreased; these data seemed to prove that the glass-electrode negative error was not a direct function of the hydrogen-ion concentration.   The alcoholic solution data also pointed to the same conclusion.   In Table 8·1 some representative data for the negative errors are tabulated along with the pH and activity of the water in the solution, the activity of the water being defined as the ratio of the aqueous tension of the solution to that of the pure water.

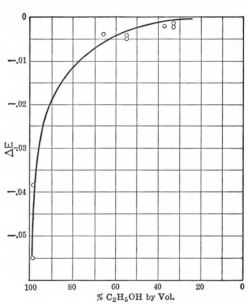

FIG. 8·2.   Errors of the glass electrode in alcoholic solutions.

A study of the data indicates that there is a much closer correlation between the activity of the water and the negative errors than between the errors and the pH, or between the errors and the concentration or type of negative ions.   In Chapter 16 it will be shown mathematically that, if certain assumptions are granted, the glass electrode will be in error if the term

$$\frac{RT}{F} \ln a_{H_2O} \qquad\qquad [8·2·1]$$

where a_{H_2O} is the activity of the water, becomes different from zero.

Amis and Gabbard [5] have measured the error of the glass electrode in a concentrated magnesium sulfate solution, and have found the error to agree with Eq. 8·2·1.

TABLE 8·1

ERRORS OF THE GLASS ELECTRODE IN ACID AND NONAQUEOUS SOLUTION AT 25°C.

DATA OF DOLE (1932)

Solution	pH	Water Activity	ΔE Millivolts
33% Ethanol.................	1.30	0.89	−1.3
33% Ethanol.................	0.413	0.89	−1.3
37% Ethanol.................	1.86	0.88	−2.0
55% Ethanol.................	1.36	0.83	−4.2
56% Ethanol.................	1.99	0.83	−4.6
66% Ethanol.................	0.712	0.79	−3.9
4.4 N LiCl..................	4 to −0.5	0.77	−7.0
H_2SO_4......................	−0.798	0.69	−6.9
H_2SO_4......................	−0.798	0.69	−3.3
HCl.........................	−0.680	0.65	−6.5
HCl.........................	−0.680	0.65	−6.8
H_2SO_4......................	−0.910	0.63	−7.8
HCl.........................	−0.730	0.62	−15.1
HCl.........................	−1.17	0.41	−18.4
HCl.........................	−1.17	0.41	−22.5
H_2SO_4......................	−1.35	0.40	−16.6
H_2SO_4......................	−1.62	0.27	−33.9
H_2SO_4......................	−1.62	0.27	−36.3
98% Ethanol.................	−0.065	0.12	−55.1
98% Ethanol.................	−0.065	0.12	−38.6

If the expression 8·2·1 correctly gives the negative error of the glass electrode, then it is obvious that the glass electrode cannot be used to measure the pH of nonaqueous solutions. This is a serious limitation of the glass electrode. In agreement with this conclusion, Goodhue and Hixon [6] found that they could not use the glass electrode to determine the dissociation constants of amines and acids in ethanol.

There has been a dearth of studies of the acid and nonaqueous solution errors of the glass electrode as a function of the composition of the glass (see remarks in Sec. 4·1), but the very suggestive work of Hub-

[5] E. S. Amis and J. L. Gabbard, *J. Am. Chem. Soc.* **59**, 557 (1937).
[6] L. D. Goodhue and R. M. Hixon, *J. Am. Chem. Soc.* **57**, 1688 (1935).

bard, Hamilton, and Finn [7] (see Fig. 4·6) indicates that their glass "A" having the approximate composition given in Table 8·2, func-

TABLE 8·2

COMPOSITION OF GLASS A IN PER CENT

SiO_2.............. 72.1
CaO.............. 10.1
Na_2O.............. 13.5
MgO.............. 3.3
R_2O_3............. 0.7

tions much better in acid solutions than does the Corning 015 glass, see Table 8·3.

TABLE 8·3

ACID ERRORS OF THE GLASS ELECTRODE IN MILLIVOLTS

DATA OF HUBBARD, HAMILTON, AND FINN (1939)

Normality of Solutions (Approximate)	Error HCl Solution		Error H_2SO_4 Solution		Error HF Solution
	015	A	015	A	015
0.001	0	0	0	0	−3
0.01	0	0	0	0	−15
0.1	−2	0	0	0	−54
1.0	−5	0	0	0	−188
5.0	−24	−1	0	0	....
10.0	−43	−9	0	0	....

Two other commercial soft glasses also gave no errors in sulfuric and hydrochloric acid solutions down to a *p*H of −1.0, but the authors state "although the data presented indicate that glass A has very desirable e.m.f. relations in the super-acid region, its resistance is so high it cannot be considered as more satisfactory than Corning 015 glass."

Acid solutions of hydrogen fluoride which, of course, attack the glass vigorously—particularly at concentrations greater than 1 *N*—cause large deviations of the Corning 015 electrodes as indicated in Table 8·3.   Hubbard, Hamilton, and Finn relate the nonaqueous solution error (except in the case of the hydrogen fluoride solutions)

---

[7] D. Hubbard, E. H. Hamilton, and A. N. Finn, *J. Research Natl. Bur. Standards*, **22**, 339 (1939).

to the repression of the swelling of the glass which normally takes place in water. Thus the superacid solutions, strong solutions of magnesium sulfate and solutions of ethanol all repress the swelling and at the same time cause the production of the negative errors of the glass electrode. In Chapter 16 we shall discuss more fully this interesting observation.

Not only does the glass electrode give incorrect pH values in nonaqueous solutions, but as mentioned in Sec. 4·2, the glass electrode may give erroneous results in aqueous solution if the glass surface has been in contact with nonaqueous solutions for any length of time. This difficulty is remedied by soaking the glass electrode in water.

Izmaïlov and Bel'gova [8] have studied the potentials of glass electrodes in alcohol-aqueous solutions as a function of the pH, finding deviations from linearity in the e.m.f.-pH curve at a pH of approximately 9.5, 8, and 7, for 40, 50, and 70 per cent alcohol, respectively.

8·3. Methods of Avoiding Acid and Nonaqueous Solution Errors

A possible method of eliminating errors arising from the change in the activity of the water would be to improve the glass along the lines suggested by the work of Hubbard, Hamilton, and Finn.[7] If this is not possible, then the error may be eliminated by applying a correction to the observed pH if the vapor pressure of the water in the solution is known. This correction is readily calculated by means of Eq. 8·2·1; it may also be calculated from the following equation if the osmotic pressure, Π, of the solution is known

$$\Delta E = - \frac{\Pi V_{H_2O}}{F} \qquad [8·3·1]$$

Equation 8·3·1 follows from the thermodynamic equation for osmotic pressure

$$\Pi = \frac{RT}{V_{H_2O}} \ln \frac{P_{H_2O}}{P_{soln.}} \qquad [8·3·2]$$

where P_{H_2O} is the vapor pressure of pure water, $P_{soln.}$ is the vapor pressure of water in the solution whose osmotic pressure is Π and V_{H_2O} is the partial molal volume of the water in the solution. (For approximate calculations it is sufficient to take V_{H_2O} equal to 18 cc.) As an example of the use of Eq. 8·3·1 let us calculate the error of the Corning 015 glass electrode in the determination of the pH of ox blood whose osmotic pressure is about 7 atmospheres. Expressing V in

[8] N. A. Izmaïlov and M. A. Bel'gova, *J. Gen. Chem.* (*U.S.S.R.*) **8**, 1873 (1938).

liters and multiplying the numerator of the right-hand side of Eq. 8·3·1 by 101.28, the factor to convert liter-atmospheres to joules, we have

$$\Delta E = -\frac{(0.018)\,(7)\,(101.28)}{96,500}$$

or

$$\Delta E \sim -\,0.0001 \text{ v.}$$

and therefore negligible.

However, it should be pointed out that the glass-electrode potentials are likely to be erratic and not very reproducible if the vapor pressure of the water becomes significantly different from that of pure water; for this reason pH measurements with the glass electrode in solutions containing only small amounts of water are not very reliable. Yet for some industrial purposes the glass electrode can be quite useful, even under these difficult conditions, see Sec. 12·3 and Sec. 15·4.

8·4. Qualitative Explanation of the Negative Errors of the Glass Electrode

The negative errors of the glass electrode are probably to be explained on the assumption that the hydrogen ion is transported by the electric current across the glass-solution interface as a hydrated ion and not as an unhydrated proton. Probably the proton migrates with one molecule of water, and since hydrogen is transferred by the hydrogen gas-platinum electrode in a dry condition, this difference in matter transferred results in an e.m.f. being developed by the glass electrode which is different from that of a hydrogen electrode. If a glass could be discovered through which the hydrogen would move in an unhydrated condition, i.e., as the proton, this glass would be free from the negative error; perhaps this is the explanation for the good data of Hubbard, Hamilton and Finn.

The mathematical theory for Eq. 8·2·1 is given in Chapter 16.

8·5. The pH of Emulsions of Sulfonated Oils

Parsy [9] has made an interesting study of the pH of sulfonated oil emulsions as a function of concentration of the oil, method, and temperature of formation of the emulsion, age, influence of potassium chloride and phosphate buffer solutions, and method of pH measurement. In Fig. 8·3 we have plotted as a function of per cent of oil the pH values as determined by the glass electrode and by the Wulff

[9] G. Parsy, *J. Intern. Soc. Leather Trades' Chem.* **21**, 261 (1937).

indicator comparison method of emulsions made from water and a sulfonated oil having the composition given in Table 8·4. Note the

TABLE 8·4

COMPOSITION OF A SULFONATED OIL

	Per Cent
Water.....................	13.25
Total Fatty Acid.............	79.00
Nonsaponifiable Matter.......	5.00
Total Sulfate as H_2SO_4........	5.50
Free Sulfate as H_2SO_4.........	0.60
NH_3.......................	0.99
Ash........................	1.62
Alkalinity of Ash.............	0
Chlorine content of Ash.......	0

sudden "break" in "glass electrode pH" as the 40 per cent mixture is approached and further note the relative insensitivity of the Wulff method to changes in composition of the system. Determination of the pH five hours after preparation of the emulsion gave no significantly different results. The emulsions were prepared at 40°C. although measured at 20°, but change of preparation temperature from 90 to 30°C. had no effect on the measured pH;

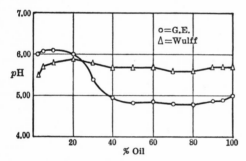

FIG. 8·3. pH of emulsions of sulfonated oils.

the manner of preparing the emulsion seemed, however, to have some influence. Thus adding the water and oil together in bulk before emulsification resulted in a mixture having a pH about 0.6 pH units below the pH of emulsions formed by adding progressively the water to the oil or vice versa; yet the Wulff method showed no difference in pH between the emulsions formed in these three ways. This led the author to suspect that a difference of potential between the oil particles and the aqueous medium of about 35 mv. could produce this discrepancy of 0.6 pH unit. On the other hand a comparison of the pH of three different emulsions by four methods revealed that the glass and quinhydrone electrodes gave identical results, but that the colorimetric and Wulff data diverged about 0.5 pH unit from the electrometric data, see Table 8·5. (The oil used was slightly different from that of Table 8·4.)

In the case of pure milk and of a 10 per cent emulsion of yolk of egg the Wulff apparatus *p*H values were identical with the glass electrode

TABLE 8·5

*p*H OF OIL EMULSIONS BY DIFFERENT METHODS AT 21°C.

DATA OF PARSY (1937)

Method	Solution			
	Phosphate Buffer	Oil Emulsion		
		2.5%	5%	10%
Quinhydrone..................	5.99	6.68	6.66	6.63
Glass electrode.................	6.00	6.67	6.61	6.57
Colorimetric				
(*a*) Buffer solutions and indicators	6.0	6.1	?	?
(*b*) Wulff apparatus............	6.0	6.1	6.1	6.3

results within the experimental limits of observation, see Table 8·6, but in the case of an oil emulsion stabilized with sodium caseinate and a

TABLE 8·6

*p*H OF SOME FAT-CONTAINING MATERIALS

DATA OF PARSY (1937)

Material	22°C.		21°C.—Five Hours Later	
	*p*H Glass Electrode	*p*H Wulff	*p*H Glass Electrode	*p*H Wulff
Phosphate buffer...............	6.00	6.0	6.00	6.0
Pure milk.....................	6.74	6.9	6.78	6.9
10% Emulsion of egg yolk........	5.86	5.7	5.90	5.7
10% Oil emulsion (containing 1% Na-caseinate)...	6.70	6.3	6.72	6.3
10% Petroleum Emulsion containing alkali.....	9.68	10.7	9.35	10.7

10 per cent petroleum emulsion containing alkali, the two methods disagreed; the large disagreement in the case of the latter solution,

however, may be due partly to the sodium error of the glass electrode (sodium-ion concentration was not given).

The emulsion of the oil can affect the e.m.f. of the glass electrode in two ways—either by causing a real change in the pH of the aqueous medium, or by modifying the difference of potential between the glass membrane and the liquid without changing the pH; if the latter occurs, then it can be said that the emulsion produces an "error of the glass electrode." Let us see if it can be demonstrated thermodynamically that a phase-boundary potential between the oil and the water phases would cause the glass electrode to be in error. Consider Fig. 8·4 in which the two possible current paths through the glass electrode-calomel electrode combination are indicated; we wish to ask ourselves whether the e.m.f. of the cell represented by path A is equal to or different from that of the cell represented by path B. If there is a

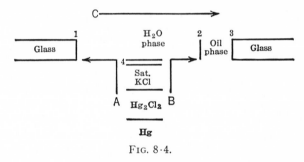

Fig. 8·4.

difference, then the glass electrode would possibly be in error since it might measure the e.m.f. of one or the other, depending on the path of the current, or its e.m.f. might take on an intermediate value. But it is easy to show that if equilibrium exists in the system, total free energy change equal to zero for the motion of electricity along the path C of Fig. 8·4, the sum of e.m.f.'s in going from one glass electrode to the other must be equal to zero, or

$$E_1 - E_3 = E_2 \qquad [8·5·1]$$

The e.m.f. of cell A is given by the equation

$$E_A = E_4 + E_1 \qquad [8·5·2]$$

and of cell B by the equation

$$E_B = E_4 + E_2 + E_3 \qquad [8·5·3]$$

or

$$E_A = E_B$$

by virtue of Eq. 8·5·1. Thus the presence of the oil phase will have no influence on the glass electrode potential at equilibrium, and the glass electrode will have no "globular error," to use a phrase of Parsy's, (unless the glass electrode potentials are irreversible). It seems much more likely to the author that the colorimetric method is in error although at the present time it is impossible to state definitely that the glass electrode method is to be preferred.

Another thermodynamic method of analyzing this complex mixture is to consider the initial and final states of the system represented by paths A and B for the passage of an infinitesimal amount of electricity; if the e.m.f. generated is to be identical, then the initial and final states of the substances transferred along the two paths by the electrical current must be identical. Suppose positive current flows into the glass electrode so that protons hydrated with one molecule of water are carried into the glass; this will happen along path A, but unless the activity of the water in the oil phase is equal to that in the aqueous phase—which it will be at equilibrium—then the proton may pass into the glass along path B in an unhydrated condition, producing thereby a glass-electrode error.

If a saturated potassium chloride solution is added drop by drop to the sulfonated oil emulsion, the pH reading of the glass electrode tends to become erratic and changes somewhat while the appearance of the emulsion also changes. If an agar-agar potassium chloride salt bridge is substituted for the ordinary aqueous solution bridge, no improvement in the stability of the readings is noted. If a phosphate salt is added to the oil before emulsification, the pH of the oil when plotted as a function of the water content of the emulsion gives almost a straight line, see Table 8·7, no peculiarities in the range of 60 per cent

TABLE 8·7

pH OF BUFFERED EMULSIONS AS MEASURED BY THE GLASS ELECTRODE AT 21 °C.

DATA OF PARSY (1937)

Parts oil mixture *	100	60	50	40	20	10
Parts water	0	40	50	60	80	90
pH	5.74	6.08	6.19	6.28	6.46	6.58

* The oil mixture contained 70 parts of sulfonated oil, 5 parts of disodium phosphate crystallized and 25 parts of water.

water being noted (the state of the emulsion is, of course, modified). The author wishes that Parsy had also determined the pH of these buffered emulsions colorimetrically for comparison purposes.

Porter's [10] report of the Committee on Methods for Analysis of Sulfonated Oils gives the pH values of Table 8·8 determined by a glass electrode. Without knowing the water content of the *pure* oils listed, it is impossible to estimate the pH error of the glass electrode for these nonaqueous liquids.

TABLE 8·8

pH OF SULFONATED OILS AS MEASURED WITH THE GLASS ELECTRODE

DATA OF PORTER (1938)

Concentration %	pH			
	Sulfonated Sperm Oil	Sulfonated Cod Oil	Sulfonated Neatsfoot Oil	Sulfonated Castor Oil
2	5.60	6.19	5.51	7.71
5	5.70	6.22	5.85	7.70
10	5.80	6.26	6.01	7.61
20	5.90	6.20	5.81	7.40
50	6.05	6.10	5.50	7.10
Pure oil	5.45	5.60	5.05	6.78

Water (filtered drinking water)   7.2

[10] R. E. Porter, *J. Am. Leather Chem. Assoc.* **33**, 509 (1938).

CHAPTER 9

TEMPERATURE EFFECTS IN GLASS ELECTRODE CELLS[1]

Introduction

In this chapter we shall study the properties of the glass electrode and component parts of its cell as a function of temperature and shall then attempt to estimate quantitatively the magnitude of the errors involved at any definite temperature arising from neglect of temperature control. Methods of avoiding or correcting for temperature difficulties and methods of standardizing glass electrodes at high temperatures will also be considered.

9·1. Electrical Resistance of Glass as a Function of Temperature

A knowledge of the electrical resistance of glass at different temperatures is important in connection with the measurement of pH with the glass electrode because errors due to electrical leakage or parallel e.m.f.'s become greater, the greater the electrical resistance of the membrane, see Sec. 4·4; conversely, the lower the electrical resistance the lower these errors.[2]

Lengyel and Blum [3] made a comprehensive study of the electrical resistance of glass as a function of temperature and composition and found that the specific conductance κ of the different glasses ($\kappa = l/RA$ where R is the resistance of the piece of glass being meas-

---

[1] We wish to express our gratitude to Dr. A. O. Beckman of the National Technical Laboratories, Pasadena, Calif., for his critical examination of and his contributions to the material of this chapter.

[2] Dr. Beckman writes, " A knowledge of the electrical resistance of a glass electrode is also important in connection with industrial applications where the electrode is connected to the measuring instrument through a long shielded cable. The electrostatic capacity from cable to shield and the 'soak charge' effects in the cable insulation shunt the electrode resistance and may introduce a long time constant in the measuring circuit if the electrode resistance is high. The consequence of the long time constant is that the null indicator responds only sluggishly to changes in the potentiometer setting and a minute or more may be required to locate the proper potentiometer setting."

[3] B. Lengyel and E. Blum, *Trans. Faraday Soc.* **30**, 461 (1934).

ured, l its length, and A its area of cross section), could be represented by the equation

$$\kappa = A e^{-\frac{Q}{RT}} \qquad\qquad [9\cdot1\cdot1]$$

Values of the empirical constants A and Q are given in Table 4·5. Lengyel and Blum did not measure the specific resistance of Corning

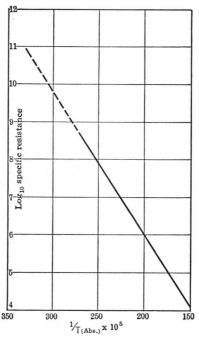

FIG. 9·1.   Resistance of Corning 015 glass as a function of temperature.

015 glass. This has been done by the Corning Glass Works [4] with the results expressed in Fig. 9·1. The author by using the logarithmic

[4] Private communication from Dr. W. C. Taylor and F. Kraissl of the Corning Glass Works. Dr. Beckman writes, "Measurements in our laboratory over the range 25 to 75°C. on 015 electrodes indicate that the resistance is given by the expression

$$R_t = R_{25} 10^{-0.034\,(t-25)}$$

to a close degree of approximation. The slight difference between our results and those obtained by extrapolation from the Corning data may be due to the error of extrapolation or to a difference in the state of the glass. Our investigations have shown that the specific resistance of a given glass electrode at room temperature may be varied by a factor of at least six by subjecting the electrode to different heat treatments. Most glass electrodes are in a 'chilled' condition for which the specific resistance is much lower than for annealed glass."

equation of the data of Fig. 9·1 calculated the change of resistance with temperature and obtained resistances of an average glass electrode at various temperatures which are collected in Table 9·1. The

TABLE 9·1

RESISTANCE OF AN AVERAGE CORNING 015 GLASS ELECTRODE
AS A FUNCTION OF THE TEMPERATURE

Temperature, °C.....	7	18	25	30	40	50	60
R in megohms.......	161	50	25	15.4	6.18	2.62	1.17

values of the resistances given in Table 9·1 which were calculated by extrapolation of data obtained at 350°C. and higher show the same proportionate change with change of temperature as found experimentally by Kahler and DeEds [5] and by Dole and Wiener [6] over the temperature range listed in the table. Increase of temperature, therefore, rapidly reduces the resistance which may increase the sensitivity of the measurement of the glass electrode e.m.f. if an ordinary galvanometer-potentiometer circuit is the measuring instrument as Schwabe [7] has noted.

9·2. High-Temperature Stability of Glass Electrodes

Schwabe stated that glass electrodes devitrify and become useless if treated with boiling solutions for a long time, but Beckman [8] writes:

"The effect described by Schwabe as 'devitrification' occurring in glass electrodes exposed to solutions at elevated temperatures would be better described as 'surface deterioration.' Whenever a glass electrode is exposed to aqueous solutions, deterioration of both surfaces immediately starts, the rate of deterioration depending upon the pH of the solution, the presence of certain specific ions, and the temperature. When the deterioration of both surfaces is the same, the asymmetry potential is zero. Badly deteriorated electrodes become sluggish in response to pH changes, show abnormally high sodium-ion errors and have an e.m.f.-pH slope less than the theoretical. The behavior of a deteriorated electrode can be completely restored to normal by etching away the deteriorated surface.

"The rapid deterioration of the conventional 015 glass electrodes was a serious limitation in industrial pH control. To overcome this limitation we have devel-

[5] H. Kahler and F. DeEds, *J. Am. Chem. Soc.* **53**, 2998 (1931).

[6] M. Dole and B. Z. Wiener, *Trans. Electrochem. Soc.* **72**, 107 (1937).

[7] K. Schwabe, *Z. Elektrochem.* **42**, 147 (1936).

[8] Private communication. Dr. Beckman's conclusions follow from experiments carried out by Dr. W. P. Baxter, H. H. Cary, and W. T. Cardwell.

oped a new 'high temperature' electrode in which the rate of deterioration is reduced by a factor of approximately 50. Under conditions where the useful life of the conventional 015 electrode might be a week, the useful life of our new electrode is estimated at at least a year. This estimate is based not only on laboratory tests but upon actual field operation for many months at temperatures up to 100°C."

Hubbard, Hamilton, and Finn [9] measured the rate of solution of the glass by the method described in Sec. 4·2 with the resulting observation that a rise in temperature of 10°C. approximately doubles the rate of solution, see Fig. 9·2. Other studies of the temperature coefficient of the electrolytic resistance of glass have been carried out by Humphreys [10] and also by Saechtling, Richter, and Rosenthal [11] who state that the resistance of Jena 4073 III glass (similar to Corning 015) is independent of pH and electric current.

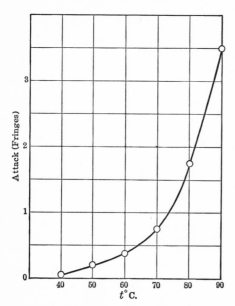

FIG. 9·2. Rate of solution of Corning 015 glass as a function of temperature.

9·3. Asymmetry Potential as a Function of Temperature

Kahler and DeEds,[12] Dallemagne,[13] and the author in collaboration with R. H. Corzo,[14] all have made measurements from which the change of asymmetry potential with change of temperature may be inferred, but with conflcting conclusions, probably because of different types of glass used, different shapes and sizes of electrodes, and different cell designs. Some data of Corzo and the author representing

[9] D. Hubbard, E. H. Hamilton, and A. N. Finn, *J. Research Natl. Bur. Standards* **22**, 339 (1939).

[10] R. G. Humphreys, *Chemistry & Industry*, **58**, 281 (1939).

[11] H. Saechtling, H. Richter and H. G. Rosenthal, *Z. Elektrochem.* **45**, 79 (1939).

[12] H. Kahler and F. DeEds, *J. Am. Chem. Soc.* **53**, 2998 (1931).

[13] M. J. Dallemagne, *Biochem. Z.* **291**, 159 (1937).

[14] M. Dole and R. H. Corzo, unpublished data.

studies on Corning 015 glass are illustrated in Fig. 9·3 from which it can be seen that at all temperatures the asymmetry potential is less than 4 mv., that elevation of temperature increases the asymmetry potential if the electrode is well aged, that the initial rise of temperature immediately after construction of the electrode tends to reduce the asymmetry potential, and that the asymmetry potential tends to decline to zero with time.

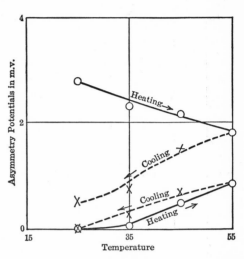

FIG. 9·3.   Asymmetry potential of Corning 015 glass electrode (Haber type).   Top curves, immediately after blowing electrode; bottom curves, four days later.

9·4. Alkaline Errors as a Function of Temperature

Gardiner and Sanders,[15] Powney and Jordan,[16] Dole and Wiener,[17] and Gabbard and Dole,[18] all have published data for the errors of the glass electrode at temperatures other than 25°C. The technique of Powney and Jordan, Dole and Wiener, and Gabbard and Dole, was essentially the same as that already described in Sec. 7·2. The saturated calomel reference electrode (Powney and Jordan used a normal calomel electrode at the higher temperatures) was always kept at the temperature of the glass electrode cell and the pH calculated by means of the equation,

$$pH = \frac{E - E^o}{2.303RT/F} \qquad [9·4·1]$$

whose constant E^o had the following values: 0.2565, 0.2452, 0.2295 at 10°, 25°, and 50°, respectively, as found experimentally, assuming that the pH of 0.05 c potassium acid phthalate was 3.98 at 10°, 25°, and 50°C.   This assumption is not quite correct as shown by the

[15] W. C. Gardiner and H. L. Sanders, *Ind. Eng. Chem., Anal. Ed.* **9**, 274 (1937).
[16] J. Powney and D. O. Jordan, *J. Soc. Chem. Ind.* **56**, 133T (1937).
[17] M. Dole and B. Z. Wiener, *Trans. Electrochem. Soc.* **72**, 107 (1937).
[18] J. L. Gabbard and M. Dole, *ibid.* **72**, 129 (1937).

recent work of MacInnes, Belcher, and Shedlovsky [19] who found the pH of 0.05 c potassium acid phthalate to be 4.000, 4.000, 4.015 at 12°, 25°, and 38°C. Gardiner and Sanders took the pH of this solu-

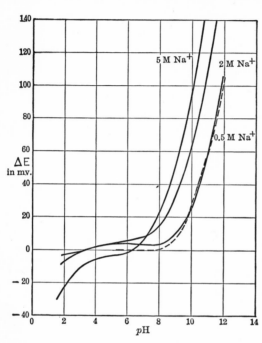

FIG. 9·4. Errors of Leeds and Northrup pH glass electrode at 50° (data of Gardiner and Sanders). Data of Dole and Wiener for 1 M Na$^+$ solutions at 50° represented by dotted line.

tion to be 3.98, 4.00, and 4.02 at 30°, 50°, and 60°C., respectively. These slight differences are less than the experimental variations among different glass electrodes in the alkaline range and are therefore negligible. Of course, different values of RT/F in the denominator of Eq. 9·4·1 must be used at the different temperatures.

Baxter,[20] after a critical study of recent literature pertaining to the E^o value of the saturated calomel electrode and on the basis of additional experimental work performed in the laboratories of the National Technical Laboratories, concludes that the standard potential of the saturated calomel electrode at t degrees C. is best given by the equation

$$E^o = 260.1 - 0.602t - 0.00115t^2 \text{ mvs.} \qquad [9\cdot4\cdot2]$$

Gardiner and Sanders, whose data are compared with those of Dole and Wiener in Fig. 9·4, were particularly interested in studying the behavior of commercial glass electrode instruments as used under

[19] See Appendix IV. Hamer (private communication to Bacon, Hensley, and Vaughn) gives the following equation for the pH of 0.05c HK C$_8$H$_4$O$_4$ (from 0° to 60°C.); pH = 5.13 log T + $\dfrac{1519.62}{T}$ + 0.01092T − 17.039 where $T = t$°C. + 273.16.

[20] W. P. Baxter. Private communication from Dr. A. O. Beckman.

the extreme industrial conditions encountered in measuring the pH of saturated sodium chloride solutions at room temperatures and higher. Sodium errors measured at 60°C. were even higher as would be expected. They state, "It was found that at pH 11.0 at 50°C., the potential of the glass was independent of the pH, but changed linearly with the pNa of the solution. Thus the hydrogen-electrode function of the glass is destroyed at a lower pH, the higher the temperature and the higher the sodium-ion concentration."

The variation of the glass electrode error with temperature as determined by Dole and Wiener is shown in Fig. 9·5. There is not much difference between the 25° and 10°C. data, the data at 10° being more scattered and less reliable. These results seem to show that not much can be gained by making glass electrode measurements at temperatures below room temperature. The useful range of the glass electrode is considerably reduced, however, by using it at elevated temperatures; high temperatures should, therefore, be avoided whenever possible. (See, however, the remarks of Beckman cited below.)

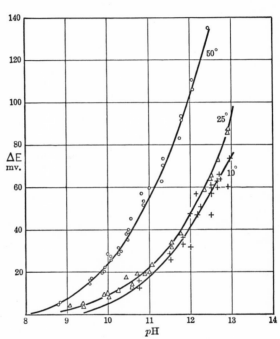

FIG. 9·5. Errors of the glass electrode in 0.5c Na$_2$HPO$_4$. (Data of Dole and Wiener.)

Powney and Jordan [21] studied glass electrodes made of a glass almost identical in composition to Corning 015 at the temperatures 22°, 40°, 60°, and 80°, and over the concentration range 0.005 to 0.1 N in sodium salts; the different temperatures and lower concentrations involved thus preventing a direct comparison of their work with the

[21] J. Powney and D. O. Jordan, J. Soc. Chem. Ind. 56, 133T (1937).

results discussed above.   They were able to express their measurements by means of the equation

$$\log \Delta\, pH = A\ pH' + 0.46 \log m - C \qquad [9\cdot4\cdot3]$$

(see Sec. 7·4) where pH' is the uncorrected pH as observed with the glass electrode, $\Delta\, pH$ the pH correction to apply, m the concentration of sodium ions and A and C empirical constants having at the different temperatures the values given in Table 9·2.

TABLE 9·2

CONSTANTS OF EQUATION 9·4·3

AFTER POWNEY AND JORDAN (1937)

Temperature	A	C
22	0.540	6.05
40	0.355	3.55
60	0.340	3.33
80	0.340	3.28

By applying corrections to the glass electrode pH as calculated from Eq. 9·4·3, Powney and Jordan were able to arrive at a good agreement between these corrected pH values and the true hydrogen electrode pH at 22° over the concentration range of sodium ions studied.   Beckman [22] and his co-workers find some variation in electrode behavior with different samples of Corning 015 glass, but they confirm essentially the data of Dole and Wiener.   Beckman points out that: "Although the useful range of the glass electrode at elevated temperatures is considerably reduced in terms of pH units, usually the electrode is just as useful at a given solution at elevated temperatures as at room temperatures.   This is because the pH of alkaline solutions decreases rapidly with increasing temperature, the net result of decreasing pH and increasing alkaline errors with increasing temeratures being to hold the sodium-ion error roughly constant."   Pchelin [23] has also studied the error of the glass electrode in alkaline solutions as a function of temperature with results similar to those described above.

9·5. Acid and Nonaqueous Solution Errors as a Function of Temperature

In contrast to the great increase of alkali error in going from 25° to 50°C. or higher, Dole and Wiener [24] found no very marked change in

22 Private communication.
23 V. A. Pchelin, *J. Phys. Chem.* (*U.S.S.R.*) **13**, 490 (1939).
24 M. Dole and B. Z. Wiener, *Trans. Electrochem. Soc.* **72**, 107 (1937).

the acid error although it should be pointed out that the glass electrode gave rather erratic results in the concentrated sulfuric acid solutions studied by them, so that comparison of the data at the two temperatures is not particularly significant.   An inspection of Fig. 9·6 in which average results of the two investigations are plotted shows a slight increase in the error at the higher temperature, but the difference between the two curves is within the experimental uncertainty.   In all probability the error at the higher temperature is also given by Eq. 8·2·1.

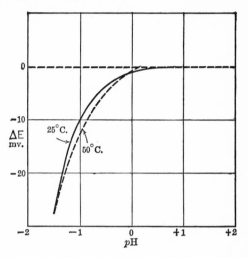

FIG. 9·6.   Errors of the glass electrode in sulfuric acid solutions at 25° and 50°C. (Data of Dole and of Dole and Wiener.)

9·6. Temperature Coefficient of Glass Electrode Surface e.m.f.

Although the glass electrode functions as a hydrogen electrode between the pH limits 0 and 7, or 8, at 50° without error, this does not mean that its surface potential does not vary with the temperature; on the contrary, its surface potential changes with the temperature in a way similar to the change in potential of a platinum hydrogen electrode (at constant partial pressure of the hydrogen gas).   Unfortunately there is no experimental or thermodynamic method by which the temperature coefficient of a single glass-electrode surface e.m.f. can be rigorously determined, but we can perhaps understand the problems involved by studying the temperature coefficient of the ordinary hydrogen electrode.   What do we know about the latter?

Consider the cell

Pt, H_2 (at 1 M) | Test Solution || Sat. KCl | HgCl | Hg   [9·6·A]

whose e.m.f. is given by the equation

$$E = E^{o,'} + E_x - 2.3RT/F \log m_{H^+} \cdot \gamma_{H^+}.   [9·6·1]$$

When the temperature of cell 9·6·A is changed, the total e.m.f., E, will be changed owing to a change in $E^{o,'}$, the standard electrode potential of the saturated calomel electrode (which is a constant only at constant temperature in a definite solvent), to a change in E_x, the liquid-junction potential, to a variation of the factor RT/F and to a change in γ_{H^+}. Thus the situation is rather complicated and in fact insoluble from a strictly thermodynamic point of view. If a definite chemical reaction for any cell can be written, and this is not possible for cell 9·6·A because of ignorance concerning the reaction at the liquid junction, then the temperature coefficient of the cell e.m.f. can be calculated by the thermodynamically exact Gibbs-Helmholtz equation

$$\left(\frac{dE}{dT}\right)_P = \frac{E}{T} + \frac{\Delta H}{nFT} \qquad [9·6·2]$$

where ΔH is the increase in the heat content or enthalpy of the cell reaction when *exactly* the same reaction is carried out in a calorimeter. The information obtained from the Gibbs-Helmholtz equation is not very useful, however, because it is usually easier to measure dE/dT experimentally than to calculate it from Eq. 9·6·2. What we need to know is the variation of the total e.m.f. of cell 9·6·A with temperature in order to calculate the pH at the different temperatures, and the temperature coefficient of the platinum electrode potential alone in order to estimate pH measurement errors due to fluctuations in its surface e.m.f.

At any definite temperature when all the different parts of cell 9·6·A are at the same temperature, the pH is calculated from the e.m.f. of cell 9·6·A by means of the equation

$$p\text{H} = \frac{E - E^o}{2.3RT/F} \qquad [9·6·3]$$

In this equation the factor RT/F and the constant E^o change with the temperature. From the most recent data of MacInnes, Belcher and Shedlovsky [25] the pH of 0.05 c potassium acid phthalate ($C_6H_4[COO]_2HK$) is estimated to be 4.000, 4.000 and 4.015 at 12°, 25°, and 38°C. so that by measuring the e.m.f. of cell 9·6·A at any of these temperatures when 0.05 c potassium acid phthalate is the test solution and inserting the e.m.f. into Eq. 9·6·3 we can calculate E^o at the temperature in question. This is certainly the most con-

[25] D. A. MacInnes, D. Belcher and T. Shedlovsky, *J. Am. Chem. Soc.* **60**, 1094 (1938); D. I. Hitchcock and A. C. Taylor, *J. Am. Chem. Soc.* **60**, 2710 (1938) give 4.010 and 4.025 as the pH of the phthalate buffer at 25° and 38°C., respectively; see also Hamer's equation.[19]

venient and most accurate way to standardize glass-electrode cells at different temperatures.[26]

By inspection of Eq. 9·6·3 it can be seen that the rate of change of E with pH is a function of the temperature even after variations in E^o have been determined or corrected for. In fact the change of slope of the pH-e.m.f. curve with temperature gives rise to the largest errors in pH measurement because of temperature fluctuations (unless corrected for). Suppose the glass electrode apparatus is standardized at 50°C. using the phthalate buffer and the apparatus is then used to measure the pH of a solution having, let us say, a pH of 8. From the change in e.m.f. of the cell between the solutions of pH 4 and 8, + 0.2564 V, we can calculate the pH increase if we use the correct value of 2.3 RT/F, namely 0.06411 at 50°C., or 4, and the pH of the test solution is $4 + 4$ or 8. But if we use the value of 2.3 RT/F, 0.05915, valid for 25°C., we find $\Delta\, p$H equal to 4.3, giving a value of 8.3 for the pH of the test solution, 0.3 pH units too high. Some commercial glass electrode outfits have their direct-reading pH dial constructed with the use of the factor 0.05915 valid only for 25°C., since the manufacturers assume that all measurements are to be made at 25°C. Use of such an instrument at any temperature other than 25°C. and at any pH other than the calibrating pH, introduces an error. The peculiar shape of the curves in Fig. 5 of the previously quoted paper by Gardiner and Sanders (where their measurement at pH 8 and 50°C. is just 0.3 pH units too high in agreement with the calculations given above) is due to this effect as the authors themselves point out. Mathematically, the error in instrument reading (or the correction to be subtracted from the measured pH) is given by the equation

$$\Delta\, p\text{H} = \frac{(t^\circ - 25)\,(p\text{H}_r - p\text{H}_s)}{t^\circ + 273} \qquad [9\cdot6\cdot4]$$

where t° is the temperature of the whole cell, in degrees Centigrade, pH$_r$ is the instrument reading, and pH$_s$ is the pH of the standardizing solution. In Appendix VII is given a curve from which can be obtained the proper pH correction to be applied to the instrument reading to correct for this temperature effect.

Many commercial pH electrometers contain temperature adjustments or compensators which allow automatically for the proper conversion of e.m.f. to pH at the temperature of the test sample, but an

[26] The National Technical Laboratories, Pasadena, Calif., is prepared to supply buffer solutions of pH values close to 4.0, 7.0, or 10.0 whose pH has been determined to ±0.01 pH unit up to 50°, 60°, and 90°C., respectively.

instrument *without* temperature adjustments or compensator, with its dial calibrated directly in *p*H units, can give the correct *p*H *only at one temperature.*

Up to this point in our discussion we have assumed that the temperature is uniform throughout all the constituent parts of the cell; although it is impossible to measure rigorously the variation in e.m.f. with temperature of a single boundary, we can calculate that a change in temperature of 5°C. changes the e.m.f. at a single glass electrode surface by 4 mv. or 0.07 *p*H unit provided there is no change in activity coefficients or in the standard electrode potential of a single glass electrode surface (which cannot be measured). This calculation is not to be taken too seriously, but it does indicate the order of magnitude of the temperature effect. (Wingfield and Acree [27] find that the apparent dE/dT of the hydrogen gas half cell together with the liquid-junction potential is 1.0 mv. per degree Centigrade.)

9·7. Temperature Coefficient of the Inner Reference Electrode

To show the relative temperature coefficients of different inner reference electrodes, let us study the behavior of complete cells made by combining these electrodes with the hydrogen gas electrode.

Morton [28] advocates the use of a quinhydrone reference electrode inside the glass electrode since the e.m.f. of the cell

$$\text{Pt, H}_2 \mid 0.1 \ N \ \text{HCl} \mid \text{Q·QH}_2, \text{Pt} \qquad [9·7·A]$$

is independent of the *p*H of the solution as long as the quinhydrone electrode acts as a perfect hydrogen electrode. But the e.m.f. of this

TABLE 9·3

STANDARD ELECTRODE POTENTIALS OF THE QUINHYDRONE ELECTRODE AND E.M.F.
VALUES OF CELL 9·7·A AS A FUNCTION OF TEMPERATURE

DATA OF HARNED AND WRIGHT (1933)

t°C.	0°	5°	10°	15°	20°	25°	30°	35°	40°
E^o	0.71790	0.71429	0.71066	0.70702	0.70336	0.69969	0.69600	0.69230	0.68858

combination is comparatively very sensitive to temperature as the data for the standard electrode potential of the quinhydrone electrode

[27] B. Wingfield and S. F. Acree, *J. Research Natl. Bur. Standards* **19**, 163 (1937).
[28] C. Morton, *J. Chem. Soc.* **1932**, 2469.

in Table 9·3 taken from the paper of Harned and Wright [29] prove. The e.m.f. values of Table 9·3 are also equal to those given by cell 9·7·A at the different temperatures listed.

In Fig. 9·7 a comparison is made between the e.m.f. of cell 9·7·A and the e.m.f. of other standard electrodes used inside the glass electrode as the temperature is varied. The temperature coefficient of the e.m.f. of the quinhydrone electrode is about four times as great as the temperature coefficient of the other electrodes, with the result that the quinhydrone electrode is not to be recommended for use as a reference electrode if the temperature of the cell is not carefully controlled. In addition to this difficulty there is the

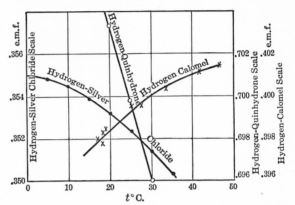

FIG. 9·7. E.m.f. of hydrogen-quinhydrone, hydrogen-silver chloride and hydrogen-calomel electrode combinations in 0.1 m hydrochloric acid.

possibility that, as mentioned in Sec. 2·2, the quinhydrone is likely to decompose or to react with the hydrochloric acid at high temperatures. In remarking on their experiences with a quinhydrone electrode in 0.01 M HCl (as measured against a silver-silver chloride electrode) Harned and Wright [29] state:

"Careful scrutiny of all the cell measurements first leads to the following conclusions. (1) In the particular type of cell employed, the time required to reach equilibrium varies from three hours at 0° to thirty to forty-five minutes at 25° and higher temperatures. (2) At low temperatures the cell is very difficult to read, both because of its high internal resistance and because of polarization of the quinhydrone electrode. (3) For unknown reasons, some cells do not reach equilibrium within a reasonable time. (4) While at low temperatures, the electromotive force first decreases with the time, in nearly all cases it eventually begins to rise. The rate of this rise varies with the individual cell, but it always increases with temperature and becomes quite pronounced above 25°. It has long been known that quinone and concentrated hydrochloric acid react to form chlorohydroquinone and it therefore seems justifiable to ascribe the cause of the drift to this reaction, even at the low concentration of hydrochloric acid present in our cells."

[29] H. S. Harned and D. D. Wright, *J. Am. Chem. Soc.* **55**, 4849 (1933).

If the quinhydrone half cell is used as the reference electrode inside the glass electrode at temperatures higher than normal, frequent calibration of the glass electrode is essential because of the drift of this electrode's potential with time; also the quinhydrone should periodically be renewed.

The silver-silver chloride electrode in 0.1 N hydrochloric acid is commonly used as the reference electrode inside the glass electrode. In Table 9·4 the values of the e.m.f. of the cell

$$\text{Pt, H}_2 \mid \text{HCl } (m) \mid \text{AgCl} \mid \text{Ag} \qquad [9\cdot7\cdot\text{B}]$$

obtained by Harned and Ehlers [30] over the temperature range 5° to 35°C. are given for two concentrations of hydrochloric acid and it is evident that a difference of temperature of 1°C. changes the e.m.f. by

TABLE 9·4

E.M.F. OF CELL 9·7·B AS A FUNCTION OF TEMPERATURE

DATA OF HARNED AND EHLERS (1932)

$t°$C.	5°	10°	15°	20°	25°	30°	35°
0.1 m	0.35487	0.35451	0.35394	0.35321	0.35240	0.35140	0.35031
0.01 m	0.45943	0.46084	0.46207	0.46319	0.46419	0.46499	0.46565

about 0.2 mv. or only 0.003 pH unit.   Note that the trend with temperature reverses its direction as the concentration changes from 0.1 m to 0.01 m.   At 0.03 m at 25°C. dE/dT is almost zero; at this temperature and concentration, the e.m.f.-temperature curve goes through a maximum.

From the data published by Lewis and Randall [31] it is evident that the temperature coefficient of the e.m.f. of the cell

$$\text{Pt, H}_2 \mid \text{HCl } (0.1\ m) \mid \text{HgCl} \mid \text{Hg} \qquad [9\cdot7\cdot\text{C}]$$

is not greatly different from that of cell 9·7·B except for a difference in sign.   In Fig. 9·7 we have plotted the e.m.f. values of both of these cells along with those of the hydrogen-quinhydrone cell for ease of comparison (the concentration of the hydrochloric acid in the hydrogen-calomel cell was not exactly equal to 0.1 m) and it can be seen

[30] H. S. Harned and R. W. Ehlers, *J. Am. Chem. Soc.* **54**, 1350 (1932).
[31] G. N. Lewis and M. Randall, "Thermodynamics," McGraw-Hill Book Co., New York, 1923. p. 391.

that as far as temperature variations are concerned neither the silver chloride-silver nor the calomel electrode is to be preferred over each other.

9·8. Temperature Coefficient of Saturated Calomel Reference Electrode and of the Complete Cell

Once again we should point out that the actual e.m.f. produced by the saturated calomel electrodes, by the reference electrode within the glass electrode, or by strains in the glass or surface irregularities at any temperature is immaterial if this resultant e.m.f. remains constant and if the system is calibrated with a buffer of known pH at the temperature in question, such as 0.05 c potassium acid phthalate. The standard electrode potential or rather the constant E^o of Eq. 9·6·3 for the saturated potassium chloride-calomel mercury half cell has been determined, however, at various temperatures so that it is possible to make pH measurements in some cases without a preliminary standardization although this procedure is not recommended because of possible fluctuations in the asymmetry potential of the glass electrode which should be corrected for.

The saturated calomel electrode is almost universally used as the reference electrode in pH measurements. Fales and Mudge [32] made an extensive study of the saturated calomel electrode with the conclusions, "The saturated potassium chloride calomel cell is the best cell for use in conjunction with a saturated salt bridge, because it has a very small temperature coefficient, is easily reproducible, can safely be used at temperatures 5° to 60°, and can be relied upon for its constancy of value over long periods of time." [33]   This reference electrode has a somewhat higher e.m.f.-temperature coefficient than do calomel cells constructed of dilute potassium chloride or dilute hydrochloric acid solutions as a study of the data in Table 9·5 [34] indicate.

As remarked before the actual e.m.f. of the saturated calomel electrode is not important if it remains constant and if it is calibrated with a known buffer. In addition to the information given in Table 9·5, it is also interesting to know how rapidly calomel electrodes respond in their temperature and e.m.f. to changes in external temperature.

[32] H. A. Fales and W. A. Mudge, *J. Am. Chem. Soc.* **42**, 2434 (1920).

[33] Dr. Beckman writes, "We have maintained calomel electrodes continuously for long periods at temperatures ranging up to 100°C. without bad effects."   Bacon, Hensley, and Vaughn (paper submitted for publication) who studied soap solutions up to 80°C. found the saturated calomel electrode to vary as much as 2 mv.

[34] Calculated from Eq. 9·4.·2.

Fortunately, Wingfield and Acree[35] have recently published the results of an extensive study of temperature and hysteresis errors in calomel half cells. In this investigation they varied the external temperature at a definite rate, then measured the temperature of

TABLE 9·5

STANDARD E.M.F. (E^o OF EQ. 9·6·3) OF THE SATURATED CALOMEL ELECTRODE

$t°C.$	0	10	15	18	20	25	30	35
E^o	0.2601	0.2540	0.2508	0.2489	0.2476	0.2443	0.2410	0.2376

$t°C.$	38	40	50	60	70	80	90	100
E^o	0.2356	0.2342	0.2271	0.2198	0.2123	0.2046	0.1966	0.1884

various parts of the calomel cell as well as its e.m.f. Their work may be summarized as follows: The temperature of the mercury and chloride solution in the half cell may differ by 0.1° to 2.2°C. depending upon the magnitude of the change in the temperature of the surrounding air bath. The use of a Dewar flask for thermal insulation of the cell reduces the temperature fluctuations but does not eliminate them completely.

"In pH measurements requiring an accuracy of 0.1 pH temperature variations of 4° to 5°C. could be tolerated without temperature corrections. For precision results to 0.01 to 0.02 pH, the measurements should be made in constant temperature air or liquid baths and after the temperature of the cell system has been uniform for several hours."

Wingfield and Acree found the temperature coefficient of the saturated calomel half cell to be 0.25 mv. per degree Centigrade over the range 22.5° to 31.3°C.[36] and the temperature coefficient of the 3.8 N KCl half cell undersaturated at all temperatures studied to be 0.47 mv. per degree Centigrade.

Up to this point we have been considering individual electrode e.m.f. fluctuations with change of temperature. It is also interesting to study the e.m.f.-temperature curve of the entire glass electrode cell to

[35] B. Wingfield and S. F. Acree, *J. Research Natl. Bur. Standards* 19, 163 (1937).
[36] Cary and Baxter find 0.20 mv. per degree Centigrade at 25°C. (Private communication from Dr. A. O. Beckman.)

see whether the trends with temperature of the separate e.m.f.'s partially cancel one another or whether they are additive. The three possible glass electrode-reference electrode combinations studied above may be represented by the following cells where a hydrogen platinum electrode is substituted for each surface of the glass electrode.

$$\text{Ag}\left|\text{AgCl}\right|\begin{matrix}\text{HCl}\\(a=1)\end{matrix}\left|\text{H}_2, \text{Pt–Pt, H}_2\right|\begin{matrix}\text{HCl}\\(a=1)\end{matrix}\left\|\begin{matrix}\text{Sat.}\\\text{KCl}\end{matrix}\right|\text{HgCl}\left|\text{Hg}\right.\qquad [9\cdot8\cdot\text{A}]$$

$E_{25°} = 0.0219 \quad E_{30°} = 0.0218 \quad \Delta E/\Delta T = -0.02 \text{ mv./°C.}$

$$\text{Hg}\left|\text{HgCl}\right|\begin{matrix}\text{Sat.}\\\text{KCl}\end{matrix}\left\|\begin{matrix}\text{HCl}\\(a=1)\end{matrix}\right|\text{H}_2, \text{Pt–Pt, H}_2\left|\begin{matrix}\text{HCl}\\(a=1)\end{matrix}\right|\text{HgCl}\left|\text{Hg}\right.\qquad [9\cdot8\cdot\text{B}]$$

$E_{25°} = 0.0249 \quad E_{30°} = 0.0271 \quad \Delta E/\Delta T = 0.44 \text{ mv./°C.}$

$$\text{Hg}\left|\text{HgCl}\right|\begin{matrix}\text{Sat.}\\\text{KCl}\end{matrix}\left\|\begin{matrix}\text{HCl}\\(a=1)\end{matrix}\right|\text{H}_2, \text{Pt–Pt, H}_2\left|\begin{matrix}\text{HCl}\\(m=1)\end{matrix}\right|\text{Q·QH}_2, \text{Pt}\qquad [9\cdot8\cdot\text{C}]$$

$E_{25°} = 0.4554 \quad E_{30°} = 0.4550 \quad \Delta E/\Delta T = -0.01 \text{ mv./°C.}^{37}$

The comparison of the temperature coefficients of cells $9\cdot8\cdot$A, B, and C shows that the cell with a quinhydrone electrode inside the glass electrode has the lowest e.m.f.-temperature coefficient and the cell using the normal calomel electrode the highest. These values vary with the concentration of the acid inside the glass electrode (except in the case of cell $9\cdot8\cdot$C); thus if the reference liquid is 0.1 m hydrochloric acid, the temperature coefficients become +0.46, +0.80, and −0.01 mv. per degree Centigrade for the cells in the order listed. If the solution on the outside of the glass electrode has a pH of 8 while the inside solution remains 0.1 m hydrochloric acid, the e.m.f.-temperature coefficient for the cells as a whole is increased to +0.74, +0.04 and +1.28 mv. per degree Centigrade; thus, the relative magnitude of this coefficient may be altered at will by changing the concentration of the solutions in the cells. It is, therefore, impossible to state which reference electrode gives the least errors as a function of temperature when the total e.m.f. of the cell is considered. (It should also be noted that the sign of the e.m.f. of cells $9\cdot8\cdot$A, B, and C depends upon the concentration of the various solutions. In this

[37] The data given below each cell were obtained from the following sources: data for the hydrogen-saturated calomel cell from Table 9·5; data for the hydrogen-silver chloride cell from Harned and Ehlers, *J. Am. Chem. Soc.* **54**, 1350 (1932); data for the hydrogen-quinhydrone cell from Table 9·3; data for the hydrogen-calomel electrode cell at 25°C. from Scatchard, *J. Am. Chem. Soc.* **47**, 696 (1925), and at 30° from the 25° value using the temperature coefficient of this cell given by J. H. Ellis, *J. Am. Chem. Soc.* **38**, 737 (1916).

discussion we have changed the order of the separate components of the cells wherever necessary to give a positive e.m.f. of the cell as a whole. The e.m.f.-temperature coefficients are, therefore, the temperature coefficients of the positive e.m.f. of the cell.)

In ending this section we can conclude that pH measurements should be made with the entire cell at a uniform temperature in order to reduce temperature fluctuations to a minimum; if, however, the saturated calomel electrode is kept at room temperature, as it is sometimes preferable (to avoid hysteresis effects), each half cell of the combination should be at a uniform temperature with the temperature gradient in the salt bridge. The standard electrode potential, E^o, of the half cell

$$\text{Hg} \mid \text{HgCl} \mid \text{KCl (sat.) at } 25°\text{C.} \parallel \text{KCl (sat.) at } t°\text{C.} \parallel \qquad [9·8·D]$$

is

$$E^o = 265.1 - 0.798t - 0.00123t^2 \text{ mv.}[38] \qquad [9·8·1]$$

9·9. Methods of Avoiding Temperature Difficulties

The only sure way to eliminate temperature fluctuations is to immerse the glass electrode cell and calomel reference cell in a constant temperature air or oil bath. A water bath must not be used since it is too conducting and may cause serious electrical leakage errors. In some cases the air or oil bath must not be stirred with an electric motor stirrer but with an air driven stirrer; the electric motor produces magnetic fields and induced currents which influence the behavior of vacuum-tube electrometers.

In many commercial pH electrometers it is inconvenient to thermostat either the calomel reference cell or the glass electrode cell; in this case the measurements should be made in a constant temperature room. When neither constant temperature baths nor constant temperature rooms are available, the glass electrode equipment should be maintained manually at a constant temperature as far as possible by controlling the temperature of the room. (If the room is not too large, it is frequently possible to prevent the temperature from fluctuating more than a degree by opening or closing windows, etc.) The actual temperature of the room is not so important as the constancy. If the temperature is known and held at a constant value, it is easy to standardize all the constant potentials in the cell and to convert e.m.f. to pH using the proper conversion factor.

The temperature of the test sample should always be given and the room temperature should always be recorded.

[38] Private communication from Dr. A. O. Beckman.

CHAPTER 10

SOME SPECIAL APPLICATIONS OF
THE GLASS ELECTRODE

In this chapter we consider some special applications of the glass electrode, particularly the use of the glass electrode in measuring the pH of pure water and of dilute unbuffered salt solutions, and in determining the salt error of the quinhydrone electrode. All of these systems represent solutions rather unstable with respect to their hydrogen-ion concentration, solutions whose pH can only be determined accurately with the glass electrode. Next comes a brief mention of some glass-electrode studies of reaction rates; and finally we describe the technique of handling the glass electrode in the tropics or in hot, humid atmospheres.

10·1. Determination of the pH of Unbuffered and Slightly Buffered Solutions

The glass electrode offers a convenient and accurate method for the determination of the pH of unbuffered solutions chiefly because no addition agents which might alter the pH of the solutions are necessary. The hydrogen gas-platinum black electrode gives unstable, erratic and too low pH readings; indicators and quinhydrone may change the pH of the pure water to which they are added (the isohydric indicator method appears to be reliable to 0.1 pH unit in pure water). However, all glass electrodes slowly give off alkali at varying rates (depending upon the softness of the glass), see Sec. 4·2 so that certain precautions in their use have to be taken. Thus Edwards and Evans [1] made the pH observations given in Table 10·1 on 200 cc. of pure water with a soft glass electrode. Stirring the water with purified air caused the pH to drop to a more correct value after the initial erroneous rise.

The absolute magnitude of the pH values of Table 10·1 include the unknown contribution of the liquid-junction potential between the salt bridge and pure water.

[1] E. G. Edwards and D. Evans, *J. Chem. Soc.* **1937**, 1938.

TABLE 10·1

pH of Pure Water in Contact with a Soft Glass Electrode as a Function of Time

Data of Edwards and Evans (1937)

	Solution Not Stirred				Solution Stirred	
Time (Min.)......	2	4	8	15	16	30
pH.............	7.15	7.17	7.20	7.25	7.13	7.12

The first investigators to measure the pH of weakly buffered solutions and pure water were Burton, Matheson, and Acree[2], whose conclusions after a rather brief investigation were as follows:

"1. The hydrogen electrode appears to be applicable in solutions whose concentrations are 0.0001 c or greater. It is not generally suitable for determining the pH of distilled water or tap water. In the case of tap water the difficulty may be a disturbance of the carbonate-bicarbonate ratio rather than too low a concentration of electrolyte.

"2. The quinhydrone electrode is not reliable in solutions whose concentrations are less than 0.001 c.

"3. The glass electrode appears to be applicable throughout the entire range of concentration from 0.1 c to double-distilled pH 7 water, with an accuracy of 0.1 pH or better. The solubility of Corning 015 glass is low enough to prevent errors even with distilled water, especially if the solution is flowed through the electrode or kept in it only long enough for measurements."

Incidentally, these authors found that the glass electrode offered the only means by which the pH of a dilute buffer solution containing 0.07 g. of chlorine per liter could be accurately measured, the chlorine attacking indicators, quinhydrone and platinum black.

Ellis and Kiehl[3] have made a most careful study of the application of the glass electrode to unbuffered systems. Their apparatus is illustrated in Fig. 10·1 where S is a vertical, thin-walled, pipet-type glass electrode (during the e.m.f. measurement, the electric current flows through the glass wall from J to S), C_1 and C_2 are two calomel reference electrodes, the second being supplied with an interchangeable tip, J is a cylinder containing 0.1 N hydrochloric acid in contact with the

[2] J. O. Burton, H. Matheson, and S. F. Acree, *J. Research Natl. Bur. Standards* **12**, 67 (1934); *Ind. Eng. Chem., Anal. Ed.* **6**, 79 (1934).
[3] S. B. Ellis and S. J. Kiehl, *J. Am. Chem. Soc.* **57**, 2139 (1935).

outside surface of the glass electrode, and V_1 and V_2 are two three-way stopcocks. The glass electrode, S, may be filled from the top by means of a siphon tube or from the bottom by means of suction; the rubber bulb, B, is a convenient aid in rinsing and filling the cell. Since, as already mentioned, the electrodes made of Corning 015 glass and other soft glasses, slowly liberate alkali to the solution, Ellis and Kiehl found it necessary not only to flow solutions through the electrode, i.e., down through S, in the case of pure water and unbuffered salt solutions in order to obtain significant *p*H measurements, but also to use a soft

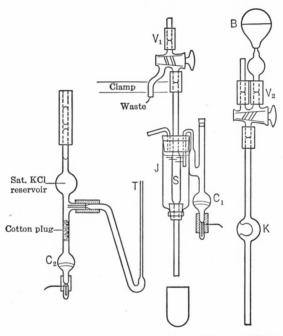

FIG. 10·1. Glass electrode assembly of Ellis and Kiehl.

glass more resistant to corrosion than Corning 015. But flowing very dilute solutions through a glass tube gives rise to a new source of e.m.f., the so-called streaming potential, as demonstrated by curves A' and B' of Fig. 10·2. In case of the measurements represented by these two curves, the tip of the potassium chloride junction, T of Fig. 10·1 was inserted into S up to a point about 9 cm. below the lowest part of the thin-walled electrode tube; since increase in velocity of flow increased the e.m.f., the latter is the sum of the true e.m.f. and the streaming potential. Curve A' shows an initial drop at very low velocities due to the glass-solubility effect. If, however, the tip T is inserted higher into S until it is located centrally with respect to the vertical length of the active part of the glass membrane, the streaming potential cancels and the e.m.f. becomes independent of the rate of flow after the flow becomes great enough to eliminate the glass-solubility effect as in curves A and B of Fig. 10·2. The stock distilled water is practically unaffected at low rates of flow by alkali from the glass (curves B and B') in contrast to the increase in pH shown by the highly purified water (curves A and A'). The ordinary laboratory

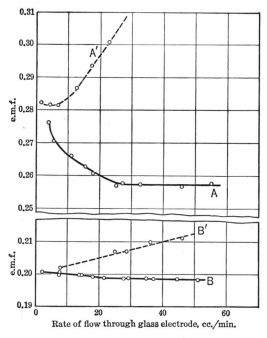

Fig. 10·2.   Curves A and A', highly purified water, curves B and B' laboratory distilled water. pH of distilled water.

distilled water is buffered by minute traces of carbon dioxide and ammonia.

In Fig. 10·3 pH measurements on very dilute phosphate buffers and potassium chloride solutions are illustrated as a function of concentration and rate of flow. Note the surprising but distinct buffering action of the chloride solution and the "inflection points" in the pH-rate of flow curves for the dilute buffers. The inflected form of the curves indicates that the buffering capacity of the extremely dilute solutions is less if they are relatively pure (flowing rapidly) than if they are contaminated by alkali from the glass. The slight buffering action of the potassium chloride solution may be due to impurities, although the authors recrystallized their salt three times from distilled water and dried it at 100°C. Ellis and Kiehl carried out their experiments at room temperature, 25° to 30°C.

Schwabe[4] has also studied the pH of unbuffered solutions as a function of rate of flow with conclusions similar to those of Ellis and Kiehl. Ball and Stock[5] found that of the three electrode systems,

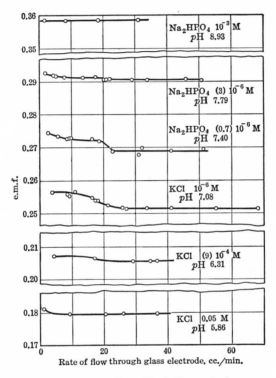

Fig. 10·3. The pH of dilute solutions.

the platinum, quinhydrone, and glass electrodes, the last is the only one with which reliable pH measurement on sea water can be made.

Values for the pH of different salt solutions obtained by Ellis and Kiehl, Edwards and Evans, and Cranston and Brown[6] are collected in Table 10·2.

[4] K. Schwabe, *Z. Elektrochem.* **42**, 147 (1936).

[5] E. G. Ball and C. C. Stock, *Biol. Bull.* **73**, 221 (1937).

[6] J. A. Cranston and H. F. Brown, *J. Roy. Tech. Coll.* (*Glasgow*) **4**, 46, 53 (1937); *Trans. Faraday Soc.* **33**, 1455 (1937); *J. Chem. Soc.* **1940**, 578.

TABLE 10·2

THE *p*H OF SALT SOLUTIONS

Salt	Concentration	*p*H	Temp. °C.	Observer
KCl.........	0.01011	6.75	20°–23.4°	Edwards and Evans
	0.00112	6.86		
	0.000132	6.90		
	1.3×10^{-5}	6.93		
Pure Water...	0	6.98		
KCl.........	1.22×10^{-6}	7.08	25.5	Ellis and Kiehl
	1.05×10^{-5}	6.80	25	
	1.44×10^{-4}	6.45	30.5	
	2.88×10^{-4}	6.29	25.5	
	9.32×10^{-4}	6.31	25.5	
	4.55×10^{-3}	6.10	27.5	
	9.98×10^{-3}	6.12	27.5	
	0.0486	5.86	27.5	
	0.102	5.78	27.5	
	0.296	5.65	27	
Pure Water...		7.01	27.5	
NH₄Cl.......	0.25	5.05	18°–19°	Edwards and Evans
	0.05	5.41		
	0.01	5.62		
NH₄Cl.......	0.10	5.42	15°	Cranston and Brown
	0.05	5.56		
	0.01	5.92		
	0.001	6.51		
Pure Water...	0	7.0 ± 0.3		
Pb(NO₃)₂.....	0.1001 *M*	4.28	20°–20.5°	Edwards and Evans
	0.0101	4.89		
	0.00402	5.11		
	0.00208	5.22		
	0.000996	5.34		
Pb(NO₃)₂.....	0.1	4.17	15°	Cranston and Brown
	0.01	4.92		
	0.004	5.11		
	0.002	5.24		
	0.001	5.34		

Amis and Gabbard[7] have carried out an interesting comparison of the hydrogen, quinhydrone, and glass electrodes in magnesium sulfate solutions at room temperature (25° to 29°C.). The extent to which the glass and quinhydrone electrodes are in error in these concentrated buffered and unbuffered solutions is indicated by the data of Table 10·3.

TABLE 10·3

ERRORS IN MILLIVOLTS OF THE GLASS AND QUINHYDRONE ELECTRODES
IN CONCENTRATED MAGNESIUM SULFATE SOLUTIONS

DATA OF AMIS AND GABBARD (1937)

Concen- tration	pH	Temp. °C.	Electrode Errors		Solution
			Glass	Quinhydrone	
2.0	3.01	29°	−1.2	1.0	Buffered
1.0	3.44	29°	0	0	Buffered
2.05	4.30	26°	−1.2	3.7	Unbuffered
1.02	4.30	26°	0	2.3	Unbuffered
2.09	5.21	27°	−1.2	8.6	Unbuffered
1.04	5.21	27°	0	3.8	Unbuffered

Note that the so-called "salt error" of the quinhydrone electrode is greater the more basic the solution and the less it is buffered. The slight error of the glass electrode in the most concentrated solutions is due presumably to the lowering of the vapor pressure of the water by the large concentration of magnesium sulfate.

10·2. Study of Reaction Rates Using the Glass Electrode

In this section we mention briefly three rather new applications of the glass electrode in the field of reaction kinetics. Cady and Ingle [8] using the glass electrode demonstrated that the pH of sucrose solutions remains constant during its inversion by hydrochloric acid. Both the hydrogen and quinhydrone electrodes give erroneous and changing results in this system, the quinhydrone electrode e.m.f. resulting in too high a pH value and the hydrogen electrode too low.

Edwards, Evans, and Watson[9] carried out an electrometric study of dilute aqueous solutions of halogenated ketones in which they determined pH and pCl or pBr as a function of time using the glass

[7] E. S. Amis and J. L. Gabbard, *J. Am. Chem. Soc.* **59**, 557 (1937).

[8] H. P. Cady and J. D. Ingle, *J. Phys. Chem.* **40**, 837 (1936)

[9] E. G. Edwards, D. P. Evans, and H. B. Watson, *J. Chem. Soc.* **1937**, 1942.

electrode and silver halide electrodes.   A rapid hydrolysis of the halogenated ketone caused a decrease in pH which was readily followed
with the glass electrode.

The technique involved consisted in the use of the glass electrode
assembly, Fig. 10·4, which was immersed in an oil bath at 30° up to
the dotted line.

"A measured volume of pure water, previously boiled to remove carbon dioxide,
was placed in the electrode vessel P, the rubber   stopper R carrying a glass electrode, and a small, stoppered glass tube was placed tightly in the mouth of the
vessel, and a current of purified air passed through the liquid to remove traces of
carbon dioxide.   Previous tests had shown that this procedure yielded water of

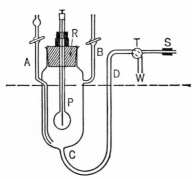

FIG. 10·4.   Glass electrode assembly
of Edwards, Evans, and Watson.

pH 6.9–7.2, and addition of 1–2 cc. of absolute alcohol did not affect the measured
pH.   A solution of ketone in absolute
alcohol was made in a 5 cc. stoppered
flask, and 1 cc. of this solution was added
quickly from a small pipette through the
stoppered glass tube in the rubber bung
to the water of pH about 7.   Aeration
was continued throughout the experiment.   This procedure ensured the rapid
solution of the ketone in water.   One
minute was allowed for thorough mixing
of the solution by the air current, and
the liquid junction between the saturated
calomel and the test solution was made in
the tap T, Fig. 10·4.   E.M.F. readings were then taken at short intervals, zero
time being the instant of half delivery of the ketone solution into the water."

Lamb and Jacques [10] were able to obtain important information
concerning the increase in hydrogen-ion concentration during the slow
hydrolysis of ferric chloride in dilute solution.   Except for the first
few minutes of the reaction, when the e.m.f. developed was estimated
from electrometer deflections rather than from balanced potentiometer
readings because of the rapidity of decrease of the pH, the glass electrode technique was not different from that described elsewhere in
this book.

10·3. The Use of the Glass Electrode in the Tropics and under Conditions of High Humidity

Thanks to the information kindly imparted to us by Dr. D. S.
Villars [11] of the United States Rubber Co. giving his experiences at the

[10] A. B. Lamb and A. G. Jacques, *J. Am. Chem. Soc.* **60**, 1215 (1938).
[11] Private communications.

Plantation Laboratory in the Dutch East Indies, and by Dr. E. B. Newton,[11] Resident Director of the Malayan Research Laboratory of the B. F. Goodrich Co. at Kuala Lumpar, F.M.S., we are able to describe the difficulties experienced in the use of glass electrodes under conditions of warm climates and very high relative humidities. Such conditions exist in many parts of the United States during the hot humid months of June, July, August, and September, so that it is of vital interest to many of us to know how to overcome the electrical errors of pH measurements introduced through the deposition of films of moisture on surfaces throughout the apparatus.

Dr. Newton, who was able to use a Coleman pH electrometer without apparent error, writes as follows:

" . . . Speaking generally, electrical equipment for use in humid climates should always be ordered with special moisture-proof insulation, and if the equipment is idle for some time or does not during operation generate some heat, it is best to arrange to dry it gently as by putting it in a room or box where carbon filament electric lamps are kept burning continuously. Large pieces of equipment can be covered with duck and lights placed underneath the cover. For use with small equipment, silica gel sprayed lightly with aqueous cobaltous nitrate or chloride is an excellent non-corrosive drying agent, being blue when dry and pink when hydrated. Activated alumina is a good substitute. Use of these agents with instruments mounted in wood cases, however, is to be avoided since their action is so severe the wood will split. Microscope accessories and lenses should be kept in desiccators over silica gel to prevent fungus growth on the glass. The same applies to cameras. The microscope stand can be placed on a plate of glass and covered with a glass bell jar carrying a basket of colored silica gel (100 to 200 grams). Mold growth on books can be kept at a minimum or prevented entirely by keeping them in closed bookcases containing several handfuls of p-dichlorobenzene. This material has a high vapor pressure and evaporates completely after some time and so requires renewing. We prefer this method to varnishing the books with "mold-proof" lacquers which usually have offensive odors. This scheme is also successful as a means of keeping mold and insects out of wool clothes when a camphor wood chest is not available. We have never noticed any indication of HCl released by possible hydrolysis of this compound."

The experiences of Dr. Villars were somewhat different as a different electrical measuring circuit was used, and the atmospheric conditions of the Sumatra East Coast seemed to be worse. The laboratory temperature ranged between 80 and 90°F. in the daytime, and dropped to the dew-point at night when a film of moisture condensed on almost all objects. A glass electrode was found to maintain its hydrogen-electrode function very well during the day, even during rainfall, but on the next day and subsequently its calibration curve became more and more erroneous because of the dew precipitated at night.

Dr. Villars' recommended technique is as follows:

"The recommended technique is to dismantle the electrode at the beginning of each working day and to immerse its top parts (a bulb type Leeds and Northrup electrode was used), including the rubber stopper serving as its support, for 60 seconds in paraffin heated to 125 to 130°C.   The electrode is removed and rotated in a horizontal position until the paraffin has solidified on both inner and outer top walls, taking care that none flows onto the thin bulb.   The top part of the inner electrode as well as its supporting stopper are likewise dehumidified by treating for 60 seconds in the hot paraffin.   The inner electrolyte is added by pipet (the outer parts of the pipet having been dried by wiping off any adhering solution with filter paper), taking extreme care not to touch or wet the upper wall of the glass electrode.   Finally, the inner electrode is inserted, taking the same care not to touch it to the top wall of the paraffined glass electrode thereby wetting it.   The system is touched by the fingers as little as possible.   The electrode is then calibrated by taking readings in at least two calibrated buffers (pH's 6.5 and 9.5 used for alkaline titrations).   This last step should be performed after each dehumidification treatment, for the slope of the calibration curve serves as an important check on the preceding technique.   (The slope usually ranges between 17 and 17.5 at 30°C.   Too high a value indicates faulty paraffining technique or wetting of top parts of the electrodes while fitting them together.)"

An oil thermostat was used.   The writer continues,

"Wires connected to the cell had to be insulated by suspending in air by paraffined silk threads and were connected at a paraffin block switchboard.   Even the latter had to be scraped from time to time to remove the layer of dew which gradually deposited.   An ordinary Bakelite tapping key was found to be a dead short and had to be replaced by a paraffin block containing two wells of mercury into which a connecting wire could be lowered at will by means of a paraffined silk thread. With these precautions, an ordinary high sensitivity d'Arsonval galvanometer set-up was used without further trouble."

In using commercial pH electrometers it is a good idea to put some sort of a heating element inside the electrical-circuit container to drive out moisture; in the electron-beam tube apparatus designed by Hill (see Sec. 3·7, Fig 3·12), the heat generated by the heater-type tubes is sufficient to prevent the occurrence of any high humidity difficulties. The glass electrode and input circuit must be maintained in a highly insulated condition, however.   Quartz insulation is decidedly inferior when the relative humidity is high with the result that the Cherry electrometer whose input circuit is insulated with quartz gives difficulties if the relative humidity remains at a high level (as already mentioned in Sec. 3·6).   The use of a calcium chloride tube attached to a glass tube through which the input wire passes will overcome this difficulty.

CHAPTER 11

SPECIAL APPLICATIONS OF THE GLASS ELECTRODE IN BIOLOGICAL CHEMISTRY

11·1. Introduction

The glass electrode finds one of its most fruitful and important fields of application in biological and clinical chemistry, in medical research, and in medical diagnosis and control. It is used chiefly to measure the pH of blood both *in vitro* and *in vivo* because the glass electrode is the only instrument by which the pH of whole blood as drawn can be directly measured. Since body reactions occur in an aqueous medium, the glass electrode can measure the pH of any body fluid, and it can be used in an exploratory way to measure the pH of wounds, of normal or malignant tissues, of the stomach or duodenum, of the cerebral cortex, etc. Its chief advantages in biological work consist in its application to very small quantities of material, to fluids possessing volatile components and to liquids containing proteins or oxidizing and reducing agents. Its chief disadvantages of giving erroneous results in highly alkaline solutions and in very acid (1 N or higher) or nonaqueous solvents are not serious in biological work where such systems are infrequently encountered.

Some workers in medical schools report that there is now routine use of the glass electrode in their laboratories for all pH measurements, for it has displaced the usually less accurate and less convenient colorimetric method, and has proved superior in many cases to the other electrometric methods. Thus, whereas with a quinhydrone electrode, pH measurements of a concentrated protein-salt solution gave fluctuating results which prevented the isoelectric point of the protein from being found, measurements with the glass electrode were reproducible at least to 0.1 pH and permitted the protein to be easily brought to its isoelectric point.

In Chapter 17 we discuss the significance and interpretation of pH measurements in general with a few specific remarks concerning pH in the biological field.

179

11·2. The Measurement of Blood pH in vitro

Concerning the problems of blood pH determinations, we quote *in extenso* from a recent paper by Sendroy.[1] "The pH of the blood is kept constant, within very narrow limits, by the operation, in large measure, of buffer systems, that is, of certain weak acids and their salts. The more important of such systems in the blood are the forms of hemoglobin and their salts, carbonic acid and carbonate, serum proteins and their salts, and monobasic and dibasic phosphate. L. J. Henderson[2] first pointed out the importance of such systems in the regulation of physiological neutrality, and indicated the applicability to the blood system of the various equilibria involved. The buffer substances permit the addition, *in vivo* or *in vitro*, of large amounts of acid or alkali with resultant small change in the pH of the solution.

"The general equation representing the equilibria in blood is

$$pH = pK'_{1,H_2CO_3} + \log \frac{BHCO_3}{H_2CO_3} = pK'_{2,H_3PO_4} + \log \frac{B_2HPO_4}{BH_2PO_4} \quad [11·2·1]$$

"Van Slyke first used the term *acid-base balance* as descriptive of the state of the body with regard to the mechanical and chemical maintenance of physiological neutrality. The term is now more generally used in connection with studies of blood, the pH and alkaline reserve of which have proved to be a reliable index of acid-base conditions in other body tissues which either cannot be studied at all, or do not lend themselves to study as well as does the circulatory fluid.

"The pH of the blood at any time may be fixed by the ratio of the two forms of carbon dioxide, free (mostly anhydrous) CO_2 and bicarbonate. Variations in the pH, the ratio of the two forms, and also the total amounts of CO_2, determine the state of the acid-base balance.[3] The pH itself may vary between the extremes of 7.0 to 7.8 and still be compatible with life. The normal limits, to the best of our present knowledge, are from 7.33–7.51, with an average value slightly above 7.40. The maintenance of the normal blood pH within such narrow limits is an indication of the efficiency of our complicated and delicate organism. Although plasma pH, more than any other chemical function of the blood, seems to influence physiological processes, the values

[1] J. Sendroy, Jr., *Trans. Electrochem. Soc.* **74**, 595 (1938); this paper, originally written at our request, was later an address delivered by Dr. Sendroy before the Chicago section of the Electrochemical Society, April 8, 1938. With Dr. Sendroy's approval, a few slight modifications have been made in the paper as originally published.

[2] L. J. Henderson, *Am. J. Physiol.* **21**, 169 (1908).

[3] J. P. Peters and D. D. Van Slyke, "Quantitative Clinical Chemistry," Vol. I. "Interpretations," Williams and Wilkins Co., Baltimore, 1931.

are important, not in themselves, but because they indicate ratios of dissociated anions to undissociated acid.

"At this point, some remarks on the technique of handling blood samples for pH determination, may be in order. In the first place, it has been shown by Parsons,[4] and probably confirmed by most workers who have done any extensive work with blood pH, that the pH of the whole blood is the pH of the plasma, the intact cells having no influence whatever on the measurement of pH itself. The pH of the cell contents is somewhat less than that of the plasma, the CO_2 and base relationships being different within the intact cells, because of the presence of hemoglobin. The tension or pressure of CO_2 is the same throughout. For purposes of measurement, then, the plasma may be used instead of whole blood. However, the blood must be so handled as to avoid loss of CO_2 from the fluid, otherwise the pH will change. It is this handling of the sample without exposure to the air, which requires the greatest of care, regardless of the ultimate method of measurement of the pH.

"The problem of keeping the pH of freshly shed blood from changing before analysis was brought into sharp focus by the observation of Havard and Kerridge[5] of an apparent sudden fall in the pH of blood within a few minutes after being drawn. This phenomenon has been reinvestigated by them and others. That lactic acid formation takes place in freshly shed blood kept at 38° has been known for some time. That there is an accompanying fall in pH of about 0.03 to 0.05, during the first half hour after bleeding, has been amply confirmed by Laug,[6] Yoshimura,[7] and Haugaard and Lundsteen.[8] However a 'first acid change' in blood pH within a few minutes, of the magnitude reported by Havard and Kerridge, is too great to be accounted for by the amount of lactic acid formed during that time, and has rarely been observed by others. The explanation seems to be that such sudden changes of pH are a temperature artifact caused by an initial difference in temperature between the electrode and the blood sample. When the temperature is carefully controlled, the 'first acid change' is not observed and only the more gradual drop in pH, caused by glycolysis, takes place.

"It is obvious from the studies cited in the literature, that almost all values of the pH of blood *as drawn*, must be at least 0.03 pH more

[4] T. R. Parsons, *J. Physiol.* **51**, 440 (1917).
[5] R. E. Havard and P. T. Kerridge, *Biochem. J.* **23**, 600 (1929).
[6] E. P. Laug, *J. Biol. Chem.* **106**, 161 (1934).
[7] H. Yoshimura, *J. Biochem. (Japan)* **21**, 335 (1935).
[8] G. Haugaard and E. Lundsteen, *Compt. rend. trav. lab. Carlsberg* **21**, 85 (1936).

acid than in the circulatory system. For comparative clinical purposes, this is of no serious consequence. However, the effects of glycolysis or conversion of sugar to lactic acid and CO_2 production should, and can, be avoided. This may be accomplished by the use of sodium fluoride to prevent glycolysis, by keeping the sample in ice water until cells and serum are separated or directly analyzed, or by prompt centrifugation and separation of the plasma or serum from the cells in the cold. In order to avoid loss of free CO_2 all of this must be done under oil, or over mercury, or in a closed tube, or by taking the sample with a syringe. The ideal method is to draw the blood without exposure to air at 38° and to measure whole blood pH at 38° immediately. In this way, the material undergoes the minimum of handling, while, at the same time, acid formation, both lactic and carbonic, is avoided.

"In the last decade or so, in addition to the classical hydrogen-electrode method, new, more convenient techniques have been developed, particularly in connection with the utilization of the glass electrode. This, especially in biological work, has not been an unmixed blessing. Such convenient methods have been, and will be, satisfactory for most physiological purposes. They afford measurements of pH under some previously impossible conditions. However, the very ease of the procedures seem to have imbued their users with some false sense of security as to an accuracy which, in many cases, does not exist. Also, the tendency to avoid any mention of the basis of standardization has often served to make the validity of the results obscure and worthless. On the other hand, as has been pointed out, the theoretical basis upon which pH values were thought to rest has become less certain, and the problem of standardization correspondingly more difficult.

"The hydrogen electrode method is confined to *reduced* whole blood, or to plasma or serum. It is impossible to determine the pH of oxygenated whole blood by the hydrogen electrode, which is extremely susceptible to the presence of oxygen or of substances giving rise to mixed oxidation-reduction potentials. In the methods used, the presence of the small amount of dissolved oxygen that is present in the serum or plasma of blood *as drawn* does not interfere.

"By methods used for pH in other substances, the sample is equilibrated, in a closed vessel, with an atmosphere of hydrogen, or hydrogen is bubbled through the solution. In the case of CO_2 containing solutions, as has been noted, it is necessary to allow the sample neither to pick up CO_2 from, nor lose CO_2 to, any gas phase above it. This may be accomplished, when pH of blood *as drawn* is desired, by

Hasselbalch's refill technique. This consists of approximating the CO_2 tension of the sample by successive wasting and refilling with another portion of sample, until constancy of E.M.F. readings to 0.01 *p*H is obtained. The bubbling electrode, when applied to blood work, is useful only for experimental studies in which the CO_2 tension can be fixed as desired, and is *known* to be the same in both the hydrogen mixture and in the sample measured. In our work we have used for both experimental and *as drawn* blood *p*H values, the Cullen modification of the Clark cell (for a digram of the Clark Rocking Cell, see Fig. 2·1) with two 120° stopcocks. The vessel is filled with hydrogen or the hydrogen-CO_2 mixture, then with 1 or 2 cc. of the sample, and allowed to rock until thermal and chemical equilibrium is attained. After the first E.M.F. measurement, a second portion of sample is allowed to enter the vessel, displacing the first, and equilibration is continued for another few minutes. The readings of the first and second portions, or sometimes the second and third, should agree to 0.01 *p*H, which is the accuracy, referred to standard solutions, of hydrogen electrode measurements of blood.

"The quinhydrone electrode may be used for measurements within the *p*H limits of biological reactions. However, because it is subject to various sources of error (salt and protein effects, drift of potential, and variation in reproducibility), it has distinct limitations with regard to accuracy for biological work. The errors cited, being caused in large measure by the presence of other oxidation-reduction systems present, make impossible an accuracy for serum comparable with that of the hydrogen electrode. Furthermore, to the best of the writer's knowledge, there is no known, successful application of this method to whole blood, even when reduced. Since the work of Cullen and Earle,[9] Laug,[10] and Yoshimura [11] have made further studies in connection with serum measurements, and have confirmed the essentially empirical character of the results. Under the best of conditions, the accuracy for serum is probably 0.03 *p*H.[12]

"The *colorimetric determination* of *p*H is based on the principle that acid-base indicators exhibit colors in solutions which are a function of the ratio of their two forms, acid and alkaline, which in turn are a function of the *p*H of the environment. One would expect that colorimetric *p*H measurements would share in the benefits of the increasing use of photometers, visual and photoelectric, and, indeed, steps have

[9] G. E. Cullen and I. P. Earle, *J. Biol. Chem.* **76**, 565 (1928).
[10] E. P. Laug, *J. Biol. Chem.* **88**, 551 (1930).
[11] H. Yoshimura, *J. Biochem.* (*Japan*) **23**, 187 (1936).
[12] For a more extensive discussion of the quinhydrone electrode see Sec. 2·2.

been taken in this direction.   However, the accuracy of any color-imetric method is limited by the reactions governing the development of the color.   The colorimetric measurement of serum pH is a good example of this.

"In the method developed by Cullen,[13] the colorimetric readings at 20° were related to hydrogen-electrode measurements at 38°, by a correction constant, C.   Hastings and Sendroy [14] subsequently made colorimetric readings at 38°, finding little variation from the electro-metric results at that temperature.   Further work revealed variations, from time to time, in the C correction, and necessitated an H correction for the Hastings and Sendroy method.   On the whole, results by either technique have been found satisfactory for most clinical work.   Since the major part of the C correction is a result of the difference in temper-ature between 20° and 38°, the Hastings and Sendroy technique should have a slight advantage in accuracy, since there is no reason to expect the temperature coefficient of the colorimetric readings to be constant from one sample to another.   The discrepancies mentioned have occurred often enough under apparently abnormal conditions to make them the subject of much study in the laboratories of Cullen and of Myers.   Robinson, Price, and Cullen [15] have recently found the C correction to vary directly with the logarithm of the protein concentra-tion of the serum.   Occasionally, they report, other factors may have even greater effect on the magnitude of the C correction than has change of protein.   Their results satisfactorily shed light on what has been a perplexing problem.   Since control of the responsible factors, even if they were all known, would be impracticable, in the writer's opinion these results indicate definitely that colorimetric serum pH measurement should be limited to work requiring an accuracy no greater than 0.05 pH.

"The *glass electrode* has become the subject of much study since 1924 and 1925 when Brown,[16] Von Steiger,[17] and Kerridge [18] called attention to its use for pH measurements of biological fluids, and considerable progress has recently been made in the development of various types of apparatus particularly designed for such work.

"Because the glass electrode is unaffected by the action of sub-stances which interfere with pH measurement by other methods

[13] G. E. Cullen, *J. Biol. Chem.* **52**, 501 (1922).
[14] A. B. Hastings and J. Sendroy, Jr., *J. Biol. Chem.*, **61**, 695 (1924).
[15] H. W. Robinson, J. W. Price, and G. E. Cullen, *J. Biol. Chem.* **114**, 321 (1936).
[16] W. E. L. Brown, *J. Sci. Instruments* **2**, 12 (1924).
[17] A. L. von Steiger, *Z. Elektrochem.* **30**, 259 (1924).
[18] P. T. Kerridge, *Biochem. J.* **19**, 611 (1925).

(mixed oxidation-reduction potentials, oxygen, protein, etc.) it has come into widespread use in the biological sciences. The results are usually empirical, and must be referred to the hydrogen electrode by standardization (preferably with two standards at *p*H values on either side of the *p*H of the unknown). Where accuracy is concerned, most of the values in the literature should be regarded with a great deal of skepticism because they lack the support of such reference values. Further confusion has been created by the lack of distinction between 'sensitivity' and 'accuracy'. An instrument sensitive to changes of 0.01 *p*H may yet show an agreement of only 0.1 *p*H with the hydrogen electrode value for a given solution.

"Stadie, O'Brien, and Laug [19] have made the best comparison of glass and hydrogen-electrode results for serum, obtaining agreement within 0.01 *p*H. Sendroy, Shedlovsky, and Belcher,[20] using a modified MacInnes and Belcher glass electrode (See Fig. 4·15) and a Clark-Cullen hydrogen electrode in which there was also inserted a thin-membrane MacInnes and Dole glass electrode (See Fig. 4·12), have made comparisons for reduced whole blood. Their results also showed agreement within 0.01 *p*H between glass and hydrogen electrodes. From this, one would expect the glass electrode to yield results of the same accuracy for the *p*H of oxygenated whole blood, or blood as drawn from the body. Such measurements can be made directly by no other method. Another task for which the glass electrode is well suited is that of automatic *p*H control. (For the use of the glass electrode in automatic *p*H control and recording, see Chapter 13).

"In summing up, it is apparent that the best method of measurement of whole blood or plasma *p*H, *as drawn*, is afforded by the glass electrode. However, the accuracy of the instrument used must first be determined, for the material being studied, by suitable standardizations and comparisons against the hydrogen electrode, in accordance with the procedures previously mentioned."

The author of this monograph feels that Dr. Sendroy has done glass electrode science a useful service by calling attention to the errors involved in indiscriminate use of the glass electrode without sufficient standardization and without sufficiently careful control of the temperature. Doctors Barron and Lyman [21] report that they find it necessary not only to standardize their Michaelis glass electrode at least once a day at a single *p*H, but also periodically (about once a month) to calibrate their glass electrode over a rather wide *p*H range.

[19] W. C. Stadie, H. O'Brien, and E. P. Laug, *J. Biol. Chem.* **91**, 243 (1931).
[20] J. Sendroy, Jr., T. Shedlovsky, and D. Belcher, *J. Biol. Chem.* **115**, 529 (1936).
[21] Private communication.

It is interesting to study the actual data obtained by Sendroy, Shedlovsky, and Belcher in their comparison of the hydrogen and glass electrodes. Their best measurements, given in Table 11·1, were obtained in the experiments in which they immersed the glass electrode (MacInnes and Dole type) into the same solution in which the hydrogen electrode was dipping, thereby eliminating liquid-junction potentials and temperature fluctuations from the comparative results.

TABLE 11·1

HYDROGEN AND GLASS ELECTRODE pH MEASUREMENTS ON REDUCED WHOLE BLOOD
AND DILUTE BICARBONATE-CARBONATE SOLUTIONS AT 38°C.

DATA OF SENDROY, SHEDLOVSKY, AND BELCHER (1936)

Exp. No.	Material	Hydrogen Electrode	Glass Electrode	ΔpH
1	Phosphate buffer	pH 7.17	pH 7.17	0.00
	Ox blood defibrinated	7.20	7.18	−0.02
	Phosphate buffer	7.42	7.42	0.00
	Ox blood defibrinated	7.40	7.38	−0.02
	Phosphate buffer	7.63	7.63	0.00
	Ox blood defibrinated	7.66	7.64	−0.02
2	NaHCO₃ + Na₂CO₃	8.483	8.491	+0.008
	total concentration	8.722	8.715	−0.007
	from 0.007 N to	8.984	9.001	+0.017
	0.01 N	9.623	9.630	+0.007
		10.302	10.314	+0.012

The glass electrode was standardized against the hydrogen electrode in 0.1 N hydrochloric acid solution at 38°C. The data in the above table show that the glass and hydrogen electrodes give identical results (within the experimental error of measurement) in the buffer solutions, but that the glass electrode potential is consistently −0.02 pH units low in the reduced whole blood. It is difficult to understand this discrepancy, unless the glass electrode membrane became contaminated with a film of solid or inert material, or unless the glass electrode was poisoned by proteins—a possibility that has not been verified in any other work. Any known causes of hydrogen electrode errors would produce a difference in the opposite direction to that given in Table 11·1. The data of Table 11·1 were based on the use of 0.1 N

hydrochloric acid as a standard; in other work using acetate buffers as a standard, the ΔpH value was only 0.01, but in this series of experiments the hydrogen and glass electrodes were not in the same cell. Calculations have shown that the water activity error of the glass electrode is negligible in the case of the ox blood measurements, see Sec. 8·3. We also wonder why a sodium error of the glass electrode does not appear in the data of Table 11·1 for the pH values of the sodium carbonate buffer at the highest pH (from Eq. 9·4·3 and the constants of Table 9·2 we can calculate an expected sodium error of the glass electrode of -0.13 pH units at 40°, pH 10.3 and 0.01 N sodium-ion concentration).

In this connection, it is worthwhile to consider the recent work of Yoshimura and Fujimoto.[22] These authors measured the pH of the same sample repeatedly with one or two previously calibrated glass electrodes and with 4 to 11 hydrogen gas electrodes and averaged the data so obtained. In Table 11·2 we have collected their data for reduced whole blood of goats as measured at 15°C. In their work no consistent difference between the hydrogen and glass electrodes could be found in contrast to the observations of Sendroy, Shedlovsky, and Belcher. The latter authors, however, worked at 37°C. where the measurements are more difficult to carry out.

TABLE 11·2

COMPARISON OF HYDROGEN GAS AND GLASS ELECTRODE pH MEASUREMENTS ON WHOLE REDUCED BLOOD OF GOATS AT 15°C.

DATA OF YOSHIMURA AND FUJIMOTO (1937)

Sample	pH with Glass Electrode	pH with H$_2$ Gas Electrode	Difference	Mean
1	7.330	7.336	-0.006 pH	
2	7.510	7.504	$+0.006$	-0.002 pH
3	7.495	7.469	$+0.026$	
4	7.317	7.349	-0.032	

Sendroy, Shedlovsky, and Belcher used ox blood in their experiments which was either defibrinated or treated with 0.2 per cent potassium oxalate plus 0.1 per cent sodium fluoride. After bleeding, the blood was kept one day before it was used, in order that the spon-

H. Yoshimura and T. Fugimoto, _J. Biochem._ (_Japan_) **25**, 493 (1937).

taneous lactic acid formation that occurs in freshly shed blood might come nearly or completely to an end. Yoshimura and Fujimoto studied chiefly oxalated goat blood whose pH remained constant for six hours when kept at 15°C.

The glass electrode cell used by Stadie, O'Brien, and Laug[23] in their blood pH determinations is illustrated in Fig. 11·1. Here we see how the thin membrane type of glass electrode can be used to measure samples of blood less than 1 cc. in volume and how the temperature of the sample can be carefully controlled. One of the two gas jets pointing toward the water jacket is the continually burning pilot light which relights the gas whose intermittent flow through the second jet is controlled by the gas thermo-regulator. An inlet for compressed air which bubbles through the water of the water jacket thus stirring it is not shown in the drawing. Stadie, O'Brien, and Laug find that the thin glass membrane may be washed with water, alcohol and ether and dried by a stream of air immediately before a pH determination without affecting its potential. They made no attempt to keep their serum covered with a second liquid to prevent the escape of carbon dioxide, but designed their glass electrode cell so that the first blood admitted to the apparatus flowed into the auxiliary reservoir above the glass electrode and was not involved in the pH measurement. Tests on a large and small cell showed that errors due to escape of carbon dioxide amounted on the average to 0.006 pH units in the alkaline direction and ±0.002 pH units for cells of capacity 0.5 and 0.2 cc., respectively. The fluctuations of the data in the case of the small cell showed no trend and were within the limits of the e.m.f. measurement.

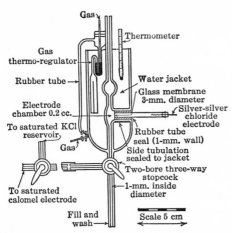

FIG. 11·1.   Glass electrode cell assembly of Stadie, O'Brien, and Laug.

In contrast to the data of Sendroy, Shedlovsky, and Belcher, on the pH of reduced whole blood quoted in Table 11·1, Stadie, O'Brien, and Laug found in their study of the pH of serum that their glass electrodes

[23] W. C. Stadie, H. O'Brien, and E. P. Laug, *J. Biol. Chem.* **91**, 243 (1931).

gave slightly higher, i.e., more alkaline, *pH* values than the hydrogen electrode when the two types of electrodes were compared at 38°C., the average difference of the alkaline deviations being 0.009 *pH* unit. Part of their data is given in Table 11·3.

TABLE 11·3

COMPARISON OF *pH* OF SERUM EQUILIBRATED WITH CO_2 AT 40 MM. BY HYDROGEN
AND GLASS ELECTRODES AT 38°C

DATA OF STADIE, O'BRIEN, AND LAUG (1931)

Specimen No.	1	2	3	4	5	6	7
pH by hydrogen electrode.....	7.420	7.438	7.437	7.430	7.438	7.445	7.444
pH by glass electrode....	7.431	7.446	7.463	7.446	7.455	7.442	7.447
Δ *pH*..........	+0.011	+0.008	+0.026	+0.016	+0.007	−0.005	+0.003

Since glass electrodes made of Corning 015 glass are known to give off slight amounts of alkali because of the solubility of the glass, one might expect the glass electrode *pH* data to be slightly higher than hydrogen gas electrode *pH* data, but considering the three investigations of Sendroy, *et al*, Stadie, *et al.*, and Yoshimura, *et al.*, one must conclude that the evidence for any significant difference between hydrogen gas and glass electrode *pH* measurements on blood or serum at 37°C. is at the present time negligible.

Stadie, O'Brien, and Laug found the glass electrode to be reproducible to ±0.0016 *pH* unit in a series of measurements at 38° on nine different samples of the same equilibrated beef serum. In the case of whole blood at 38° they demonstrated that equilibrium between the blood and glass electrode was complete in 30 seconds (within 0.3 mv.). Other studies of the *pH* of blood as measured by the glass electrode have been published by DuBois,[24] Haugaard and Lundsteen,[25] and Seekles.[26] DuBois' arrangement is illustrated in Fig. 11·2.

[24] D. DuBois, *Science* **76**, 441 (1932).
[25] G. Haugaard and E. Lundsteen, *Compt. rend. trav. lab. Carlsberg*, **21**, 85 (1936); *Biochem. Z.* **285**, 270 (1936).
[26] L. Seekles, *Biochem. Z.* **288**, 402 (1936).

"Blood, taken by the method described by Himwich and Castle,[27] enters the containing vessel without exposure to air at A. The blood is let in slowly and at first stopcocks B and C are turned to divert the flow of blood towards the vent D. As soon, however, as stopcock C is full of blood it is turned to shut off the flow in that direction and stopcock B is given a quarter turn, allowing fresh blood to rise up and around the tip of the electrode. The blood should stand from $\frac{1}{2}$ cm. to 1 cm. above the electrode tip. Stopcock B is then given a final quarter turn, to the position illustrated, and the tonometer is then disconnected."

About $\frac{1}{4}$ cc. of blood is necessary for a filling and connection to the salt bridge of the calomel electrode is made at E. DuBois designed his apparatus to eliminate the settling of blood corpuscles about the electrode, which he says causes a drift in the potential of the glass

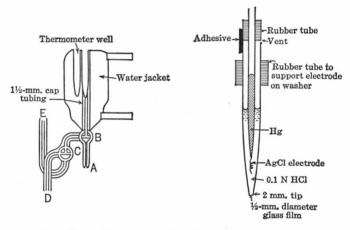

FIG. 11·2.   Glass electrode cell assembly of DuBois.

surface; the shank of the electrode fits so tightly into its well that the settling of the corpuscles is prevented.

Haugaard and Lundsteen keep their blood-drawing equipment in an air bath at 37° before use; during the operation of obtaining the blood they attempted as far as possible to keep the apparatus warm with the hands, and they returned it to the air bath immediately after the drawing of the blood was complete. Seekles states that the decomposition products of egg albumen produce an irreversible error of the

[27] Himwich and Castle, *Amer. J. Physiol.* **83**, 92 (1927). For detailed directions for the drawing and handling of blood see J. P. Peters and D. D. Van Slyke, "Quantitative Clinical Chemistry," Vol. II, p. 52, The Williams and Wilkins Co., Baltimore, 1932.

glass electrode since these substances can not be washed off the surface, thereby changing the calibration e.m.f. of the electrode. Cleaning with chromic acid and washing with water for at least 24 hours are required to restore the normal function of the electrode. Whether any of the difficulties in the determination of blood *p*H mentioned by DuBois and Seekles can explain the difference between the results for the hydrogen and glass electrode observed by Sendroy, Shedlovsky, and Belcher, it is impossible to say at the present time.

Thiesse, Verain, and Ziegler,[28] using a Thompson glass electrode obtained agreement between the hydrogen electrode and glass electrode measurements of the *p*H of blood plasma.

Harris, Rubin, and Shutt [29] modified the Kerridge glass electrode to make it serviceable for blood *p*H determinations; they demonstrated that the "first acid change" in blood observed by some workers was probably a temperature effect as already remarked above. Falk and McGuire [30] found that *p*H determinations by the colorimetric method might be as much as 0.8 *p*H units more alkaline at *p*H 3.2 than glass electrode *p*H data on diluted horse serum to which acid had been added. They recommended that colorimetric determinations be checked whenever possible by application of the glass electrode.

A commercial micro-glass electrode for blood *p*H measurements is illustrated in Fig. 11·3.

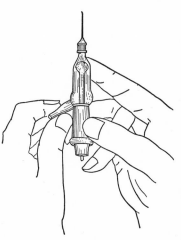

FIG. 11·3. Glass electrode cell for determining the *p*H of blood.

Horwitt [31] shows how a MacInnes and Dole glass electrode can be adapted to serve as the plunger in a syringe, the membrane of the electrode being about 0.25 mm. thick. After drawing the blood the whole electrode is immersed in a relatively large volume of potassium chloride solution serving as the salt-bridge liquid heated to 38°C. Behrmann and Fay [32] describe methods of adapting the commercial Beckman glass electrode to blood *p*H measurements.

[28] X. Thiesse, M. Verain, and A. Ziegler, *Bull. soc. chim. biol.* **18**, 203 (1936).
[29] I. Harris, E. L. Rubin, and W. J. Shutt, *J. Physiol.* **81**, 147 (1934).
[30] K. G. Falk and G. McGuire, *J. Biol. Chem.* **105**, 379 (1934).
[31] M. K. Horwitt, *Ind. Eng. Chem., Anal. Ed.* **11**, 30 (1939).
[32] V. G. Behrmann and M. Fay, *Science* **90**, 188 (1939).

11·3. The Measurement of the *p*H of Blood *in vivo*

Voegtlin, DeEds, and Kahler [33] were the first to use the glass electrode for the measurement of the *p*H of blood *in vivo*. Their technique was to fill the cannula containing the glass-electrode bulb, see Fig. 11·4, with normal saline solution, to tie one cannulated end into the central portion of a carotid peripheral to a "bull dog" clip which had been placed on the carotid, to tie the other cannulated end into the peripheral part of the artery and to allow the blood to flow past the electrode membrane by simultaneously removing the two clips. The dog had been anesthetized with morphine-ether and had been given heparin intravenously through the femoral vein (1 mg. heparin per 5 cc. of total blood assuming total volume of blood equivalent to 10 per cent of body weight). The heparin treatment was necessary to prevent the formation of fibrin deposits on the glass electrode which would otherwise occur because of calcium in the glass. The vertical shank of the electrode was filled with a buffer solution and held in place by one arm of the potassium chloride agar bridge which led to the saturated calomel electrode. The circuit was closed by placing one end of a third potassium chloride agar bridge on a moistened portion of the body of the dog, the other end making contact with a calomel cell.

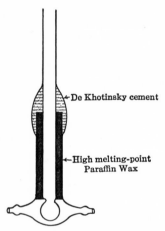

FIG. 11·4. Manner of mounting glass electrode in a Pyrex cannula for continuous blood *p*H measurement *in vivo*.

This method of completing the circuit does not eliminate the erratic and unknown skin-to-blood e.m.f. differences so that the *p*H values given by Voegtlin, DeEds, and Kahler are uncertain by several tenths of a *p*H unit in their absolute magnitude. In a study of skin potentials in a later publication [34] these authors recommended eliminating the skin potential uncertainty by bringing the salt bridge into contact with a freshly made cut on the leg of the animal.

Their glass electrodes were carefully standardized with known buffers before use. It was found by direct experimentation with flowing buffer solutions of known *p*H that

[33] C. Voegtlin, F. DeEds, and H. Kahler, *U. S. Pub. Health Reports* **45**, 2223 (1930); *Amer. J. Physiol.* **90**, 546 (1929).

[34] C. Voegtlin, H. Kahler, and R. H. Fitch, *U. S. Nat. Inst. of Health Bulletin* **164**, 15 (1935); *Science*, **75**, 362 (1932); **77**, 567 (1933).

"1. Two carefully calibrated glass electrodes agree within 0.02 pH to 0.03 pH, on steady flows, and over short-time periods are capable of detecting pH changes of a much smaller magnitude.

"2. Change of rate of flow of a given buffer is without effect on the potential.

"3. Lag is dependent upon flow when changing from one pH buffer to another. With rates comparable to blood flow in the carotid artery of a dog the lag is negligible."

Comparison of the glass electrode with a MnO_2 electrode demonstrated the superiority of the former, leading the authors to conclude

"The independence of the glass electrode from variation in rate of flow and the presence of oxidizable organic substances is the strongest possible argument in favor of selecting this electrode for the measurement of the pH of the circulating blood under all sorts of conditions.   The same advantages obtain in the use of the glass electrode for the continuous measurement of the pH of tissues *in situ.*"

Nims and Marshall [35] have recently studied the blood pH *in vivo* with particular emphasis on the changes of blood pH due to changes in the respiration rate. They eliminated skin and other extraneous d.-c. potentials by placing a normal saline salt bridge close to the glass electrode (they do not describe the type of glass electrode used), both electrodes being in contact with the circulating blood. Of particular interest in their work is the discovery of single fluctuations in the pH of the blood for each single inspiration of a cat or dog if the respirations were slow enough. The

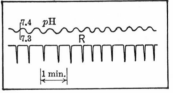

FIG. 11·5. pH fluctuations of blood in left carotid artery as a function of time and respiration (R).   Cat Nembutal.   Chlorazol fast pink.

type of pH-time curve in this case is illustrated in Fig. 11·5, and was obtained by using, in connection with a potentiometer and vacuum-tube microvolt meter,[36] a recording galvanometer whose writing pen was connected vertically in such a way as to record the pH directly on the smoked paper of a kymograph.   Single fluctuations in pH equal to 0.05 pH unit can be noted in the figure.

Nims and Marshall demonstrated that the latency of changes in the pH of blood in the carotid artery following spontaneous variations in respiration is 6 seconds or less.

[35] L. F. Nims and C. Marshall, *Yale J. Biol. Med.* **10**, 445 (1938); Nims, Marshall, and H. S. Burr, *Science* **87**, 197 (1938).

[36] L. F. Nims, H. S. Burr, and C. T. Lane, *Yale J. Biol. and Med.* **9**, 65 (1936). See also the recent note of C. E. King and E. W. Benz, *Science* **92**, 409 (1940).

11·4. The Measurement of pH *in vitro*

In Sec. 11·2 we have described methods of measuring the pH of blood *in vitro*. Here we consider the measurement of the pH of other systems of biological interest.

One of the chief advantages of the glass electrode is the ease with which it can be used to measure the pH of very small quantities of materials. This is demonstrated in the work of Campaigne and Fosdick [37] who succeeded in measuring the pH of a dental plaque which had been dislodged from a tooth by a stiff Nichrome wire. The plaque was placed on the flat horizontal tip of a vertical capillary tube containing the potassium chloride salt bridge (see Fig. 14·1), and a specially constructed membrane type glass electrode lowered until it was in complete contact with the plaque material. In this way a satisfactory pH reading could be made.

Wolfers [38] compared pH measurements taken with the glass electrode and quinhydrone electrode in urine and in diluted urine; in the former the quinhydrone values averaged 0.14 pH units higher than the glass results, but for the diluted urine satisfactory agreement between the two methods was obtained. Colorimetric pH determinations fluctuated $\pm$ 0.2 pH units about the glass electrode data.

Shedlovsky [39] found that with the glass electrode a precision of ± 0.02 pH units was attainable in the determination of the pH of contraceptive jellies and creams, but that the presence of glycerol or other substances capable of lowering the vapor pressure of water produced a "medium effect" (the nonaqueous errors of the glass electrode).

11·5. The Measurement of pH *in vivo*

In Sec. 11·3 we have described the measurement of the pH of blood *in vivo*. In this section other systems will be considered.

In 1915 McClendon [40] made pH measurements of the stomach contents by swallowing a tiny hydrogen gas electrode-calomel electrode system and measuring the difference in potential across the thin silk-insulated lead wires coming out through his mouth. He also had passing through his mouth a tiny rubber tube which was connected to the

[37] E. E. Campaigne and L. S. Fosdick, *Bull. Northwestern Univ. Dental School*, **38**, 27 (1938).

[38] D. Wolfers, *Bull. soc. chim. biol.* **17**, 1559 (1935).

[39] L. Shedlovsky, *J. Contraception* **2**, 147 (1937).

[40] J. F. McClendon, *Am. J. Physiol.* **38**, 180 (1915).

little glass tube cell so that a bit of hydrogen could be run in to convert the platinum wire into a hydrogen electrode.

Glass electrodes can be more accurately and simply used to measure the pH of the stomach and other internal parts of the body; only the small bulb of the electrode is exposed, the shank being imbedded in rubber and surrounded by a compensator shield which runs all the way up the lead. The salt bridge to the calomel electrode has sometimes been attached to the patient on the outside of the stomach, but in this case some uncertainty having to do with skin potentials is introduced into the results.

The question concerning the extent to which skin potentials can invalidate the measurement of pH is easily answered by means of the data recently obtained by Quigley, Barcroft, Adair, and Goodman.[41] These investigators measured the skin-stomach potentials by attaching the salt bridge from one calomel electrode to freshly abraded skin, and a second salt bridge to the point in the stomach at the junction of the body of the stomach with the pyloric antrum. The potentials varied at first with time after eating, but finally became practically constant, varying less than 5 mv. in 30 minutes. The skin-stomach e.m.f.'s of about 22 mv. with the stomach negative were independent of hunger contractions, of respiratory or other somatic movements, of states of repose or restlessness, of subcutaneous injections of histamine or atropine (although these substances affect the secretory and motor activity of the stomach), of intravenous injections of alcohol, and of the presence of salts in the stomach. The potentials were increased by dextrose in the stomach, but were quickly brought to zero by the intravenous injection of potassium cyanide (thus proving that the skin-stomach e.m.f. is a vital phenomenon). These skin e.m.f.'s probably have little influence in affecting pH measurements as a function of time, but they must affect the absolute magnitude of the pH. Since the stomach is negative to the skin, the pH measurement by means of a glass electrode in the stomach must be 0.3 to 0.4 pH units too great. However, since the approximate magnitude of the skin-stomach e.m.f. is known, the pH reading can be corrected for this phenomenon. Yet it would be still better to eliminate this uncertainty by building into the glass electrode cell a tiny calomel reference electrode which also could be swallowed as McClendon did in 1915, or to bring the cotton wick moistened with saturated potassium chloride into contact with a bleeding cut in the skin. This technique eliminates the skin contact potential in the case of measurement of the pH of liv-

[41] J. P. Quigley, J. Barcroft, G. S. Adair, and E. N. Goodman, *Am. J. Physiol.* **119**, 763 (1937).

ing tissue according to Voegtlin, Kahler, and Fitch [42] and possibly would eliminate the skin-stomach difference of e.m.f.

While not exactly being *p*H measurements *in vivo*, Osterberg [43] has succeeded in withdrawing and measuring the *p*H of the gastric and duodenal fluids at intervals of one minute

"and thus obtained accurate information as to the emptying of the stomach into the duodenum and the variation in *p*H values which occur following various types of test meals and other gastric and duodenal stimulants." His procedure can be described as follows: "Two-lumen tubing is swallowed, one opening remaining in the stomach and the other in the duodenum as determined by x-ray, and the two tubes are kept under constant suction by means of two gastric evacuators. By means of a Y-tube glass electrodes are inserted into each circuit and the flow of duodenal or gastric content controlled by means of stopcocks. We have adapted for this purpose the glass electrode ordinarily used for the determination of the *p*H of blood, in which the glass electrode is attached directly to the venipuncture needle."

Voegtlin, Kahler, and Fitch [42] have applied the glass electrode (after

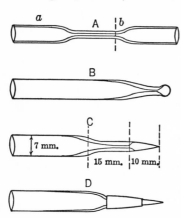

FIG. 11·6. Steps in the construction of the Voegtlin and Kahler capillary-tip glass electrode for tissue *p*H measurement.

making a study of skin and other extraneous potentials) in a most interesting way to the measurement of the *p*H of living tissue, both normal and malignant. Preliminary observations made with a bulb type glass electrode inserted into the skeletal muscle of living dogs showed that it is feasible to obtain rough estimations of *p*H changes in this tissue, but insertion of the bulb caused severe tissue injury with consequent shift of *p*H. These authors also realized from the work of Kahler and DeEds (see Sec. 4·4) the necessity of keeping constant the glass membrane area which is exposed to the system to be measured. Accordingly they designed and constructed from Corning 015 glass the type of capillary tip electrode illustrated in Fig. 11·6.

[42] C. Voegtlin, H. Kahler, and R. H. Fitch, *U. S. Nat. Inst. of Health Bulletin* **164**, 15 (1935); Science **75**, 362 (1932).

[43] Private communication from Dr. A. E. Osterberg, Mayo Clinic, Rochester, Minn.

"Tubing of approximately 7 millimeters outside diameter and 1 millimeter wall thickness is melted down to a thick-walled tube with a capillary bore (A, Fig. 11·6). The tube is cut off and a bulb of about 3 mm. diameter blown on the end (B). The bulb is gently heated in a cool flame and pulled out to a thin-walled capillary (C). This procedure was adopted because it gives the most rapid transition between the thick-walled tube serving as the shank of electrode and the thin-walled capillary which serves as the actual measuring membrane. (In this manner there is maintained a low resistance ratio between the measuring immersed part of the electrode and the unexposed insulating part of the electrode.) The end of the thin-walled capillary is sealed in a flame, care being taken to have a perfect seal and a straight, smooth and sharp point. The lower part of the shank is covered with a cement such as DeKhotinsky or Kronig's 'Special Micro' glass cement. The cement should extend down to the junction of the thick and thin glass walls and its thickness should be about 2 mms. (D, Fig. 11·6, sealed and coated electrode.) Kahler and DeEds have shown that elimination of the hygroscopic film on the glass surface above the liquid surface of the solution whose pH is to be measured greatly improves the reliability of the glass electrode. We have found as the result of many experiments that the cement coating applied as described above reduces the electrode drift, gives more reproducible results and a nearer approach to the theoretical number of millivolts per unit pH difference between solutions. (After several weeks the cement usually is penetrated by the solution and the readings become very erratic.)

"The shank (20 to 30 cms. in length) is then partly filled with phosphate buffer (about pH 7 is satisfactory), and connected with the pressure rubber tubing leading to a vacuum pump. With the glass tubing in the vertical position, the capillary being at the bottom, the vacuum pump is then started. The air in the capillary is thus removed and completely replaced by the buffer solution. The shank is now almost filled with the same phosphate buffer."

Voegtlin, Kahler, and Fitch recommend that air-insulated wires be used wherever possible, that the relative humidity of the room air be kept down to 55 per cent, that a well-insulated switch for the electrometer be used and that the whole equipment including the animal, but not the electrometer, be screened by surrounding it with a large fine-mesh grounded wire cage. The upper shank of the glass electrode is kept at room temperature, but the capillary tip at 37°. The e.m.f.'s arising from the temperature inequalities in the electrode are eliminated in the calibration.

Measurements carried out by the authors demonstrated that the contact potential at the junction agar bridge cut skin was negligibly small and that it was immaterial where the skin was cut. By cutting the skin direct contact was made between the Ringer solution of the agar bridge and the blood, thereby eliminating the troublesome skin potentials. A large volume of Ringer solution was used so that its composition was kept constant. The authors recommend that the tip of the bridge containing the saturated potassium chloride be not allowed to remain standing in contact with the Ringer solution indefinitely as dilution of the saturated chloride solution with the Ringer solution produces additional liquid-junction potentials.　The cell actually used in estimation of the pH of tissue was

Calo-mel Cell	KCl Agar	Ringer	Blood	Tissue	Glass Elec-trode	Phos-phate Buffer	KCl Agar	Calo-mel Cell	[11·5·A]

Voegtlin, Kahler, and Fitch found it advantageous to immobilize completely the animal under investigation by a suitable anesthetic, because slight motions might break the electrode tip or injure the tissue.　Pentobarbital (nembutal) was found satisfactory as the anesthesia produced was slight, easily controlled, and did not influence the pH of the tissue (at least not to 0.02 pH).　After cutting the animal slightly on the foot and immersing in 50 cc. of Ringer solution:

"The tissue to be studied is now exposed by a small skin incision.　When subcutaneous tissue is used, the incision need not be much greater than the diameter of the glass capillary, so that after insertion of the electrode the skin opening is completely sealed by the insulating electrode coating.　This assures against loss of CO_2 from and access of atmospheric O_2 to the tissue.　With voluntary muscle it is necessary to cut the tough fascia.　There must not be any bleeding on the tissue surface and any blood clots are carefully removed with absorbent cotton. The full length of the capillary of the electrode is now cautiously inserted into the tissue, usually in a vertical direction, and is held in place by an insulated clamp or the agar bridge which makes contact with the inside of the electrode. The second agar bridge is now taken from the concentrated KCl solution and dipped into the Ringer solution in contact with the foot."

The e.m.f. is next measured and the pH calculated.

The chief difficulty of this method lies in the production of lactic acid by the injury to the tissue, but by waiting 45 to 60 minutes this effect usually disappears.　The glass electrode is in contact simultaneously with different cells composing the tissue and intercellular tissue fluid, so that it measures some sort of an average pH of these bodies. The temperature of the tissue is somewhat uncertain since it is probably not at 37°; as the authors realize, the temperature of the tissue should be measured with a sensitive thermocouple.

The reader is referred to the papers of Voegtlin, Kahler, *et al.*, for the tabulation of the pH measurements and for a discussion of their physiological significance.　Subjects studied have been the pH of normal and malignant tissues, the effect of the parenteral administrations of sugars on the pH of tissues, and the pH of mammalian voluntary muscle under various conditions.

Nungester and Kempf [44] have used a Beckman penetrating glass electrode to measure the pH of normal and pneumonic lung tissue in animals kept alive by artificial respiration after having the lungs exposed.

Beck, Musser, Carr, and Krantz [45] followed a glass electrode technique similar to that of Voegtlin, Kahler, and Fitch described above in measuring the pH of skeletal muscle and of Walker sarcoma 319.

Blank [46] has succeeded in applying the MacInnes and Dole glass electrode to the determination of the pH of the skin surface. This type of electrode seemed to be more serviceable than the Haber bulb type because of the possibility of the relatively thick-walled shank rather than the thin walls of the bulb-type electrode taking up the strain when the electrode is pressed against the skin. The flat shape of the membrane also served to make a uniform contact with the skin, but the membrane was thicker than 0.001 mm. (but less than 0.015 mm. thick) which probably accounts for Blank's success in using electrodes of this type. His procedure consisted in first washing the area to be tested with ethyl ether, a manipulation that had little effect, if any, on the final measurement, but was necessary to obtain stable and reproducible readings; second, moistening the area with a thin film of a contacting solution, containing 0.1 per cent sodium chloride whose pH was adjusted to 5.0, a procedure also without effect on the final reading; third, applying the electrode (contact between the salt bridge of the calomel electrode and the skin was made about one cm. away from the glass electrode through a thin film of saturated potassium chloride solution in a ground glass joint) lightly to the skin, moving it around over a small area for a few seconds and reading the pH. Finally, the electrodes were moved around again for a few seconds and the pH redetermined. Usually after the third or fourth reading was made, constant pH values were obtained which were believed to be significant.

Dusser deBarenne, McCulloch, and Nims [47] have measured the pH of the cerebral cortex by bringing a MacInnes and Dole thin membrane type of electrode directly into contact with the cerebral

[44] Private communication from Dr. Walter J. Nungester.

[45] F. F. Beck, R. Musser, C. J. Carr, and J. C. Krantz, Jr., *Amer. J. Cancer*, **32**, 434 (1938).

[46] I. H. Blank, *J. Investigative Derm.* **2**, 67, 75, (1939).

[47] J. G. Dusser deBarenne, W. S. McCulloch, and L. F. Nims, *J. Cell and Comp. Physiol.* **10**, 277 (1937).

cortex of fully anesthetized monkeys.   Their electrode arrangement is
shown in Fig. 11·7.   Instead of a saturated potassium chloride salt

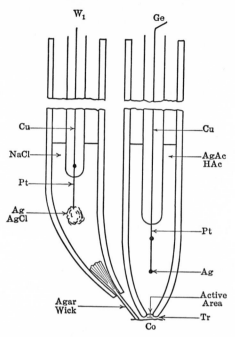

FIG. 11·7. Ge, diagram of glass electrode; Tr, minute quantity of transudate underneath glass electrode; Co, cortex; W_1, wick electrode; NaCl, normal saline solution.

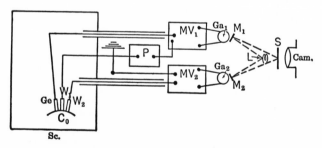

FIG. 11·8.   Apparatus and circuit for continuous pH measurement of cerebral cortex. Sc, shielded cage for animal. Co, cortex. Ge, glass electrode. W_1 and W_2, wick
electrodes. P, potentiometer. MV_1 and MV_2, vacuum-tube microvoltmeters, Ga_1 and
Ga_2, galvanometers, M_1 and M_2, mirrors of Ga_1 and Ga_2. L, light source. S, ground
glass screen. Cam., camera for moving paper with its F/1.25 anastigmatic lens.

bridge and calomel reference electrode, they used for physiological
reasons a normal saline solution and silver-silver chloride reference elec-

trode.   The glass electrode was supported by a spring in such a way as to exert a small constant pressure on the cortex, and to seal effectively from contact with the air the minute volume of cerebro-spinal fluid between the electrode and the cortex.   The authors do not state whether the small amount of base which is continually given off by

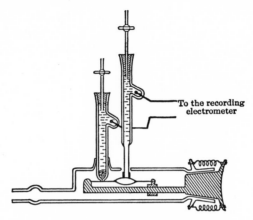

To the recording electrometer

FIG. 11·9.   Electrode arrangement for measuring the *p*H changes of frog muscle on stimulation.

Corning 015 glass is sufficient to affect their *p*H measurements.   If the cerebro-spinal fluid trapped under the glass electrode is in continual motion and in circulation with the main volume of cerebro-spinal fluid, this error is probably not serious.   A study of their data indicates no appreciable drift of the glass electrode potentials in the alkaline direction under normal physiological conditions, so that the solubility of the glass does not seem to be serious in their work.

The apparatus and circuit assembly used by Dusser deBarenne, McCulloch, and Nims is illustrated in Fig. 11·8.

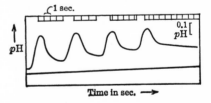

FIG. 11·10.   Fluctuation of muscle *p*H on electrical stimulation.

Dubuisson [48] has succeeded in recording the *p*H changes that occur in muscle during activity in less than a second by means of an automatic *p*H recording device described in Sec. 13·1.   His electrode arrangement is illustrated in Fig. 11·9 and some observations are

[48] M. Dubuisson, *Proc. Soc. Exp. Biol. Med.* **35**, 609 (1937); *Proc. Physiol. Soc.* **5** *June*, 1937; *J. Physiol.* **90**, 47 P (June, 1937).

schematically plotted in Fig. 11·10; the periods of stimulation of the muscle by means of an induction coil are represented by the gaps in the time scale. No changes in pH were observed when the muscle was surrounded by an atmosphere entirely of nitrogen, 5 per cent carbon dioxide had to be present. Furthermore, the tip of the glass electrode in contact with the muscle had to be surrounded by a rubber ring, see Fig. 11·9, in order to exclude the atmosphere from the bit of liquid between the muscle and the flat glass membrane surface, otherwise the carbon dioxide exchange between the muscle and the film of liquid would not be able to produce an observable rise and fall of pH.

CHAPTER 12

APPLICATIONS OF THE GLASS ELECTRODE IN INDUS-TRIAL RESEARCH AND CONTROL LABORATORIES

12·1. The Glass Electrode in Food Industries

Through the generous collaboration of a number of industrial chemists, we have been able to accumulate enough unpublished information to report in this chapter not only on the success of the glass electrode in actual routine plant operation, but also on certain interesting experiences and difficulties which users of glass electrodes have encountered.

First of all let us state that the simplicity of pH measurement by means of commercial glass electrode pH meters commends the instrument to many industrial concerns. Thus one industrialist writes, "It has been particularly useful because none of our staff is expert in the theory of hydrogen-ion concentration."

Second, the versatility of the instrument is of great convenience; as an example, we give a partial list of materials whose pH must be measured in the routine operation of a chemical laboratory in a great meat packing house.[1]

Adhesives
Bacteriological cultures
Brines (cooling system)
Blood solutions
Buffers
Butter serum
Cheeses
Cloth (water extract)
Curing pickles (meat)
Earth (clay and extract)
Eggs (whites and yolks)
Flexible glue
Fruit juices
Gelatin
Gelatin liquors
Ink
Invert syrup

Meat extracts
Meats (fresh and cured)
Meat juices
Milk
Paper (water extract)
Reagents (oxygen absorbent)
Reconstituted powdered milk
Sewage
Soap and soap powder solutions
Solutions for sulphide precipitation from
    various determinations
Water
    Boiler water
    City water supply
    Wash waters
    Blue gas and hydrogen scrubber waters

[1] Private communication from R. C. Newton, Chief Chemist, Swift and Co., Chicago.

Needless to say, the glass electrode is the only instrument which can be applied quite generally to the materials in the list.

Third, and most important of all, the glass electrode apparently gives the correct pH in many cases where other instruments, notably the quinhydrone electrode, fail; this is particularly true in the determination of the pH of canned foods and fruit juices as the careful study made by Blair [2] proves. In Blair's laboratory the hydrogen electrode was found to give satisfactory results except under certain unfavorable conditions, but the time consumed to bring the hydrogen electrode to complete equilibrium with the sample seriously limited the applicability of this electrode, particularly in situations where significant conclusions could only be drawn after a comparative examination of a large number of samples. Turning to the quinhydrone electrode Blair discovered that it gave three types of errors when compared with the glass or hydrogen electrode, depending on the foodstuff under investigation.

"In the first type, exemplified by canned tomatoes, the quinhydrone electrode does not exhibit drifting potentials, but the steady potential corresponds to a pH value, as calculated by the usual quinhydrone equation, which is characteristically too high."

The data of Table 12·1 illustrate this effect; the buffer used for standardization was a "citrate-phosphate buffer of the McIlvaine series; nominal pH value 4.00," and pH_q and pH_g refer to the pH as calculated from the e.m.f. of the quinhydrone and glass electrodes respectively. Note that the quinhydrone electrode gives a pH 0.11 units higher than the glass electrode, probably because the quinone has oxidized some of the reducing substances in the tomato juice such as ascorbic acid, thereby lowering the concentration of the quinone and changing the e.m.f. of the quinhydrone electrode in the same direction that an increase of pH would change it as one can readily see by referring to Eq. 2·2·11. In fact, Blair proved that the addition of pure ascorbic acid (cebione) to the citrate-phosphate buffer produced just this sort of quinhydrone electrode error, (as one would expect, because the oxidation-reduction potential of the quinhydrone is about 0.3 v. higher than that of the ascorbic acid system at pH 4.0). The e.m.f. of the glass electrode, however, was independent of the addition of the ascorbic acid.

"The second type of error is encountered with canned chocolate syrup and is not exhibited by any other canned product, so far as is known. In this case the

[2] J. S. Blair, *Trans. Electrochem. Soc.* **74**, 567 (1938) and private communication.

quinhydrone electrode pH value shows an upward drift, beginning (if one works rapidly) only slightly above the hydrogen electrode value but increasing within 30 minutes as much as 0.3–0.4 pH unit. It is noteworthy that the same sort of upward drift is encountered with a slurry of cocoa powder in water."

TABLE 12·1

Comparison of Quinhydrone and Glass Electrodes in Canned Tomato Juice

Sample	Temperature °C.	pH$_q$	pH$_g$
Buffer.................	21.3	3.964	Set at
	21.3	3.964	3.96
Tomato juice...........			4.22
			4.22
	21.3	4.339	
	21.3	4.326	
			4.22
	21.0	4.327	
			4.22
	20.7	4.327	
			4.22
Cleaned out cell and inserted buffer.			
Buffer......................................			3.97
			3.97

In studying chocolate syrups, Blair diluted these viscous liquids with an equal volume of water "to facilitate continuous equilibration with quinhydrone and to increase the sharpness and stability of the liquid junction"; he also added hydroquinone in addition to quinhydrone, for if the solution is saturated simultaneously with both of these substances, the activity of both quinone and hydroquinone is fixed (at constant temperature and pressure) and there can be no quinhydrone electrode error due to the reduction of the quinone by reducing substances (see Sec. 2·2). Blair's data illustrating the second type of quinhydrone error are listed in Table 12·2 where the slow rise of pH of the chocolate syrup as measured with the quinhydrone electrode is readily seen. It is also evident that the addition of hydroquinone reduces this error and gives the proper pH (the glass electrode pH at the end should be lowered by 0.05 pH units, apparently because of a slow drift during the four-hour period—as indicated by a recalibration of the electrode—which brings the two electrodes into fairly close

agreement).   However, the slowness with which the hydro-quinhydrone electrode attains its equilibrium value prevents its use in rapid
routine work.

TABLE 12·2

COMPARISON OF QUINHYDRONE, HYDRO-QUINHYDRONE, AND GLASS ELECTRODES IN
CANNED CHOCOLATE SYRUP

Sample	Time Minutes	e.m.f. Quin-hydrone Cell	Tempera-ture °C.	pH_q	pH_{hq}	pH_g
Buffer plus Quin-hydrone	3	−0.2152	27.2	3.999	....	....
	23	−0.2157	27.0	3.993	....	....
Buffer plus Hydro-quinone and Quinhydrone	7	−0.1350	25.3	....	3.932	Set at 3.99
	36	−0.1299	26.0	....	4.009	....
	48	−0.1298	26.2	....	4.008	....
Chocolate Syrup and Quinhy-drone	2	−0.1392	28.0	5.263	....	5.23
	8	−0.1320	27.8	5.387	....	5.23
	24	−0.1261	27.2	5.495	....	5.22
	140	−0.1219	27.7	5.556	....	5.17
Chocolate Syrup and Hydroquin-one plus Quin-hydrone	4	−0.0808	26.2	....	4.883	5.12
	52	−0.0681	28.2	....	5.015	5.12
	82	−0.0663	28.6	....	5.036	5.11

Blair postulates "that some reducing agent is present in chocolate
products, which is 'electromotively sluggish,' so that it does not directly
affect the potential of the platinum electrode, but which manifests
itself by its reaction with the hydroquinone-quinone system."   A certain pigment, "cacao red," is present in chocolate products, and this
may possibly be the reducing agent in question.

"The third type of error is the most common, and is characteristic of canned
grapefruit, orange juice, lemon juice, prunes, apple products, etc., and is also very
characteristic of canned bean sprouts.   In this case the apparent quinhydrone pH
value drifts downward with time over a range of 0.5 pH unit or more, and finally
comes to equilibrium at an apparent pH value which may be about equal to the
hydrogen electrode pH value, but most commonly is still about 0.1 unit higher
than the hydrogen electrode value."

By way of variation, this type of error and behavior of the quinhydrone electrode is illustrated by means of Fig. 12·1 which is self-

explanatory, yet the cause of the error of the quinhydrone electrode is far from clear. Blair postulates a sort of mixed electrode mechanism by which the platinum electrode assumes a potential in the direction of that of the organic oxidation-reduction system present (more negative than that of the quinhydrone electrode), and after the quinhydrone is added, the potential slowly becomes more positive (corresponding to an *apparent* drop in the *p*H) and finally attains the correct value of the quinhydrone electrode which is, however, not positive enough to give the true *p*H by about 0.1 *p*H unit because of the reduction of the quinone.

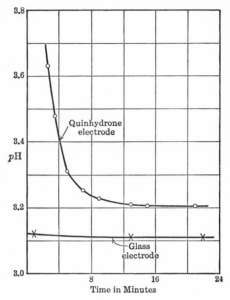

FIG. 12·1. *p*H of canned grapefruit juice. (Data of Blair, 1938).

In certain rather exceptional samples of foodstuffs, addition of the quinhydrone may actually lower the true *p*H of the sample; thus the step-wise addition of quinhydrone to a sample of "hydrogen-swelled" bean sprout brine changes the *p*H as determined with the glass electrode from 4.7 to 4.2, see Fig. 12·2. By the term "hydrogen-swelled" brine we mean brine taken from cans which have swelled due to the internal production of hydrogen; the data of Fig. 12·2 refer to a brine from a can in which the excess pressure over that of the atmosphere was approximately 0.5 atm. If the brine is agitated and oxidized with air for 30 minutes, the reaction with the quinhydrone is reduced somewhat, but it is still considerable, indicating that oxidation by air

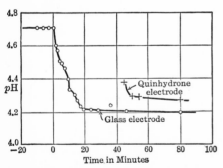

FIG. 12·2. Influence of quinhydrone on *p*H of hydrogen-swelled bean sprout brine. Addition of quinhydrone begins at zero time. Solution saturated with quinhydrone at 45 minutes.

is much slower than oxidation by the quinone. In Figs. 12·1 and 12·2, time is computed from the moment of the first addition of the quinhydrone; in Fig. 12·2 the pH as measured by the quinhydrone electrode is given only after saturation of the solution with the quinhydrone has become complete.

Sourness, one of the four elements of flavor, is directly related to titratable acidity and indirectly to pH, so that a pH measurement is helpful in controlling the flavor of food products, but the determination of the pH of colored fruit juices, and such darkly colored liquids as coffee, tea and cocoa infusions by the colorimetric method is difficult if not impossible, while use of the quinhydrone electrode may give errors similar to those already described by Blair. Thus Elder [3] finds that the pH of a coffee infusion as calculated from the e.m.f. of the quinhydrone electrode drifts slowly upward (5.03 to 5.12 in 60 minutes) and does not agree exactly with the pH as given by the glass electrode (5.01). His infusions were prepared "by steeping 32 grams of ground coffee in 600 cc. freshly boiled water for 15 minutes which was then cooled, centrifuged, and filtered."

TABLE 12·3

pH Values on Fruit Materials by Glass and Hydrogen Electrodes

("The pH Values in this table for the various substances mentioned were selected at random from laboratory data and should not be considered as typical or average values for the substances, but merely as actual pH values for certain individual samples.") [4]

Substance	pH Value	
	Glass	Hydrogen
Fresh burred navel orange juice...............	3.78	3.77
Fresh lemon juice...........................	2.24	2.22
Lemon beverage materials.....................	2.52	2.50
Concentrated lemon juice.....................	1.86	1.86
Concentrated lemon juice.....................	2.13	2.13

From G. H. Joseph we learn that quite similarly the quinhydrone electrode gives erroneous (too high) pH values in fresh lemon juice,

[3] Private communication from Dr. L. W. Elder, Jr., of the General Foods Corporation.

[4] Private communication from W. E. Baier, Manager, Research Dept., California Fruit Growers' Exchange.

but that the glass and hydrogen electrodes agree as proved by the data in Table 12·3.[4]

In Table 12·4 are collected the interesting comparative pH values of various dairy products obtained by Parks and Barnes [5] using the glass, quinhydrone (gold), hydrogen, and antimony stick electrodes at 25°C.

TABLE 12·4

COMPARISON OF GLASS, QUINHYDRONE (GOLD), HYDROGEN, AND ANTIMONY
ELECTRODES IN DAIRY PRODUCTS

DATA OF PARKS AND BARNES (1935)

Substance	pH			
	Glass	Quinhydrone	Hydrogen	Antimony
Pasteurized whole milk	6.585	6.589	6.585	6.96
	6.587	6.586	6.583	6.94
Avg.	6.586	6.587	6.584	6.95
Pasteurized buttermilk	4.305	4.302	4.304	4.87
	4.307	4.305	4.301	4.84
Avg.	4.306	4.304	4.303	4.85
Pasteurized single cream	6.603	6.00	6.605	6.88
	6.601	6.598	6.603	6.98
Avg.	6.603	6.600	6.605	6.91
Commercial ice cream mix	6.614	6.617	6.615	7.09
	6.615	6.615	6.617	7.05
Avg.	6.614	6.616	6.615	7.07
Butter serum	5.993	6.003	6.001	6.64
	5.995	6.005	5.990	6.64
Avg.	5.994	6.004	5.995	6.64

These data are important because they prove quite definitely that the glass electrode and the hydrogen electrode agree in their pH readings of these substances, but that the antimony electrode is in error, because of the presence of citrates and lactates, to the extent of 0.3 to 0.6 pH unit. The authors noted a decided drift in the e.m.f. of the quinhydrone electrode when made of platinum, particularly with the

[5] L. R. Parks and C. R. Barnes, *Ind. Eng. Chem.* **7**, 71 (1935).

ice cream mix and butter serum, but were able to eliminate the drift by gold plating the platinum electrode.

The experimental technique used in pH determinations by the Continental Can Company [6] may be described as follows:

"Semi-solid materials are macerated with a small amount of water prior to placing them in the cup. Due to the high buffer capacity of most food products, we find that the addition of small amounts of water causes no error in the pH values obtained. All samples are brought to the same temperature as the buffer prior to the determination.

"For total titratable acidity, a weighed amount of the food product is transferred to a 250 cc. beaker, in which are placed an outside calomel half cell and glass electrode which are connected to the electrometer. Water is added and with constant stirring the sample is titrated to pH 7 with $N/10$ sodium hydroxide. The results are reported as ccs. of $N/10$ sodium hydroxide per 100 grams of sample. We realize that for truer determinations of acidity, the titration should be carried to pH 8 or 9, but since the buffer capacity of food products complicates the accuracy of the determination so much anyway, we have found titration to pH 7 to be most satisfactory for our purposes."

From the Research Laboratory of Swift and Company we have received the following outline of their procedures adopted in the use of the glass electrode.

"In general, the standard technique employed in making pH measurements with the glass electrode can be followed. In dealing with protein solutions such as gelatin and egg albumen, particular care must be given to keeping the glass electrode surface free from an adsorbed layer of the protein material. The measurement of concentrated brines involves application of extreme care to prevent contamination of the calomel half-cell with the brine. Necessarily, the measurement of the pH of brine solutions in the alkaline range involves considerable error and not too accurate values can be expected. While most glass electrode pH meters include a correction device for the effect of temperature on the glass electrode system, still fairly large temperature changes can bring about true changes in the pH of the material in question; consequently, it has been necessary to more or less standardize on certain temperatures for making pH measurements. For materials which are normally liquid, this has been merely a matter of convenience, and usually temperatures in the neighborhood of 25 to 30°C. have been used. Gelatin solutions, however, frequently jel at ordinary room temperatures; and, in order to have them in the liquid state, it is necessary to raise the temperature to nearly 40°C. Consequently, the record of the pH measurement must also include the temperature at which the measurement was made.

"Butter consists of approximately 80% butter fat and 20% serum, which is

[6] Private communication from Dr. W. H. Harrison, Director of Research, Continental Can Company.

a fairly strong salt solution. It is the pH of this serum which is to be measured. In order to do this satisfactorily with the glass electrode, it is necessary to separate this serum from the butter fat. This is done by heating the butter to approximately 50°C. The butter fat melts, floats to the top, and the serum can then be pipetted off the bottom. It is cooled to the desired temperature and the pH measurement obtained in the usual manner.

"Cheese is a more or less plastic solid, and the measurement can be made directly, provided the electrodes are strong enough. For this purpose we have used a pointed glass electrode. In most cases all that has been necessary is to obtain a slice of cheese about a centimeter and a half thick and lay it on a glass plate and gently push the cheese up to the electrode. (Beckman pH meter used for this purpose.) In this way a quick and accurate measurement can be made without the necessity of adding any material such as water to make the cheese fluid. Other materials of a similar consistency such as gelatin, flexible glue, and so on can be measured by the same technique. Meats are somewhat firmer; and, while the same technique may be used to obtain the pH of this class of materials, still it is more desirable to take a sharply pointed object and make a depression in the tissue into which the electrode can be inserted."

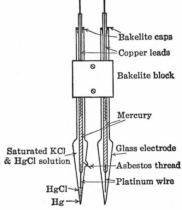

FIG. 12·3. Spear-type electrode cell.

Where the amount of liquid in contact with the glass electrode is minute, as it must be in the measurement of the pH of cheese and meat, the pH reading should be taken as rapidly as possible before alkali from the Corning 015 glass dissolves in the liquid, making the solution more basic and causing the pH reading to be too high.

In the determination of the pH of semi-solid materials, Shaw and Swenson [7] support the calomel and glass electrodes close together with a separation of 1 to 2 mm., and use the asbestos wick of the calomel electrode to form the salt bridge according to the method of ZoBell and Rittenberg [8] as illustrated in Fig. 12·3.

They also use solid glass stylets, made up in approximately the same manner as the electrodes, to pierce the semi-solid material whereupon the electrodes may be introduced into the openings made by the solid glass units.

[7] Private communication from T. L. Swenson, Chemist of the Food Research Division, U. S. Dept. of Agriculture.

[8] C. E. ZoBell and S. C. Rittenberg, *Science* **86**, 502 (1937); see also Sec. 6·3.

Hinton [9] recommends the use of the quinhydrone electrode as the most convenient tool in the scientific control of jam pH, but the fruit pulps must be diluted with four times their bulk of water and boiled down to half to remove sulfur dioxide before making the pH measurements. Furthermore, a drift of e.m.f. readings is noticed in the case of some fresh fruit jams and marmalades with the result that Hinton recommends making the pH determination as rapidly as possible. Application of the glass electrode, we believe, would probably overcome these two difficulties.

Landis [10] finds that the glass electrode offers a convenient means of following the pH changes in fermenting doughs.

12·2. The Glass Electrode in the Rubber and Leather Industries

It would be expected that interesting applications of the glass electrode are found in the fabrication of rubber and leather, two substances whose preparation and properties depend so much on the hydrogen ion concentration of the medium from which they are precipitated. Rubber latex is a milky fluid from the plant *Hevea braziliensis* consisting chiefly of colloidal rubber hydrocarbon globules (28 per cent) suspended in an aqueous medium or serum containing a small amount (1 to 2 per cent) of proteins, and about the same proportion of resins and quebrachite.[11]

Mineral substance, determined as ash, is less than one per cent, and the ash itself contains very little sodium salts (12.4 per cent Na_2O), but mostly potassium salts (43 per cent K_2O); this is of some importance as such a low concentration of ions in the latex means a negligible salt error of the glass electrode in the pH region of normal latex.

McGavack and Rumbold [12] followed later by Jordan, Brass, and Roe,[13] have made a study of the various methods of measuring the pH of latex with the conclusion that indicators are unsatisfactory even for approximate measurements because of protein errors and difficulties in matching colors, that the hydrogen electrode is inapplicable because of the sulfur-containing proteins and traces of hydrogen sulfide present, because of frothing of the latex and tendency of the rubber to deposit on the electrode, and that the quinhydrone electrode is not generally useful since the pH values of the solutions of greatest prac-

[9] C. L. Hinton, *Food Manuf.* **13**, 154 (1938).

[10] Q. Landis, *Cereal Chem.* **11**, 313 (1934).

[11] R. P. Dinsmore, "Physico-Chemical Aspects of Hevea Rubber" in Alexander's "Colloid Chemistry," Vol. IV, p. 283, Reinhold Publishing Corp., New York, 1932.

[12] J. McGavack and J. S. Rumbold, *Ind. Eng. Chem., Anal. Ed.* **3**, 94 (1931).

[13] H. F. Jordan, P. D. Brass, and C. P. Roe, *ibid.* **9**, 182 (1937).

tical interest are higher than eight, and thus greater than the upper limit of validity of the quinhydrone electrode.

A comparison of the antimony and glass electrodes in solutions of different latex samples was made for the purpose of testing the antimony electrode, but this electrode which they found to be not very accurate even in pure buffer solutions (variations of 0.1 to 0.3 pH) was even less accurate in the latex suspension as indicated by the data of Table 12·5.

TABLE 12·5

COMPARISON OF THE ANTIMONY AND GLASS ELECTRODES

DATA OF JORDAN, BRASS, AND ROE (1937)

Sample	Total Solids %	Glass Electrode pH	Antimony Electrode pH	Difference
Normal latex				
A	37.9	9.89	10.26	0.37
B	36.9	10.31	10.70	0.39
C	39.3	9.61	10.03	0.42
Concentrated latex				
A	30	9.46	9.58	+0.12
B	30	9.14	9.32	0.18
C	30	9.32	9.56	0.24
3 Times creamed latex				
A	30	11.16	11.26	+0.10
B	30	10.60	10.51	−0.09

As the latex was purified and rediluted with water the agreement between the two methods of pH measurement became closer, probably because of the elimination of substances like citric and tartaric acids which are known to affect the potential of the antimony electrode. Jordan, Brass, and Roe recommend the use of the glass electrode, but state that it is advisable to calibrate the electrode daily in solutions of pH 4.5 (50 cc. 1.0 N KOH + 50 cc. 2.0 N acetic acid and diluted to 500 cc.) and of pH 10.0 (10 g. anhydrous $KHCO_3$ + 50 cc. 1 N KOH diluted to 500 cc.). These buffers were "found to be particularly practical for this purpose, and if properly stored in stoppered Pyrex containers, they will remain at a constant pH for a period of 2 or 3 months." Finally the authors point out that pH measurements of alkaline latices containing sodium hydroxide or sodium soaps would be considerably in error because of the sodium-ion effect (see Chapter 7).[14]

The Crude Rubber Committee [14a] of the Division of Rubber Chemistry, American Chemical Society prescribes the glass electrode as the instrument to use in determining the pH of latex, stating "The only suitable means for the accurate determination of pH in latex is the glass electrode." This committee recommends that two buffer solutions be prepared from 50 ml. of 1 N potassium hydroxide plus 50 ml. of 2 N acetic acid solution diluted with distilled water to 500 ml., and from 10 g. of anhydrous potassium bicarbonate in water plus 50 ml. of 1 N potassium hydroxide diluted with distilled water to 500 ml. After a determination of the pH of these buffers with a hydrogen electrode, they should be used to standardize the glass electrode. The committee further states, "When the glass electrode is used in latex, it should always be washed free of latex as soon as the determination is finished; otherwise coagulation may take place on the fragile glass membrane. In case a light skin of coagulum does form, it may be removed by rubbing the bulb with a soft wet brush." Other details of technique suggested by the committee are similar to the methods already discussed in this book.

The concentration of hydrogen ions is of great influence in the tanning of leather whether by the vegetable or mineral tanning method, but as McLaughlin [15] remarks, "both laboratory determinations and practical experience have proved that the pH value is one of many factors determining the action of a tan-liquor; considered alone, pH value means little. This is because the 'pH' may result from the presence of any one of a number of acidic substances some of which are desirable in vegetable tanning, others being undesirable. Adequate methods for the identification and estimation of these substances have, until recently, been lacking. This need has recently been successfully met by the work of Cameron and McLaughlin."[16] These authors were pioneers in the use of the glass electrode in the investigation of tanning liquors, some of their first results being illustrated in Fig. 12·4. The curves represent the change in pH of a "Chestnut-Liquid Extract C," 27° barkometer, on titration with 0.1 N sodium hydroxide, and similar

[14] For a review of the influence of pH on rubber and rubber latex see M. Deribere, *Le Caoutchouc et la gutta-percha* **32**, 17333, 17365 (1935).

[14a] *Ind. Eng. Chem., Anal. Ed.* **11**, 594 (1939).

[15] G. D. McLaughlin in Alexander's "Colloid Chemistry," Vol. IV, p. 447, Reinhold Publishing Corp., New York, 1932.

[16] D. H. Cameron and G. D. McLaughlin, *J. Am. Leather Chem. Assoc.* **25**, 325 (1930); D. H. Cameron, *ibid.*, **26**, 7 (1931).

*p*H changes of additional samples of the extract after having been put through various chemical purification and separation procedures.

Burton, Matheson, and Acree [17] mention the use of the glass electrode in measuring the *p*H of a leather extract, and Wallace,[18] after a study of the glass electrode as applied to the determination of the *p*H of leather states, "it is recommended that the procedure for determining the *p*H value of leather proposed in the report of the committee on the determination of acid in leather be revised to permit only the use of the glass electrode. The method should read as follows: Weigh 5 g. of leather as prepared for analysis, into a flask, add 600 ml. of distilled water and stopper the flask tightly. Agitate the mixture immediately and allow it to stand for four hours. Again agitate the mixture and allow it to settle for ten minutes, and determine the *p*H of the decanted extract with the glass electrode."

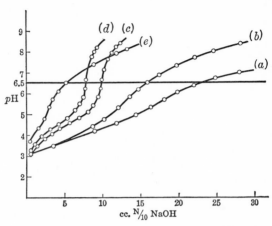

FIG. 12·4. Tanning liquor titrations with a glass electrode. (*a*) whole liquor; (*b*) diffusibles (liquor less colloids); (*c*) ether extract—acetic, lactic, and gallic acids; (*d*) ether extract—gallic only; (*e*) diffusibles after ether extractions.

The determination of the *p*H of tanning extracts and liquors and of vegetable materials containing tannin is now done by means of the glass electrode according to the official recommendation of the American Leather Chemists' Association [19] and of the International Society of Leather Trades Chemists.[20] Methods selected involve the standard practice of using a saturated (or 3.5 *N* potassium chloride) calomel electrode, glass electrode made from Corning 015 glass, electrometer amplifying device, controlling or measuring the temperature, etc. The British committee recommends the standardization of the glass elec-

[17] J. D. Burton, H. Matheson, and S. F. Acree, *Ind. Eng. Chem., Anal. Ed.* **6**, 79 (1934).

[18] E. L. Wallace, *J. Research Natl. Bur. Standards* **15**, 5 (1935).

[19] *J. Am. Leather Chem. Assoc.* **33**, 504 (1938).

[20] *J. Intern. Soc. Leather Trades' Chem.* **17**, 345 (1933)

trode in three buffer solutions having pH's equal to 3.0 (50 cc. $c/5$ acid potassium phthalate and 20.3 cc. $N/5$ HCl diluted to 200 cc. with distilled water), 3.97 (0.05 c potassium acid phthalate) and 5.5 ($c/5$ potassium acid phthalate and 37.6 cc. $N/5$ NaOH diluted to 200 cc. with distilled water). Both the British and American committees recommend that the pH determination be made on 50° Bkr. solutions in the case of the extracts.

The determination of the pH of alkaline lime liquors containing sodium sulfide or other sodium salts presents a difficult problem inasmuch as the hydrogen electrode is poisoned by the sodium sulfide, the pH is too high for the quinhydrone electrode, and the glass electrode becomes partly a "mixed" or sodium electrode in these solutions.[21]

The behavior of the hydrogen and glass electrodes is illustrated by the data of Pleass [22] in Table 12·6. See also the paper of Atkin, Goldman, and Thompson.[23]

TABLE 12·6

COMPARISON OF HYDROGEN AND GLASS ELECTRODES IN A SATURATED SOLUTION OF BUXTON LIME CONTAINING VARYING AMOUNTS OF SODIUM SULFIDE

DATA OF PLEASS (1929)

Sample No.	% Na₂S Crystals	pH	
		Hydrogen Electrode	Glass Electrode
1	10	9.20	12.40
2	5	10.03	12.45
3	2	10.87	12.45
4	1	11.47	12.41
5	0.5	11.82	12.39
6	0.2	12.07	12.38
7	0.1	12.35	12.38
8	0	12.38	12.38

Addition of the sodium sulfide actually causes the pH as measured by the hydrogen electrode to decrease whereas one would expect the pH to increase by virtue of the hydrolysis of the sodium sulfide. Pleass states "the quinhydrone method was unreliable for all the trade tan

[21] The sodium error of glass electrodes is nearly eliminated if Beckman "E-type" glass electrodes are used. Private communication from Dr. A. O. Beckman.

[22] W. B. Pleass, *J. Soc. Chem. Ind.* **48**, 152T (1929).

[23] W. R. Atkin, L. Goldman, and F. C. Thompson, *J. Intern. Soc. Leather Trades' Chem.* **17**, 568 (1933).

liquors examined." The hydrogen electrode, however, was found to be valid for tan liquors below 60° Bk. strength.

Fritsch [24] experimentally demonstrated this increase of pH on the addition of sodium sulfide to a lime liquor by the chemical method of Atkin, Goldman, and Thompson. The glass electrode pH values in Table 12·6 hardly change, probably because the increase in concentration of the sodium ion produces a positive change in potential which practically balances the negative e.m.f. change expected on the lowering of the hydrogen-ion concentration.

Fritsch made a study of the glass electrode at room temperature (24°–27°) in a saturated (and unsaturated) lime solution containing sodium chloride; on the addition of the sodium chloride practically no change in the e.m.f. of the hydrogen electrode could be detected, but that of the glass electrode dropped, see Table 12·7. In the fifth column of the table we give pH values of the solution as calculated from the glass-electrode e.m.f. data assuming that the pH error of the glass electrode in a saturated lime solution is -0.27 pH unit, the latter error being calculated from the equation given by Jordan.[25] If we know the pH as observed with the aid of the glass electrode, we can use this value to calculate the error of the glass electrode in sodium solutions with the aid of Jordan's equation for the sodium errors. The sixth column of Table 12·7 contains pH values calculated from the glass electrode e.m.f. data but including a correction for the sodium error; the ΔpH values in the last column enable one to see at a glance how closely these corrected pH numbers correspond to the true pH as given by the hydrogen electrode. Application of the correction factor computed from the Jordan equation has helped very materially although fluctuations of ±0.2 or more pH units still persist. The situation is far worse, however, if we apply a similar procedure of computing corrections for the glass-electrode pH readings in the saturated lime-sodium sulfide solutions whose pH was determined by Fritsch using the above mentioned chemical method of Atkin, Goldman, and Thompson, see Table 12·8. For low values of the sodium-ion concentration; or for values of the pH not greater than 12.5, it seems justifiable to apply a sodium correction to the glass electrode in the lime-liquor solutions, but if the true pH is above 12.5 (*not* the pH as measured by the glass electrode), and the sodium-ion concentration 0.1 N or more, the glass electrode cannot be used; for in these very alkaline solutions, the glass surface ceases to respond to changes in pH and acts, apparently, solely as a sodium-ion electrode. (The pH values of the sodium

[24] A. Fritsch, *J. Am. Leather Chem. Assoc.* **33**, 592 (1938).
[25] D. O. Jordan, *Trans. Faraday Soc.* **34**, 1305 (1938). See Chapter 7, Sec. 4.

sulfide solutions determined by Fritsch using the calcium hydroxide solubility method are consistent with the hydroxyl-ion concentration

TABLE 12·7

BEHAVIOR OF THE GLASS ELECTRODE IN SATURATED LIME SOLUTIONS CONTAINING SODIUM CHLORIDE

DATA OF FRITSCH (1938)

NaCl g./l.	N_{NaCl}	pH Hydrogen Electrode	E.M.F. Glass Electrode, Volts	pH Glass Electrode	Corrected pH Glass Electrode	ΔpH
0	0	12.45	0.2965	12.18	....	....
0.5	0.0086	12.50	0.291	12.11	12.52	+0.02
1.0	0.0171	12.49	0.290	12.09	12.65	0.16
2.4	0.0410	12.51	0.2845	11.99	12.74	0.23
9.7	0.167	12.48	0.269	11.73	12.72	0.24
24.3	0.415	12.50	0.255	11.50	12.67	0.17
48.7	0.832	12.44	0.243	11.30	12.58	0.14
97.3	1.665	12.40	0.227	11.00	12.24	−0.16

TABLE 12·8

BEHAVIOR OF THE GLASS ELECTRODE IN SATURATED LIME SOLUTIONS CONTAINING SODIUM SULFIDE

DATA OF FRITSCH (1938)

$Na_2S \cdot 9H_2O$ g./l.	Normality Na^+ Ions	pH A.G.T. Method	Glass Electrode E.M.F.	pH Glass Electrode	Corrected pH Glass Electrode	ΔpH
0	0	12.48	0.302	12.21	12.48	....
1	0.0083	12.49	0.2905	12.02	12.38	−0.11
2	0.0167	12.49	0.286	11.96	12.40	−0.09
5	0.0415	12.54	0.280	11.84	12.46	−0.08
10	0.0832	12.61	0.2735	11.73	12.46	−0.15
20	0.1665	12.71	0.2675	11.61	12.48	−0.23
50	0.415	12.96	0.2575	11.45	12.52	−0.44
100	0.832	13.05	0.246	11.26	12.43	−0.62
200	1.665	13.24	0.230	10.99	12.14	−1.10

estimated by Jellinek and Czerwinski [26] from the hydrolysis of sodium sulfide.)

[26] K. Jellinek and J. Czerwinski, Z. physik. Chem. 102, 438 (1922).

The data of Pleass (Table 12·6) are not in agreement with those of Fritsch in regard to the behavior of the glass electrode in the sodium sulfide solutions for reasons at the present unknown to us.

For reviews of the application of the glass electrode in the leather industry see papers by Parsy [27] and Haugaard.[28]

12·3. Miscellaneous Applications of the Glass Electrode

The glass electrode is useful in the determination of the pH of soils but as W. T. McGeorge [29] has found, the pH determination of an alkaline soil mixed with an excess of water gives a pH value which is never reached in the field; therefore, the pH must be taken when the soil has its normal moisture content. The technique for the soil-pH determination developed by McGeorge consists in taking 25 grams of soil, placing it in a 50 cc. beaker, adding water to give roughly the normal water content of the soil (if the soil had become dry), tapping the beaker with the hand to make the soil more compact, pressing in a spear-shaped electrode and calomel cell, and finally making the pH reading. In Fig. 12·5, McGeorge has plotted the pH of a number of soils as measured first with the normal moisture content (dotted line) and second with the soil diluted with ten times its weight of water. Note that between the pH limits 6.5–3.5, there is not much difference between the two methods of measuring the pH, but at pH's higher than 6.5 or lower than 3.5, the curves spread apart, indicating an error of a whole pH unit at the extreme limits of the plot. McGeorge investigated the influence of drying and rewetting the soil on its pH, and found a negligible effect; it is permissible, therefore, to dry the soil and then to bring it back to its normal water content before making pH measurements.

Dean and Walker [30] recommend the use of a glass electrode with silver chloride electrode insert for soil pH determination because of ruggedness, adaptability and ease of construction; they suggest, furthermore, that the glass electrode be moved up and down only two or three times in the soil-water mixture immediately after immersion and then be left undisturbed until the pH reading is taken, otherwise too acid readings will be observed. However, the author wishes to

[27] G. Parsy, *J. Intern. Soc. Leather Trades' Chem.* **20**, 84 (1936).

[28] G. Haugaard, *ibid.*, **21**, 582 (1937).

[29] Private communication from W. T. McGeorge, Dept. of Chemistry and Soils, Arizona Agricultural Experiment Station, Tucson, Arizona. Some of his studies with the glass electrode have been published in the *J. Am. Soc. Agron.* **29**, 841 (1937).

[30] H. L. Dean and R. H. Walker, *Proc. Iowa Acad. Sci.* **41**, 127 (1934); *J. Am. Soc. Agron.* **27**, 429, 519, 585 (1935).

point out that the soft glass surface of glass electrodes slowly gives off alkali in contact with water (see Sec. 4·2), so that a thin, stagnant, not strongly buffered film of liquid about the electrode might have too high a pH for this reason. The recommendation of Dean and Walker seems, therefore, to be ill-advised. On standing from 6 to 12 hours,

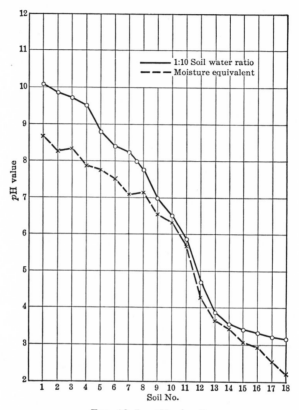

FIG. 12·5. pH of soil.

the pH of acid soils increases and that of basic soils decreases according to the findings of Dean and Walker.

The pH of soils containing manganese dioxide cannot be measured with the quinhydrone electrode, not only because of a drift in the quinhydrone electrode e.m.f. as indicated by the data of Table 12·9 taken from the report of Hissink, Crowther, and Heintze,[31] but also because the addition of the quinhydrone to the soil actually changes

[31] D. J. Hissink, E. M. Crowther, and S. G. Heintze, *Trans. Intern. Congr. Soil. Sci. 3rd Congr.*, Oxford, **1**, 127 (1935).

its pH as measured by the glass electrode, see Table 12·10. This committee's report concluded that the glass electrode was satisfactory for all soil pH determinations.

TABLE 12·9

COMPARISON OF GLASS ELECTRODE AND QUINHYDRONE ELECTRODE pH
MEASUREMENT OF SOILS

DATA FROM HISSINK *et al.*, 1935

Soil No.	pH					
	Glass Electrode	Quinhydrone Electrode				
		15	30	60	300	900 secs.
1 (Greenville).....	5.88	5.85	5.95	6.12	6.82	6.84
2 (Alabama)......	5.56	5.74	6.42	6.89	6.73	6.47
3 (Honolulu)......	6.46	6.50	7.13	6.73	6.17	5.80

TABLE 12·10

EFFECT OF QUINHYDRONE ON THE pH OF SOILS AS MEASURED WITH THE GLASS
ELECTRODE

DATA FROM HISSINK, *et al.*, 1935

Soil	pH		Soil	pH	
	Quinhydrone			Quinhydrone	
	Without	With		Without	With
1 (Berlin)	4.38	4.40	1 (Groningen B)	7.14	7.69
2 (Gro-ningen C)	6.65	6.73	2 (Scherf B)	8.24	8.60
3 (Sigmond E)	10.13	9.08 (not stable)	3 (Bradfield)	5.23	7.30

Naftel, Schollenberger, and Bradfield [32] in a comprehensive comparison of the behavior of the glass and quinhydrone electrodes in a

[32] J. A. Naftel, C. J. Schollenberger, and R. Bradfield, *Soil Research* 3, 222 (1933); Naftel, *ibid.*, 4, 41 (1934).

number of soils conclude that the rise in pH on the addition of quinhydrone is due to the reaction

$$MnO \cdot MnO_2 + C_6H_4(OH)_2 \rightleftharpoons 2MnO + C_6H_4O_2 + H_2O$$

They demonstrated that the glass electrode e.m.f. was constant for
20 minutes after insertion into the soil, that gold or gold-plated electrodes were no better than the usual bright platinum type of quinhydrone electrode, that the antimony electrode may be in error by 0.3
pH unit and that the barium sulfate colorimetric method is the least
accurate of all.

The use of the glass electrode in silicate solutions is interesting as
one might expect difficulties to occur owing to the well-known cor-
rosive properties of silicate solutions on glass, but Rambo [33] and his
co-workers at the Emeryville Chemical Company have developed
satisfactory procedures for the pH determination of these solutions.

"In equipment in which the bridge is a KCl solution and enters at the bottom
of the sample container, such as in the Coleman pH electrometer, the dense
sodium silicate solution tends to settle into the mouth of the bridge and in contact
with the saturated KCl solution a silica gel is formed. After this has occurred
and before another sample can be run, it is necessary to remove all of the silica
gel. As this gel cannot be removed by simple washing, it must be scraped and
wiped out. This introduces too much uncertainty as to cleanliness; as well as
involving considerable work, so it is better to modify the equipment and have
the KCl bridge enter at the top of the sample container. (Equipment allowing
this modification is now optional with the Coleman.) This laboratory introduced
this modification at the very start of our work and we have found it completely
satisfactory.

"After a sample of sodium silicate has been tested and before another sample
is run, extraordinary washing is required. By extraordinary is meant, not a few
extra squirts from a wash bottle or filling the sample container with water and
making a couple of rinsings, but thorough, complete washing of both the sample
container and glass electrode with tepid water. This washing must be continued
until the instrument gives no erratic deflections after the electrode has been
immersed in distilled water over a period of several minutes.

"When the work is finished and before putting the glass electrode away, the
above washing procedure should be followed and the glass electrode alternately
wiped with moist filter paper and washed with tepid water until the operator is
certain that no silicate remains. This precaution is imperative, because once
sodium silicate solution has dried upon glass, the damage to the glass surface is
irreparable. The sample container and the portion of the bridge in contact with

[33] Private communication from A. I. Rambo, Chief Chemist, Emeryville Chemical
Company, Emeryville, Calif.

the sample should receive the same thorough cleaning. If these precautions are not taken, the sodium silicate very rapidly attacks the glass electrode, rendering it unreliable. One glass electrode in this laboratory has had intermittent service in sodium silicate solutions for about a year and appears to be in as good condition as when placed in service."

Hurd and Carver [34] mention the use of the glass electrode in testing the accuracy of the quinhydrone electrode in silicic acid gels; a more detailed study of the quinhydrone electrode in these colloidal systems was made by Hurd and Griffith who found it to be satisfactory for pH measurements.

The glass electrode is particularly useful in determining the pH of hypochlorite bleaching liquids used in the paper industry,[35] inasmuch as no other accurate method exists which can be applied to these solutions; indeed experiments with the glass electrode have demonstrated errors existing in previous colorimetric pH estimates, and have enabled for the first time the dissociation constant of hypochlorous acid to be accurately calculated (see Chap. 15). Yorston [36] and Voigtman and Rowland [37] were pioneers in advancing the application of the glass electrode to the paper industry. For sizing, dyeing, and sulfite solutions the glass electrode is also serviceable, and it is probably the best tool for the titration of black liquors.

H. C. Wall [38] writes

"The principal uses we have for the glass electrodes are for the determination of the pH of 'white water' from the paper machines. This water contains fine fibres, starch, dyestuff, alum and various salts, all in small amounts. The samples are usually dipped from the flowing stream and the measurements made immediately at the temperature existing when the samples are taken.

"Another use is made of the glass electrode during the various steps in chlorination, neutralizing, bleaching and washing of kraft pulps. In these operations oxidizing agents are usually present.

"Another use is in measuring the pH of kraft pulp mill waste liquors, which are composed of mixtures of organic soaps, salts and alkalies.

"The glass electrode is used for the measurement of pH in the routine analysis of boiler waters. In this case samples are drawn in Pyrex flasks and cooled to room temperature before making the pH determination."

[34] C. B. Hurd and D. H. Carver, *J. Phys. Chem.* **37**, 321 (1933); C. B. Hurd and R. L. Griffith, *ibid.* **39**, 1155 (1935).

[35] G. F. Davidson, *Paper Trade J.* **99**, 24, 46 (1934).

[36] F. H. Yorston, *Pulp Paper Mag. Can.* **1931**, 31, 374.

[37] E. H. Voigtman and B. W. Rowland, *Paper Trade J.* **95 TAPPI**, Sec. 96 (1932).

[38] Private communication from Harold C. Wall, Chief Chemist, Longview Fibre Company, Longview, Wash.

Wall states, however, that "When we work with solutions having a pH less than 7.0, we prefer to use the quinhydrone cell, as our experience has shown it to be less subject to errors and electrical difficulties, and that it is always ready for instant use without elaborate schemes for accurate standardization."

Chalon [39] points out that too much emphasis can be placed on pH control, particularly of dyeing solutions when the pH at which the dye functions best does not coincide with the optimum pH of the paper, " · · · too much importance is being given to the pH optima of dyestuffs, which optima with a few exceptions, are of purely theoretical, but of no practical value."

In a recent valuable study entitled "Determination of the pH Value of Papers," Launer [40] states, "The pH of a paper extract is now usually considered one of the most reliable indices of the permanence of a paper, although the first application of pH values for papers were reported scarcely a dozen years ago." Launer made a comprehensive investigation into the proper technique of measuring the pH of papers with the conclusion that the following recommended procedure should be universally adopted in paper pH determinations.

"On the basis of the experimental results of this investigation, the following procedure is recommended for obtaining the pH value of paper. Weigh 1.0 gr. of ground, air-dry paper, and transfer to a 100-ml. beaker. Instead of grinding the paper it may be cut into pieces of roughly 1 cm.^{2} if the paper is not especially thick. Add 20 ml. of distilled water and macerate with a flattened stirring rod until the specimen is uniformly wet. Then add 50 ml. more of the distilled water, stir well, cover with a watch glass, and allow to stand approximately 1 hour. If the paper is thick or dense, and if no grinder is available, the extraction time must be prolonged to 20 hours. The entire procedure is carried out at room temperature. After stirring the mixture once more, measure the pH of the unfiltered mixture with a glass electrode and report to the nearest 0.1 pH. Duplicate determinations should agree within 0.1 pH. The distilled water used in the extraction should not contain more CO_2 than corresponds to a pH = 5.9, but it must be tested for alkaline impurities by boiling a small portion to expel the CO_2. If the pH of the water, after boiling, is definitely above 7.0, it should be redistilled, preferably from alkaline permanganate, to oxidize organic substances."

Launer found that the pH of a paper mixture, if near the neutral point, would be too high as measured by the glass electrode if the electrode had previously stood in an extract of higher pH, and too low if the electrode had stood in an extract of lower pH, but the alkaline

[39] O. T. Chalon, *Paper Trade J.* **104**, 26 (1937).

[40] Private communication from H. F. Launer; see also *J. Research Natl. Bur. Standards* **22**, 553 (1939).

effect was more serious than the acid effect. As an example of this behavior, we give in Table 12·11 the data obtained by Launer for his paper sample No. 21 whose pH was near the neutral point and for a similar sample, No. 24, having a more acid pH. Note that for the latter sample no measurable error could be detected while in the case

TABLE 12·11

GLASS ELECTRODE pH OF PAPER EXTRACTS AS A FUNCTION OF THE PREVIOUS HISTORY OF THE GLASS ELECTRODE

Paper Sample No. 21

Previous Treatment of Electrode	Minutes in Extract No. 21	pH	Relative Error (pH Units)
One hour in distilled water............	10	6.65	....
Ten minutes in paper extract of pH = 9.4	1	7.78	1.13
	9	6.93	0.28
	14	6.72	0.07
Twenty minutes in solution of pH = 4.0	1	6.42	−0.23
	3	6.45	−0.20
	11	6.52	−0.13
One hour in distilled water...........	10	6.65	....

Paper Sample No. 24

Fifteen minutes in distilled water.......	10	5.65	....
Ten minutes in solution of pH = 4.0....	1	5.65	....
	10	5.65	....
Ten minutes in paper extract of pH = 9.4	1	5.65	....
	10	5.65	....

of sample No. 21, the error of pH measurement was less when approached from the alkaline side. For this reason, before measuring the pH of a solution near the neutral point Launer preferred to dip his electrodes in a solution of pH 4.0 after they had been used in an alkaline solution.

The glass electrode is used to measure and control the pH of aqueous plating solutions, but for alkaline plating baths Thompson[41] writes, "In this field of application; the chief handicaps have been found to be the large sodium salt error and the difficulty of rinsing fairly concentrated solutions."

Powney and Jordan [42] have recently given a concise summary of the different experimental methods of estimating the degree of hydrolysis or the pH of aqueous soap solutions; the hydrogen electrode (bubbling type) seems to be unsuitable because of frothing with consequent disturbance of the hydrolytic equilibrium by the removal of acid soap while if unsaturated fatty acid soaps are present, hydrogenation takes place and a film of the corresponding saturated soap is formed on the platinum electrode. The colorimetric method has been shown to lead to erroneous results, as has the method based on the measurement of the rate of catalytic decomposition of nitroso triacetonamine. Powney and Jordan used the glass electrode with success, no significant difficulties were noted nor was it necessary to apply a sodium-ion correction as both the pH and the sodium-ion concentration were too low to cause such an error. The amount of free alkali present in the soaps was negligible. For more alkaline soap solutions or for soap solutions containing additional sodium salts, such as sodium carbonate, sodium phosphate, etc., it is quite probable that the observed pH should be corrected for the sodium ion error according to the suggestion of Sec. 7·4.

Wiegand [43] describes his technique of determining the pH of colloidal carbon in the following way: "If one part of colloidal carbon pigment is boiled for fifteen minutes or more with three to ten parts of distilled water and cooled, the supernatant liquid decanted, and the sludge placed in contact with the glass electrode of a pH electrometer, a reading is obtained which is characteristic of the material."

Winter and Moyer [44] used the glass electrode to measure the pH of blue print sensitizing solutions, other methods being impractical, while Snyder [45] titrated Prussian Blue by means of the glass electrode.

By using a glass electrode, Schicktanz and Etienne [46] were able to obtain some nice titration curves in the titration of whiskies of various

[41] Private communication from M. R. Thompson; *J. Research Natl. Bur. Standards*, **24**, 423 (1940).
[42] J. Powney and D. O. Jordan, *Trans. Faraday Soc.* **34**, 363 (1938).
[43] W. B. Wiegand, *Ind. Eng. Chem.* **29**, 953 (1937).
[44] P. K. Winter and H. V. Moyer, *Ind. Eng. Chem.* **25**, 461 (1933).
[45] A. J. Snyder, *Am. Ink Maker* **14**, 19 (1936).
[46] S. T. Schicktanz and A. D. Etienne, *Ind. Eng. Chem.* **29**, 157 (1937).

ages and dilutions; it should be pointed out, however, that the actual pH readings given by the glass electrode were probably in error due to change in concentration of the water (see Chapter 8). At a concentration of 66 per cent ethanol by volume the error is only 0.10 pH unit, but it increases to 0.92 pH unit at 98 per cent alcohol. If the vapor pressure of the water in the whiskey is known, a correction could be applied, see Sec. 8·3, but of course this would not be necessary for the titration experiments in which only the location of the end point on the titration

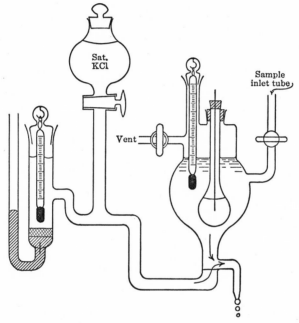

FIG. 12·6.   Cell for the measurement of the pH of boiler water.

curve is desired.   Other applications [47] not mentioned above can be listed as follows:

1. High temperature (85–100°C) pH measurements in carbonation of beet sugar juices.

2. Measurement of pH in ore flotation.

3. Use of pH data in control of still corrosion in oil refineries.

4. Measurement of pH of oil-well drilling mud.

5. Deep sea pH measurements in study of plankton growth in which the electrodes are lowered 100 feet below the surface for measurements *in situ*.   Haber type glass electrodes made by Dr. Beckman

[47] Private communication from Dr. A. O. Beckman.

have been able to withstand hydrostatic pressures exceeding 450 lb. per sq. in. and a direct applied force against a flat surface of 75 lb. or more.

6. Measurement of pH of sewage.[48]

Reichert and Hull [49] have demonstrated the usefulness of the glass electrode in the control of pH of peroxide solutions. Colorimetric indicator data coincided within 0.4 pH of the glass electrode pH values.

Hanlon [50] describes a flowing-junction glass electrode cell particularly adapted for the measurement of the pH of boiler waters, see Fig. 12·6. The boiler water is cooled under purified nitrogen, and the asymmetry potential of the glass electrode is balanced by changing the concentration of the 0.1 N hydrochloric acid inside the glass electrode.

[48] R. S. Ingols and H. Heukelekian, *Ind. Eng. Chem.* **32**, 401 (1940).
[49] J. S. Reichert and H. G. Hull, *Ind. Eng. Chem., Anal. Ed.* **11**, 311 (1939).
[50] R. T. Hanlon, *Combustion* **11**, 41 (1939).

CHAPTER 13

CONTINUOUS pH RECORDERS AND AUTOMATIC pH CONTROL WITH A GLASS ELECTRODE

13·1. Continuous Recording of pH.

As far as the author is aware, Vickers, Sugden, and Bell[1] were the first to use the glass electrode in an apparatus for the continuous recording of pH (although Kahler, DeEds, Rosenthal, and Voegtlin[2] mention the use of an oscillograph with a period of 1/300 second in the plate circuit of the last tube of a three-tube thermionic amplifier for the purpose of automatically recording rapid changes in the e.m.f. of glass electrode cells). They designed a balanced Wheatstone-bridge circuit, Fig. 13·1, in which two of the arms of the bridge consisted of the resistances R_1 and R_2 and the other two arms contained two matched vacuum tubes. A commercial recording device, M, whose microampere reading could be calibrated in terms of pH, served as the

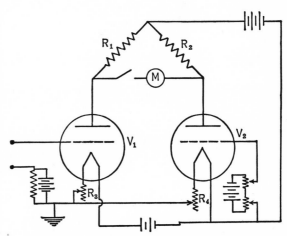

FIG. 13·1. Thermionic amplifier circuit of Vickers, Sugden, and Bell (1932)

instrument to indicate unbalance of the bridge. The chief problem in the construction of a thermionic apparatus to record the pH over a long period of time is the attainment of sufficient stability of the system to assure a constant zero point. Vickers, Sugden, and Bell meas-

[1] A. E. J. Vickers, J. A. Sugden, and R. A. Bell, *Chem. and Ind.* **51**, 545 (1932).
[2] H. Kahler, F. DeEds, S. Rosenthal, and C. Voegtlin, *Am. J. Physiol.* **91**, 225 (1929).

ured the characteristics of their vacuum tubes in order to obtain two tubes so similar that fluctuations in filament current and grid and plate battery voltage would not upset the balance of the Wheatstone bridge. They inserted the resistances R_3 and R_4 in order to secure

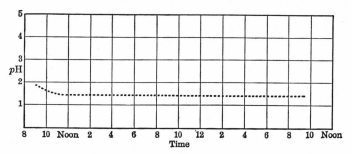

FIG. 13·2. Variation of *p*H-recorder with time.

separate control of the filament current of each tube, and the grid-biasing potentiometers were identical in voltage and resistances. (It would have been better if the operating grid voltage had been at earth potential.) By adjusting the operating conditions to maximum stabil-

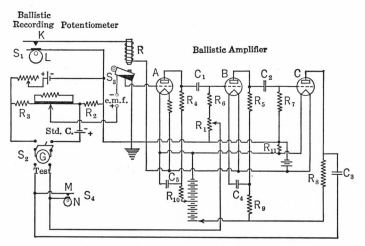

FIG. 13·3. Continuous recording circuit of Morton.

ity and by allowing the battery currents to run for twenty hours, they were able to attain readings constant to 0.02 *p*H over long periods of time, see Fig. 13·2. (A slight upward drift which may not be apparent in Fig. 13·2 is due to a change in the zero reading of the commercial recorder.)

Shortly after the appearance of the paper of Vickers, Sugden, and Bell, Morton [3] published a description of a circuit for the automatic recording of glass-electrode e.m.f. readings by means of a ballistic instrument whose action is independent of zero shift. Details of the circuit illustrated in Fig. 13·3 may be listed as follows:

A	triode electrometer tube, average grid current 10^{-15} amp.
B	triode tube possessing a high amplification factor
C	power tube of high mutual conductance
C_1, C_2	1-microfarad mica-dielectric condensers
C_3, C_4, C_5	2 to 4-microfarad condensers
R_2, R_3	10,000-ohm potential divider with sliding contact
R_4, R_5	100,000-ohm resistances
R_6	0.5-megohm resistance
R_7	2-megohm resistance
R_8, R_9, R_{10}	20,000 to 40,000-ohm resistances
R_4, R_5, R_8, R_9, R_{10}	should be noninductive and wire-wound
S_1	a cam-operated switch so arranged that contacts K and L are closed about once every 10 seconds.
S_2	a switch to connect the galvanometer to the standard cell-potentiometer combination or to the ballistic amplifier.
S_3	a mercury-cup switch operated when contacts K and L are closed by means of the relay R_e. Its purpose is to connect the grid of the input tube alternately to ground and to the unknown e.m.f.-potentiometer combination.
S_4	a cam-operated switch similar to S_1 which short-circuits the galvanometer during the time interval that a reverse or discharge current flows through the galvanometer leads when the grid is earthed.

The amplification circuit is regeneratively coupled through the resistance R_1 to increase the sensitivity by using some of the output power of the last tube to reinforce the initial impulse.

The sequence of events in Morton's apparatus during operation consists first in the usual standardization of the potentiometer using the standard cell; second, throwing of switch S_2 to the test position; then intermittent closing of switch S_1 and S_3 to apply any unbalanced e.m.f. to the grid of the electrometer tube. Amplified impulses of the charging of the first grid are impressed on the grids of the tubes B and C ultimately causing the ballistic galvanometer G to deflect. This deflection in its turn causes the potential in the automatic recorder to be readjusted to balance and then to be graphically recorded.

Morton's circuit is to be recommended for long continued operation, but it is incapable of recording sudden changes or fluctuations in

[3] C. Morton, *J. Chem. Soc.* **1932**, 2469.

*p*H such as those observed by Dubuisson [4] in muscles under stimulation (see Sec. 11·5). Dubuisson photographically recorded the deflections of the galvanometer in the FP–54 circuit shown in Fig. 3·7*b*. He reported that his recording device was "absolutely steady" and probably was over the short time intervals (less than a minute) during which he observed the rise and fall of the muscle *p*H. Dusser de Barenne, McCulloch, and Nims,[5] have also made continuous recordings of animal *p*H *in vivo*, see Sec. 11·5.

In many continuous *p*H measuring appliances an aliquot (if not the whole) part of the main body of the unknown liquid is continuously circulated past or over the outside surface of a glass electrode held in a small cup, the liquid then being returned to the main sample. Morton's continuous flow cell is illustrated in Fig. 13·4 (compare Fig. 6·5).

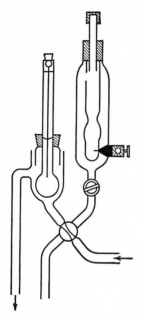

FIG. 13·4. Glass electrode cell for continuous *p*H measurement.

13·2. Automatic Control of *p*H.

The first investigator to design an apparatus for the automatic control of *p*H with the glass electrode was Whitnah,[6] who used a balanced Wheatstone-bridge circuit similar to that described in Sec. 13·1. Whitnah also measured the amount of base necessary to maintain a constant *p*H during acid production in the lactic fermentation of milk and in the methylation of lactose and glucose (actually the glass electrode was used only in the last experiment; it proved to be more satisfactory than the antimony electrode used in the first two experiments). For automatic control, base was admitted at regular intervals from a buret whose stopcock was joined by means of a universal joint to a disk which rocked back and forth causing the buret to open and close. The flow from the buret was divided into two arms before finally issuing from the buret tip so that the flow through one arm could be automatically

[4] M. Dubuisson, *Proc. Soc. Expl. Biol. Med.* **35**, 609 (1937); *Proc. Physiol. Soc.*, June 5, 1937; *J. Physiol.* **90**, page 47P (1937).

[5] J. G. Dusser deBarenne, W. S. McCulloch, and L. F. Nims, *J. Cellular Comp. Physiol.* **10**, 277 (1937).

[6] C. H. Whitnah, *Ind. Eng. Chem., Anal. Ed.* **5**, 352 (1933).

controlled while the flow through the second arm was intermittent as described above. The second stopcock was also connected by a universal joint to a disk whose operation was controlled by the armature of a solenoid, the action of the latter being governed by a

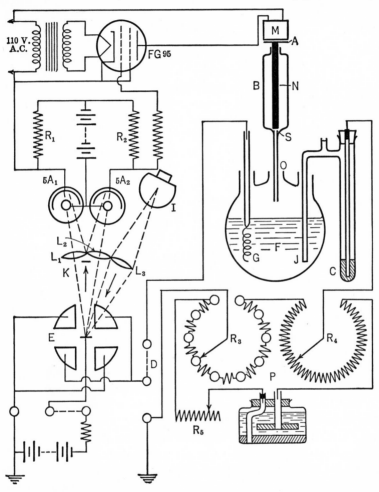

FIG. 13·5. Longsworth and MacInnes constant pH apparatus.

Leeds and Northrup recording potentiometer. For details of the mechanically operated buret, the reader is referred to the original paper of Whitnah.

Longsworth and MacInnes [7] have invented an apparatus having

[7] L. G. Longsworth and D. A. MacInnes, *J. Bact.* **29**, 595 (1935).

the same purpose as that of Whitnah, but built somewhat differently. In their case the Wheatstone bridge contained two Western Electric phototubes $5A_1$ and $5A_2$, see Fig. 13·5, and two high resistances (R_1 and R_2) whose resistances were comparable to the resistances of the illuminated phototubes.   A B-battery of 45 volts provided the necessary voltage for the bridge, any unbalance of which caused the double grid thyratron FG–95 to operate, the magnet M to become energized and the special buret, B, to open, allowing base to flow into the reaction chamber F.

"When current is passing, the magnet armature, A, lifts a glass rod, N, which extends the full length of the burette and carries a small rubber plug.   The capillary outlet, O, is sealed through the lower end of the burette with a projecting shoulder S against which the rubber plug normally presses.   When the plug is lifted from the shoulder, the liquid flows under gravity from the burette.   Since the magnet armature moves only 1 mm. in opening and closing the valve, a sufficiently strong pull can be obtained with a small current through the magnet. The valve avoids the lubrication necessary with ordinary stopcocks, a decided advantage in dealing with strong alkali, as in this work.   The rate of flow from the burette may be adjusted by varying the length and bore of the capillary outlet."

The mechanism of the automatic control of the pH depends upon the ability of the Compton quadrant electrometer E to indicate differences of e.m.f. between the glass electrode-calomel cell combination, C, and the specially constructed potentiometer, P.   If the pH in the reaction chamber changes, the e.m.f. at the surface of the glass electrode becomes greater or less so that the electrometer needle swings slightly because of the electrical unbalance, allowing more light to fall upon one of the phototubes than upon the other, thus upsetting the balance of the Wheatstone bridge and causing the armature of the magnet to operate.

Longsworth and MacInnes list the following possible sources of difficulty in connection with a change in the zero setting of the apparatus.

1. *Variations of the Potentiometer Current.*   To avoid frequent standardization of the potentiometer e.m.f. against a standard cell, the authors used a high resistance potentiometer and a Hulett [8] standard cell, a heavy-duty unsaturated type of Weston cell having low internal resistance and very little concentration polarization during operation. They used this cell as the working battery of their potentiometer and found that its e.m.f. remained constant to better than one millivolt for over a month when furnishing current for the potentiometer.   The

---

[8] G. A. Hulett, *Phys. Rev.* **27**, 33 (1908).

potentiometer was constructed of one decade resistance box having 10,000-ohm units and one with 100-ohm units, the current being adjusted so that the voltage drop across each 100-ohm unit was 1 mv. Using this type of potentiometer and the Hulett standard cell, variations in the potentiometer potential differences were made negligible.

2. *Variations in the Light Source.* The light source I of Fig. 13·5, was a 32-candle power automobile headlight bulb, operated from the line voltage using a stepdown transformer. Since two phototubes were used in the circuit, any variation in the intensity of the light from I would presumably affect each tube similarly without unbalancing the Wheatstone bridge.

3. *The Zero Shift of the Electrometer.* At the start of each experiment the Wheatstone bridge containing the phototubes was given a fine adjustment to balance by a slight motion of the light screen K; after a period of operation variations in the zero setting were tested for by reversing the position of the double-throw switch D which grounded the quadrants and noting whether any readjustment of the screen K was necessary to rebalance the Wheatstone bridge. The authors found such readjustments necessary twice a day.

4. *Variations of the Glass Electrode.* Variations in the asymmetry potential of the glass electrode were avoided by using a glass electrode of the spiral type, see Fig. 13·5, which had been allowed to soak in water for a month. Later the authors used the MacInnes and Dole membrane type of electrode.

5. *The Liquid-Junction Potential.* The salt-bridge solution was 3.5 N potassium chloride which made contact with the test liquid through the dense plug type of tip described in Sec. 6·3.

Longsworth and MacInnes used their automatic pH control apparatus to measure the acid formation, at constant pH, during the growth of *Lactobacillus acidophilus.* The rate at which base was added could be determined by readings of the buret B at appropriate time intervals.

Müller and Dürichen [9] have described an interesting automatic pH control apparatus which avoids the use of a potentiometer and standard cell, and relies solely on the maintenance of equality between the pH of the test sample on the outside of their Haber glass electrode and the pH of a standard solution on the inside of the bulb. A normal calomel electrode dips into the liquid in this glass electrode and another one into the test sample so that the e.m.f. of the whole cell is zero except for a small asymmetry potential of the glass electrode which is bal-

[9] Fr. Müller and W. Dürichen, *Z. Elektrochem.* **42**, 730 (1936).

anced out by adjustment of the variable resistance R of Fig. 13·6. If, however, the *p*H of the test sample becomes greater, let us say, than that of the standard liquid in the bulb, the control grid of the top electrometer tube in Fig. 13·6 will become more negative than the control grid in the lower tube, upsetting the balance of the Wheatstone-bridge circuit and causing the sensitive galvanometer S to deflect. The latter deflection changes the intensity of the light impinging on the photocell P with consequent operation of the relays necessary to open the buret B, thereby allowing more acid to enter the solution to bring the *p*H back to the condition of zero e.m.f. across the glass membrane.

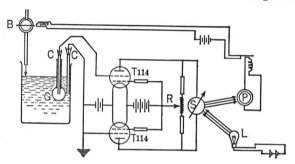

FIG. 13·6.   Constant *p*H apparatus of Müller and Dürichen.

The electrometer tubes, T–114, were operated with a grid-biasing voltage of −3 v., and the whole apparatus was very sensitive, 0.1 mv. being the limit of accuracy. Stability of the circuit was enhanced by using the two electrometer tubes in opposition as illustrated, but the authors do not state the limits of constancy. Sensitivity of the instrument could be easily altered by changing the light path, or by use of a more or less sensitive galvanometer, S, and the whole circuit was constructed without difficulty.

Nottingham [10] shows that the current through the galvanometer in circuits like those of Figs. 13·1 and 13·6 will be independent of the B-battery voltage if

$$\frac{Z_1}{Z_2} = \frac{R_1}{R_2}$$

where Z_1 and Z_2 represent the plate impedances of the tubes V_1 and V_2, and R_1 and R_2 the resistances in the other two arms of the Wheatstone bridge, as designated in Fig. 13·1. For this relation to hold, it is necessary that the tube characteristics do not change over the range

[10] W. B. Nottingham, *J. Franklin Inst.* **209**, 287 (1930).

of variation of the B-battery voltage (allowable variation of the latter being about 1 to 3 per cent). Although the sensitivity of the Wheatstone-bridge arrangement is only half that of certain single tube circuits, nevertheless, the advantages of partial compensation for variations in A-, B-, and C-battery voltages and for aging of the tubes more than outweigh the disadvantage in the loss of sensitivity.

Schwabe [11] describes a rather simple glass electrode apparatus for the automatic control of *p*H based on his independently invented principle of maintaining the difference of e.m.f. across the glass membrane equal to zero. By making a large Haber electrode of thin glass and by operating at temperatures of 30 to 40°, the resistance of the circuit is lowered to the point where the current through the cell is sufficient to operate directly a fine relay which in turn makes or breaks contacts controlling larger relays which open or close the acid and base reservoirs. A light system of red, green, and white lights is also included in the system so that the operator can tell at a glance whether the solution *p*H is acid, basic, or equal to the *p*H of the reference liquid on the inside of the glass bulb. Most of the leading manufacturers of glass electrode equipment now offer for sale automatic *p*H recorders and *p*H control devices.

[11] K. Schwabe, *Z. Elektrochem.* **43**, 152 (1937).

CHAPTER 14

MICRO METHODS WITH THE GLASS ELECTRODE

14·1. Introduction

The ability of the glass electrode to measure the pH of small quantities of materials is one of its great merits; indeed the volume of liquid required for pH measurements in the case of most of the commercial instruments is so small that one might say that practically all glass electrode techniques are micro, or at least, semi-micro methods. Not only is valuable material saved in many instances, but no addition agents are necessary and the method is rapid and convenient for routine work. Two difficulties, however, are encountered in micro work; the Corning 015 glass is sufficiently soluble to contaminate significantly small quantities of test liquid, and as the size of the glass electrode is made smaller and smaller, its resistance increases correspondingly. Yet these difficulties are not insuperable.

In Sec. 2·4 the Kerridge reentrant bulb type semi-micro glass electrode has already been described and in Sec. 4·5 the thin membrane type of electrode used in micro work is discussed. Youden and Dobroscky's capillary type of glass electrode also mentioned in Sec. 4·5 requires only 0.01 cc. for a pH determination. Small glass electrode systems used by biological workers are described in Chapter 11 and in Chapter 15 can be found the explanation of a micro titration cell.

14·2. Micro Apparatus for pH Determination

The first glass electrode apparatus capable of measuring the pH of a single drop of material was that of MacInnes and Dole,[1] see Fig. 14·1. In this drawing A represents the calomel reference electrode filled with saturated potassium chloride solution from the reservoir B. The tip of capillary tubing is ground off flat at D so that a single drop of liquid can be supported on it. Operation of the apparatus consists in tightening a screw clamp on a piece of rubber tubing attached to the tube C, sweeping out the capillary tube with the saturated chloride solution, wiping off the ground-glass surface at D with a piece of filter paper,

---

[1] D. A. MacInnes and M. Dole, *J. Gen. Physiol.* **12**, 805 (1929).

placing a drop of the test sample on the tip at D, unloosening the screw clamp at C a bit so that the test liquid is sucked back into the capillary tubing about 1 or 2 mm., wiping off the top surface again, putting a second drop of test liquid on the flat tip, and surrounding the drop with the shield G.   A fresh drop is used inasmuch as the first drop may have become contaminated with the potassium chloride solution.   By means of a mechanical holder and worm-gear device, not shown in Fig. 14·1, the glass electrode E, is next cautiously lowered until contact of the thin membrane F with the test sample is made as illustrated.   The e.m.f. can then be quickly measured.   It should be

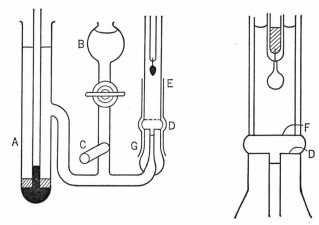

Fig. 14·1.   MacInnes and Dole micro-*p*H apparatus.   Sketch at right shows enlarged view of thin membrane and drop.

noted that it is necessary to put a thin coating of paraffin on the outside of the tubing up to the edge of the tip, D, and on the lower outside vertical surface of the glass electrode to prevent the drop of solution from spreading.   Excellent results were obtained on minute quantities of sap from *nitella*.   Fosdick and his co-workers at the Northwestern Dental School have also used a similar apparatus with considerable success.

MacInnes and Dole[2] also succeeded in making a capillary-tip glass electrode with active glass surface only 0.5 to 0.75 mm. in diameter, an electrode whose hydrogen electrode function was well developed. This electrode was made by the difficult method of passing a glass capillary tip through a flame just slowly enough to heat the thin glass edges of the tip so that they would fuse onto the membrane held underneath, but not so slowly that the glass tip fused together.

[2] D. A. MacInnes and M. Dole, *Ind. Eng. Chem., Anal. Ed.* **1**, 57 (1929).

In using the electrodes the pH readings should be made as quickly as possible, inasmuch as the Corning 015 glass slowly gives off alkali in sufficient quantities to contaminate the small volume of test sample. The smaller the buffer capacity of the unknown, the more serious is the difficulty; for highly unbuffered solutions a continuous flow method should be used, see Sec. 10·1.

Duspiva[3] has modified the MacInnes and Dole apparatus as illustrated in Fig. 14·2. Here the salt bridge makes contact with the test liquid placed on the thin membrane F from above rather than from below, and the apparatus is so designed as to enable the pH of alkaline liquids to be measured without contact of the sample with the carbon dioxide of the air and without evaporation taking place. The glass electrode is filled through A with a buffer mixture, water is run in at B_2 and out at B_1 to provide a moist atmosphere. The sample can be introduced either at C_1 or C_2, following which these openings can be closed with soda-lime tubes. D is a mercury cup enabling the salt bridge E to be raised or lowered out of contact with air, and the narrow capillary tube is filled with a saturated potassium chloride, agar-gel salt bridge.

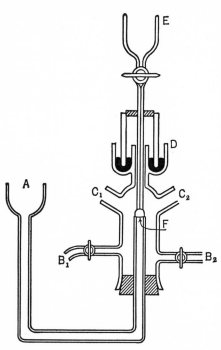

FIG. 14·2. Duspiva's micro-pH apparatus.

Duspiva used his apparatus to determine the pH of the intestinal juice of clothes and wax-moth larvae.

Païc[4] uses his protected type membrane electrode in a manner somewhat similar to Duspiva; with the glass electrode bent in a U-shape, see Fig. 4·13c, the drop of unknown liquid is placed in the little cup formed by the membrane and protuding glass walls and the saturated potassium chloride salt bridge brought down to make contact from above. To reduce the volume of test sample required, Païc

[3] F. Duspiva, Z. physiol. Chem. 241, 168 (1936).
[4] M. Païc, J. chim. phys. 35, 327 (1938).

forms his membrane between two tubes drawn out to a diameter of 3 mm.

Miss Pickford[5] has constructed a sealed-in micro glass electrode (Fig. 14·3) serviceable for the measurement of the *p*H of as little as 0.06 cc. of liquid. Made of Corning 015 glass, the electrode *D* in Fig. 14·3, is a very thin and small copy of the Michaelis[6] modification of the MacInnes and Belcher type. The reservoir *E* on the outer side of the membrane is filled with 0.1 *N* hydrochloric acid or suitable buffer which is connected to a silver-silver chloride or saturated calomel reference electrode. In using the electrode, the narrow capillary tube is first rinsed out with distilled water after a calibration with standard buffer, dried with alcohol and ether and filled from a Luer syringe as indicated in Fig. 14·3. If more than the minimum volume of sample is available, the first part of the sample is forced up into the small bulb *F* above the electrode, thus eliminating the part of the solution which has come into contact with the atmosphere. Connection of the unknown sample with the saturated potassium chloride salt bridge *A* is made by turning the three-way stopcock (due to Stadie, O'Brien, and Laug[7]) in a clockwise direction after rinsing out the base with the stopcock in the position shown in Fig. 14·3. However, actual contact of the unknown with the chloride solution in the base of the stopcock is unnecessary, provided that the inner race of the stopcock is ungreased and is wet with the salt bridge solution. Asymmetry potentials of these electrodes drop nearly to zero on long standing while the resistance is of the order of magnitude of 200 to 300 megohms.

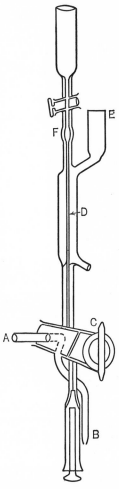

FIG. 14·3.   Pickford micro-*p*H apparatus.

The micro glass electrode described by Yoshimura[8] is very similar to that of Youden and Dobroscky mentioned in Sec. 4·5.

[5] G. E. Pickford, *Proc. Soc. Exptl. Biol. Med.* **36**, 154 (1937).

[6] L. Michaelis, *Science* **83**, 213 (1936).

[7] W. C. Stadie, H. O'Brien, and E. P. Laug, *J. Biol. Chem.* **91**, 243 (1931).

[8] H. Yoshimura, *J. Biochem.* (*Japan*) **23**, 335 (1936).

CHAPTER 15

POTENTIOMETRIC TITRATIONS WITH
THE GLASS ELECTRODE

Most of the advantages of the glass electrode over other hydrogen-ion indicating electrodes for pH measurements are to be found also in the field of potentiometric titrations; indifference of the glass surfaces to poisons, oxidation-reduction potentials, and gases; applicability of the electrode to sludges, densely colored and turbid mixtures; freedom from the necessity of introducing addition agents or of excluding oxygen and reliability of the electrode in highly unbuffered solutions may be listed in favor of the glass electrode. The high internal resistance and fragility of the electrode are disadvantages, but the sodium error of the glass electrode does not reduce the accuracy of potentiometric titrations because the end point of the titration is reached before the glass electrode is seriously in error. Similarly, the acid and nonaqueous solution errors can sometimes be made negligibly small.

Glass electrodes have been used in the estimation of total acidity in solutions of amino acids,[1] in insulating oils,[2] pulp liquors,[3,4] and mixtures of organic acids [5] to cite a few examples; they have also been used in related studies of the dissociation constants of hypochlorous acid,[6] chromic acid,[7] and carbonic acid; [8] in studies of cupric hydroxy-acid complexes,[9] of basic precipitates,[10] and of the oxyacids of phosphorus.[11] This list makes no claim to being exhaustive, but it

---

[1] M. S. Dunn and A. Loshakoff, *J. Biol. Chem.* **113**, 359 (1936).

[2] R. M. Evans and J. E. Davenport, *Ind. and Eng. Chem., Anal. Ed.* **8**, 287 (1936).

[3] K. Schwabe, *Wochbl. Papierfabrk.* **67**, 926 (1936).

[4] R. S. Neumann, W. A. Kargin, and E. A. Fokima, *Cellulosechem.* **17**, 16 (1936).

[5] J. M. Lupton and D. M. Smith, Private communication.

[6] J. W. Ingham and J. Morrison, *J. Chem. Soc.* **1933**, 1200.

[7] J. D. Neuss and W. Riemann, *J. Am. Chem. Soc.* **56**, 2238 (1934).

[8] D. A. MacInnes and D. Belcher, *J. Am. Chem. Soc.* **55**, 2630 (1933); **57**, 1683 (1935).

[9] C. Morton, *Trans. Faraday Soc.* **28**, 84 (1932).

[10] H. T. S. Britton and R. A. Robinson, *Trans. Faraday Soc.* **28**, 531 (1932).

[11] C. Morton, *Pharm. J.* **125**, 102 (1930); *Chemist and Druggist* **113**, 138 (1930).

is sufficient to show the versatility and usefulness of the glass electrode in this type of acidity measurement.

15·1. Glass Electrode Titration Cells

For a direct experimental potentiometric titration it is necessary that the active surface of the glass electrode be immersed in the unknown solution to be neutralized, that contact of the solution with the salt bridge solution to the calomel reference electrode be made,

that a proper opening in the titration vessel for the addition of the titrating fluid be provided, that some form of stirring be included in the procedure, that the atmosphere in the reaction chamber be controlled in some instances, and finally that the escape of volatile acids, when present, be prevented. There are numerous ways of setting up a titration apparatus; in a manufacturer's circular [12] pictures of

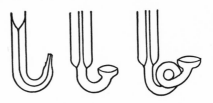

FIG. 15·1.   Capillary hooks of salt bridge.

a titration assembly show the unknown solution contained in an open beaker which is under a buret held by ring stand and clamp. The glass electrode is simply loosely laid in the beaker and a capillary hook containing the saturated potassium chloride salt bridge and turned up at the end, see Fig. 15·1, inserted into the solution. (There are now available special glass shields to protect the electrode in titrations.) The salt-bridge capillary tip is turned up at the end to prevent the lighter test solution from flowing up into the capillary tube. Fig. 15·2 illustrates a 2- or 3-ml. capacity micro-titration cup (invented by K. J. Bauer of the Abbott Laboratories), showing manner of inserting glass electrode. The micro buret is clamped above the cup, the capillary side arm allows nitrogen gas to be blown in for stirring and the connection to the salt bridge occurs *via* the bottom capillary tube.

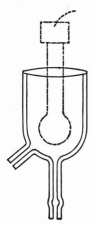

FIG. 15·2. Micro-titration cup with glass electrode.

Figure 15·3 which is self-explanatory illustrates another commercial titration assembly.[13] The tip of the salt bridge is filled with an

[12] That of the Wilkens-Anderson Co., Chicago, Ill, showing the Cameron glass electrode and accessories.

[13] That of Hellige, Inc., Long Island City, N. Y.

agar-potassium chloride jelly to prevent mixing of test solution with the salt bridge solution.   According to the directions of Michaelis and Fujita,[14] this agar jelly is made as follows: Three grams of agar are melted in 100 g. of hot water and 40 g. of potassium chloride dissolved.   After the mixture has been made uniform by stirring, it is poured into the salt-bridge tube and is allowed to solidify on cooling.   The solution in the titration vessel of Fig. 15·3 is mixed by gently shaking the flask by hand.

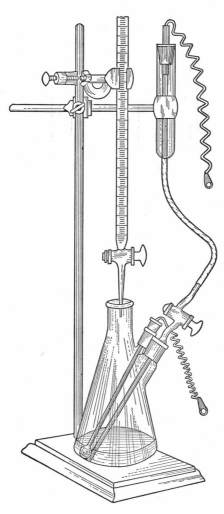

FIG. 15·3.   Titration assembly similar to that used by Lupton and Smith.

Evans and Davenport[15] have described a glass-electrode titration assembly in which water vapor can be excluded by controlling the atmosphere and volatile acids removed if desired.   In Fig. 15·4, B is the glass electrode containing a quinhydrone reference electrode, A is a silver-silver chloride reference electrode in a saturated potassium chloride solution having as solvent n-butanol, C is the capillary tip of a buret graduated to 0.02 cc., D is the acid solute in n-butanol solvent, E is a ground joint, F is an opening for the addition of sample and G is the buret.   The fluid to be titrated can be stirred by a gas stream issuing from the perforated glass tube at the bottom of the beaker or by a glass-covered ball which revolves by means of electro-magnetic action.

14 L. Michaelis and A. Fujita, *Biochem. Z.* **109**, 165 (1923).
15 R. M. Evans and J. E. Davenport, *Ind. Eng. Chem., Anal. Ed.* **8**, 287 (1936).

In Fig. 15·5 a glass electrode titration cell described by Païc [16] is illustrated. The unknown sample is placed in the right-hand compartment of the apparatus whose opening allows base from a buret to be admitted; the left-hand compartment contains a buffer solution

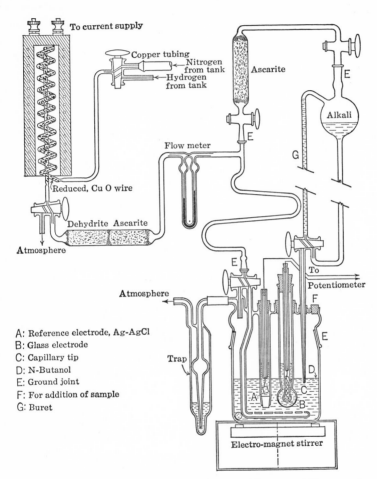

To current supply

Copper tubing
Nitrogen from tank
Hydrogen from tank

Ascarite

E

Alkali

Flow meter

G

Reduced, Cu O wire

Dehydrite Ascarite

Atmosphere

E

Atmosphere

To
Potentiometer

F

E

A: Reference electrode, Ag-AgCl
B: Glass electrode
C: Capillary tip
D: N-Butanol
E: Ground joint
F: For addition of sample
G: Buret

Trap

D

C

A

B

Electro-magnet stirrer

FIG. 15·4.   Glass electrode titration assembly of Evans and Davenport.

which is easily connected to the calomel reference electrode. The glass electrode is prepared as described in Sec. 4·5. A differential titration according to the method of Cox [19] can also be carried out in this apparatus. (See Sec. 15·2.)

[16] M. Païc, *Compt. rend.* **207**, 151 (1938).

Bowles and Partridge [17] studied the precipitation, by change of pH, of the rare earth salts with the glass electrode, stating, "two calibrations, even after a titration lasting 18 hours, were never found to vary by more than 0.02 or 0.03 pH unit and this difference was in the low and high pH regions."

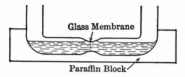

FIG. 15·5. Titration apparatus using Païc electrode.

As an example of the e.m.f. values obtained in potentiometric titrations we illustrate in Fig. 15·6 some data of Auerbach and Smolczyk's [18] pertaining to the titration of 0.1 N acetic acid with approximately 0.1 N sodium hydroxide, the hydrogen electrode being the pH indicating device. The end point of the titration

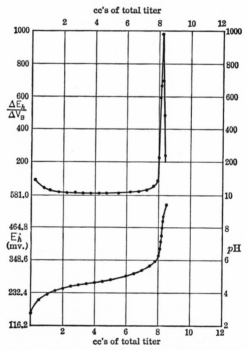

FIG. 15·6. Lower curve: Direct potentiometric titration of acetic acid. Upper curve: Slope of direct titration curve.

is the point at which the bi-logarithmic curve goes through its second inflection point; this point is more easily found, however, by plotting

[17] J. A. C. Bowles and H. M. Partridge, *Ind. Eng. Chem., Anal. Ed.* **9**, 124 (1937).
[18] Fr. Auerbach and E. Smolczyk, *Z. physik. Chem.* **110**, 65 (1924).

the change in e.m.f. ΔE_h on the addition of equal increments of base, ΔV_B as a function of total base added, see Fig. 15·6. In this case the end point is readily located by noting the total volume of base added at the maximum in the curve.

15·2. Differential Titration Cells

Although in Fig. 15·6 we have plotted differential changes in e.m.f. of the hydrogen electrode on addition of alkali thereby obtaining a so-called "differential titration curve," the differences in e.m.f. were obtained by calculation from direct e.m.f. values measured in the usual manner as described in the preceding section. Yet it is possible to measure these e.m.f. differences in a straightforward experimental way by the use of differential titration cells. The differential method was first invented by Cox,[19] shortly after modified and extended by MacInnes[20] and co-workers, applied to glass electrode titrations by MacInnes and Dole,[21] and further modified and used by Clarke, Wooten, and Compton,[22] Clarke and Wooten,[23] Hall, Jensen, and Baeckström,[24] and Païc.[25] Païc suc-

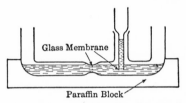

Glass Membrane

Paraffin Block

FIG. 15·7. Combination direct and differential titration assembly of Païc.

ceeded in combining two glass membranes into a single cell in such a way that a direct and potentiometric titration could be simultaneously performed, see Fig. 15·7. The differential titration was carried out according to the method of Cox[19] by adding to the acid solution in the right-hand compartment of the cell an amount of base always in a slight excess, ΔV_B, of the amount of base added to the acid solution on the left. The vertical glass electrode e.m.f. was determined by the pH of the right-hand solution while the e.m.f. across the glass membrane separating the two acid

[19] C. D. Cox, J. Am. Chem. Soc. **47**, 2138 (1925).

[20] D. A. MacInnes and P. T. Jones, J. Am. Chem. Soc. **48**, 2831 (1926); D. A. MacInnes, Z. physik. Chem. **130A**, 217 (1927): D. A. MacInnes and I. A. Cowperthwaite, J. Am. Chem. Soc. **53**, 555 (1931).

[21] D. A. MacInnes and M. Dole, Ind. Eng. Chem., Anal. Ed. **1**, 57 (1929), J. Am. Chem. Soc. **51**, 1119 (1929).

[22] B. L. Clarke, L. A. Wooten, and K. G. Compton, Ind. Eng. Chem., Anal. Ed. **3**, 321 (1931).

[23] B. L. Clarke and L. A. Wooten, J. Phys. Chem. **33**, 1468 (1929).

[24] N. F. Hall, M. A. Jensen, and S. Baeckström, J. Am. Chem. Soc., **50**, 2217 (1928).

[25] M. Païc, Compt. rend. **207**, 151 (1938).

solutions depended on the difference in pH between the two acid solutions during the titration, and was a maximum at the end point.

Clarke, Wooten, and Compton's method in the strictest sense was not entirely a differential method since they accomplished the differential measurements by using a thermionic titrimeter in which the galvanometer was set back to zero after reading the galvanometer deflections on each addition of base. They actually obtained

$$\frac{\Delta(\text{Galvanometer deflection})}{\Delta V_B}$$

and only used one hydrogen-ion indicating electrode.

A convenient differential titration cell (that of MacInnes and Dole) making use of two glass electrodes is illustrated in Fig. 15·8. E and E'

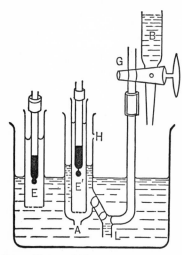

FIG. 15·8. Differential titration assembly of MacInnes and Dole.

represent two similar membrane-type glass electrodes immersed in the solution to be titrated; there is no salt bridge leading to a reference electrode and no pH measurements in this cell are possible. The solution in the main part of the beaker is carried into the small titration cell H by means of the air-lift pump L. When the solution has become uniform, the difference in e.m.f., ΔE, between the two electrodes should be zero (except for the small residual asymmetry potentials of the glass electrodes), but by turning the stopcock G in such a way as to stop the air supply and to admit base from the buret B, a difference in hydrogen-ion concentration between the main body of solution and that trapped in the little cell can be produced and an e.m.f. established. After measuring and recording this e.m.f., the air pump is started, and the solutions mixed until once again the e.m.f. returns to zero. Thus one continues repeating the whole procedure until all the acid in the beaker has been neutralized, but just at the equivalence point the addition of the constant increment of base produces the greatest difference in pH between the main body of fluid and that around the inside electrode and the maximum in ΔE between the two electrodes results. If the experimental readings are plotted as a function of base added, the end point can be found quite accurately by extrapolating the straight line drawn through the last two readings just before the end point is reached to a point of contact with a similarly extrapolated straight line drawn through the two experimental points just beyond the maximum. This procedure is illustrated in Fig. 15·9 where the excellent data obtained by Dunn

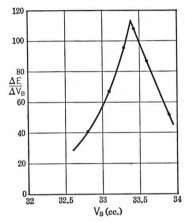

FIG. 15·9.   Electrometric formol titration of glycine with the glass electrode.

and Loshakoff [26] in an accurate formol titration of a glycine solution are illustrated.   Incidentally, use of the glass electrode constitutes a general method for the analysis of all amino acids with errors not greater than ± 0.1 per cent, whereas the error of the best of other methods has been in general five times as great.

From experimental experience, but more exactly from the approximate theoretical Eq. 15·2·1.[27]

$$\frac{dE}{d\left(\dfrac{V_B}{V_B^e}\right)_{V_B = V_B^e}} = \frac{0.059}{4.604}\sqrt{\frac{nK_A}{K_W}} \qquad [15\cdot2\cdot1]$$

where V_B is the volume of base added, V_B^e the volume of base added at the end point, K_A the acid dissociation constant, K_W the ionic product of water, and n is given by the equation

$$\frac{1}{n} = \frac{1}{N_A} + \frac{1}{N_B} \qquad [15\cdot2\cdot2]$$

[26] M. S. Dunn and A. Loshakoff, *J. Biol. Chem.* **113**, 359 (1936).
[27] P. S. Roller, *J. Am. Chem. Soc.* **50**, 1 (1928); **54**, 3485 (1932).

where N_A and N_B are the normalities of the original acid and base, it can be seen that the magnitude of ΔE at the end point in the titration of a weak acid with strong base is increased by increase in the increment of titer, by increase in concentration of the solution, by increase in the dissociation constant of the acid and decreased by increase in the value of K_W. It would probably be increased by rise of temperature. However, to find the end point accurately, it is necessary to make ΔV_B, the increment of base added, as small as possible; hence, in practice,

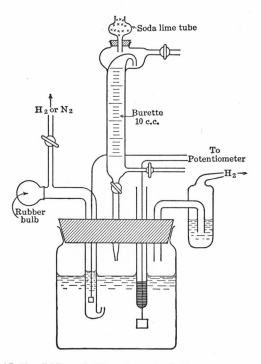

FIG. 15·10. Differential titration cell of Clarke and Wooten.

one reduces the increment of base either by reducing the volume added or by reducing the concentration of the base, to the point where the maximum of ΔE is just detectable experimentally.

Clarke and Wooten,[28] using the apparatus illustrated in Fig. 15·10, passed the inert gas nitrogen or hydrogen through their cell to stir the solution. One electrode was enclosed in a modified medicine dropper whose rubber bulb could be pressed and released to eject the trapped liquid from the inner cell or to suck in an additional sample.

[28] B. L. Clarke and L. A. Wooten, *J. Phys. Chem.* **33**, 1468 (1929).

In Table 15·1 we give some of the values of $\Delta E/\Delta V$ obtained by them in the titration of dilute solutions of the weak acetic acid.

TABLE 15·1

TITRATION OF 0.001 N ACETIC ACID BY THE DIFFERENTIAL METHOD

DATA OF CLARKE AND WOOTEN (1929)

0.001 N Ba(OH)$_2$ cc.	ΔE (Increment of Alkali 0.5 cc., Volume of Acid, 20 cc.)
17.50	4.0
19.00	6.6
19.50	8.9
20.00	14.6
20.50	16.9
21.00	22.1
21.50	18.8
22.00	16.1
22.50	9.9
23.00	7.6

The average error of their titrations of these extremely weak solutions was ±1.7 per cent.

15·3. Analysis of Acid Mixtures

Under certain conditions it is possible to analyze mixtures of acids, not only for the total acid content of the solution, but also for the separate amounts of different acids present in any given volume of the mixture. If the dissociation constants of the acids differ markedly, two end points will appear, the first end point indicating the neutralization of all of the stronger acid present and none of the weaker acid, and the second end point showing the point of complete neutralization of both acids. From the volume of base added between the two end points the normality of the weaker acid can be calculated. Acetic acid whose dissociation constant at 25° is 1.75×10^{-5} cannot be separately distinguished from the strong hydrochloric acid in water, but hypochlorous acid $(K = 3 \times 10^{-8})$ is so weak that when mixed with nitric acid and titrated with the glass electrode, two end points in the titration can be located. When the pH or e.m.f. corresponding to the neutralization of each acid present in the unknown mixture can be calculated in advance, or determined by calibration with known mixtures, it is possible to analyze the mixture by measuring the volume of base necessary to bring the solution to the predetermined pH. Schwabe [29] recommends filling the inside of the glass electrode with a

[29] K. Schwabe, *Wochbl. Papierfabrk.* **67**, 926 (1936).

solution having the correct pH of the desired end point and then titrating until the difference in e.m.f. across the glass membrane has fallen to zero; in this clever way, the end point is readily located. Schwabe also points out that two or three glass electrodes, each filled with a solution of different pH, can be immersed into the unknown substance, thus enabling the solution to be quickly analyzed for the several acids present.

In a research designed to test the possibility of analyzing mixtures by titrating with the glass electrode the separate components to the arbitrary pH 3 and the mixture itself to the same pH, Lupton and Smith [30] found that the amount of base used in the two cases was not additive, but that more base was required to bring the mixture to the pH 3 than the sum of the volumes of base used in the individual titrations. This effect, illustrated by the data of Table 15·2, was greater the weaker the acid; but by careful standardization the error of the analysis could be reduced to ± 0.2 per cent.

TABLE 15·2

ANALYSIS OF MIXTURES

DATA OF LUPTON AND SMITH (1939)

Acid Content (20 ml. each component)	Titer to reach pH 3.00	Acid Content (20 ml. each component)	Titer to reach pH 3.00
a HCl	19.82 ml.	HCl	19.8 ml.
b CCl_3COOH	20.07	$CH_2ClCOOH$	12.1
c $\Sigma(a+b)$	39.89	$\Sigma(a+b)$	31.9
d $HCl + CCl_3COOH$	40.13	$HCl + CH_2ClCOOH$	33.0
e $\Delta = d - c$	0.24	$\Delta = d - c$	1.1

By carrying out the titration of an acid mixture in a nonaqueous solution, two acid end points which coincided in the aqueous solution sometimes separate with the production of two inflections in the e.m.f. curve. In Fig. 15·11 we reproduce two curves plotted from the results of Lupton and Smith which serve to illustrate this phenomenon; curve A represents the pH of a concentrated mixture of hydrochloric and formic acids as measured with a glass electrode during a potentiometric titration using 0.5 N $NaOCH_3$ as the base. At the hydrochloric acid equivalence point the solvent was 93 per cent water and 7 per cent methanol, but the inflection point, if any existed, was not pronounced enough to detect experimentally. Yet when the titration

---

[30] Private communication from Dr. J. M. Lupton.

was carried out in methyl alcohol so that the solvent consisted of 9 per cent water and 91 per cent methanol, at the hydrochloric acid end point a marked rise in the e.m.f. occurred, enabling the concentration of hydrochloric acid in the presence of formic acid to be determined (curve B).

In Fig. 15·12 titration curves calculated from theory for the titration of mixtures of two weak acids with a strong base are given and it can be seen that when the titration curves differ by a factor of 10^3, curve 2, the intermediate inflection point is sufficiently pronounced to be experimentally observable.

Auerbach and Smolczyk [31] have derived theoretical equations which

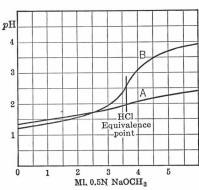

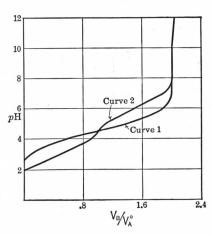

FIG. 15·11. Titration of hydrochloric-formic acid mixture. Curve A, aqueous environment; curve B, alcoholic environment.

FIG. 15·12. Theoretical titration curves of dibasic acids.

enable the percentage composition of mixtures of two weak acids to be calculated from data obtained in a single titration if the dissociation constants are known.

For the general theory of potentiometric titrations the reader is referred to the papers of Auerbach and Smolczyk, Eastman,[32] Roller,[33] Kilpi,[34] Clarke and Wooten,[35] Morton,[36] and Giraut-Erler.[37]

[31] Fr. Auerbach and E. Smolczyk, Z. physik. Chem. 110, 65 (1924).

[32] E. D. Eastman, J. Am. Chem. Soc. 47, 332 (1925); 50, 418 (1928); 56, 2646 (1934).

[33] P. S. Roller, J. Am. Chem. Soc. 50, 1 (1928); 54, 3485 (1932).

[34] S. Kilpi, Z. phys. Chem. 172A, 277 (1935); 173A, 223, 427 (1935); 174A, 441 (1935); 175A, 239 (1935); Z. anal. Chem. 104, 390 (1936).

[35] B. L. Clarke and L. A. Wooten, J. Phys. Chem. 33, 1468 (1929).

[36] C. Morton, Trans. Faraday Soc. 24, 14 (1928).

[37] L. Giraut-Erler, Compt. rend. 208, 1220, 1399 (1939).

15·4 Use of the Glass Electrode in Nonaqueous Solution Titrations

Glass electrodes made of Corning 015 glass are unsuited for the exact determination of pH in nonaqueous solutions, as has been pointed out in Chapter 8, but under certain conditions they serve as satisfactory electrodes for potentiometric analysis, inasmuch as with their aid titration end points can be located even if the absolute magnitude of the e.m.f. reading may be somewhat in error. In order to determine total acidity in insulating oil, Evans and Davenport[38] set up the e.m.f. cell (see also Fig. 15·4).

$$\text{Pt,} \atop QH_2 \cdot Q \left| {0.003\ c \atop \text{Picric Acid} \atop \text{in } n\text{-butanol}} \right| \text{Glass} \left| {\text{Oil sample} \atop \text{in} \atop n\text{-butanol}} \right\| {\text{sat. KCl} \atop \text{in} \atop n\text{-butanol}} \left| \text{AgCl} \right| \text{Ag} \quad [15 \cdot 4 \cdot A]$$

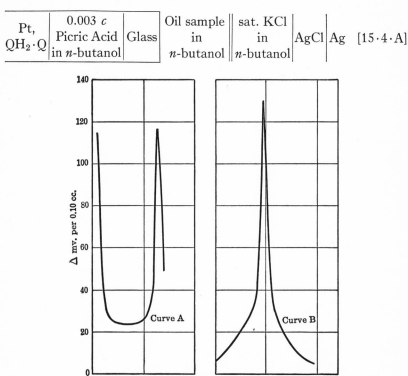

FIG. 15·13. Glass electrode titration of stearic acid in n-butanol.

in which $QH_2 \cdot Q$ represents quinhydrone. But they found that the glass-electrode potential was extremely erratic during the addition of alkali; however, when sufficient water had been formed in the neutralization reaction, the potentials became steady, the change of potential

[38] R. M. Evans and J. E. Davenport, *Ind. Eng. Chem., Anal. Ed.* **8**, 287 (1936).

uniform and end points in agreement with theory were obtained. When they used sodium butylate as the base instead of sodium hydroxide, no water formed during the titration of the acid, the potential readings fluctuated haphazardly, and no weak acid inflection point could be found. They concluded that for routine work, the nonaqueous solvent n-butanol should contain approximately 1 per cent of water by weight because of the difficulties with the glass electrode. This proportion of water was not large enough to interfere with the solubility of the insulating oil in the n-butanol. Some of their data are plotted in Fig. 15·13, where curve A represents the titration of 1 cc. of 0.0052 c stearic acid (requiring 0.63 cc. of 0.0097 c alkali, about 0.10 cc. in excess because of residual acidity in the solvent) and B represents a second titration of the same solution after 1 cc. of the acid had been added to the basic solution resulting from the first titration. Note that the presence of the sodium stearate in the second titration has reduced the ionization of stearic acid to such an extent that the sharp rise of e.m.f. on the addition of the first bit of base shown in curve A is missing from curve B, i.e., $\Delta E / \Delta V_B$ is low at the start of the titration.

Lupton and Smith have also used the glass electrode in nonaqueous solution titrations as already mentioned, see Fig. 15·11. The theoretical equations applicable to aqueous solution titrations have been found by Lupton and Smith to be applicable to water and the lower alcohols and to mixtures of these substances as solvents, but not to dioxan solutions. The glass electrode proved to be quite erratic in its potentials when immersed in dioxan with errors 0.3 to 0.5 pH. Lupton and Smith found that continued use of the glass electrode in these nonaqueous solvents induced instability in the electrode, producing changes in the asymmetry potentials and shifts in the slope of the e.m.f.-pH calibration curves. Fresh electrodes should therefore be used when dealing with nonaqueous solutions.

No difficulties were encountered by Schicktanz and Etienne [39] in the titration of whiskies using the glass electrode.

[39] S. T. Schicktanz and A. D. Etienne, *Ind. Eng. Chem.* **29**, 157 (1937).

CHAPTER 16

THE THEORY OF THE GLASS ELECTRODE

16·1. Thermodynamics of the Glass Electrode

When the glass electrode acts as a perfect hydrogen gas electrode, it is obvious that from a thermodynamic standpoint the electrode reactions for the two different types of electrodes must yield the same result; that is, the initial state of the system and the final state of the system must be exactly the same in the case of both the glass and hydrogen gas electrodes as the electrode reaction occurs regardless of

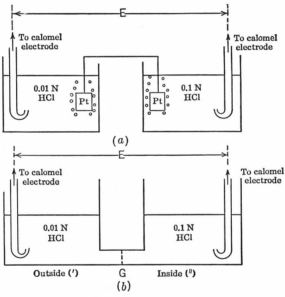

FIG. 16·1. Diagram illustrating thermodynamics of glass and hydrogen gas electrodes.

the mechanism of the reaction. By studying the thermodynamics of the hydrogen electrode, therefore, we gain an insight into the thermo-dynamics of the glass electrode.

Consider the hydrogen gas electrode system illustrated in Fig. 16·1a which is so drawn that the calomel electrode on the left is the positive electrode in contradiction to our usual convention. When positive current flows through the cell from left to right, as it does during glass electrode e.m.f. measurements when the outside reference electrode on the left is a hydrogen electrode, and the inside reference electrode a silver chloride electrode (in making any e.m.f. measurement a minute current must flow in one direction or the other in obtaining the required balance), the following reactions occur at the right and left platinum electrodes, respectively (per faraday of electricity passed).

$$\tfrac{1}{2}H_2 \rightarrow H^+ (0.1\ N) + \epsilon^- \qquad \text{(Right electrode)} \qquad [16 \cdot 1 \cdot 1]$$

$$H^+ (0.01\ N) + \epsilon^- \rightarrow \tfrac{1}{2}H_2 \qquad \text{(Left electrode)} \qquad [16 \cdot 1 \cdot 2]$$

The net result of the passage of the faraday of electricity is (neglecting the electrode reactions at the two calomel electrodes which cancel and neglecting the reactions at the two liquid junctions which do not entirely cancel, but which can not be treated thermodynamically)

$$H^+ (0.01\ N) \xrightarrow{\ H_2\ } H^+ (0.1\ N) \qquad [16 \cdot 1 \cdot 3]$$

The symbols in these equations represent one mole of hydrogen ions, and the symbol H_2 over the arrow indicates that the hydrogen is transferred in the form of unhydrated hydrogen gas. It should be noted that if the cells illustrated in Fig. 16·1 were allowed to operate spontaneously, the current would flow from right to left and the left-hand calomel electrode would be positive. For practical reasons we wish to develop this treatment in such a way that hydrogen ions pass from the outside to the inside solution as the current flows. The reason for this will be apparent when we come to consider errors of the glass electrode.

When reaction 16·1·3 occurs, there is a certain gain of chemical energy of the cell, or a gain of free energy or better still a gain of chemical potential μ_{H^+} of the hydrogen ions (the chemical potential is the partial molal free energy at constant temperature and pressure). The measured e.m.f., E, is a measure of the gain of chemical potential, the relationship being

$$\Delta\mu = -n\ FE \qquad [16 \cdot 1 \cdot 4]$$

where n is the number of faradays of electricity necessary to carry out reactions 16·1·1 and 16·1·2 as written (n equals unity here), and F is the faraday.

The chemical potential of any solute species, μ_i, is expressed in terms of the solute concentration m_i (in moles per 1000 g. of solvent) and the activity coefficient of the solute γ_i by the equation

$$\mu_i = \mu_i^0 + 2.303\ RT \log m_i\gamma_i \qquad [16 \cdot 1 \cdot 5]$$

where μ_i^0 is a constant at constant temperature, pressure and solvent. Equation 16·1·5 defines the activity coefficient γ_i. The change in chemical potential $\Delta\mu$ is defined as the chemical potential of the final state less that of the initial state, or for the reaction 16·1·3

$$\Delta\mu = \mu_{H^+(0.1\,N)} - \mu_{H^+(0.01\,N)} \qquad [16·1·6]$$

On introducing the concentration and activity coefficient by means of Eq. 16·1·5 we obtain

$$\Delta\mu = 2.303\,RT\log\frac{m_{H^+(0.1N)}\cdot\gamma_{H^+(0.1N)}}{m_{H^+(0.01N)}\,\gamma_{H^+(0.01N)}} \qquad [16·1·7]$$

which gives as the equation for E through 16·1·4

$$E = \frac{2.303\,RT}{F}\log\frac{m_{H^+(0.01N)}\,\gamma_{H^+(0.01N)}}{m_{H^+(0.1N)}\,\gamma_{H^+(0.1N)}} \qquad [16·1·8]$$

the usual equation for the hydrogen electrode e.m.f.

Equation 16·1·8 makes E negative, which is the opposite sign the cells of Fig. 16·1 would have if they operated spontaneously, but we wish to determine the e.m.f. of the glass electrode as the positive current flows in the direction, outside solution to inside solution as already mentioned above.

Consider the analogous glass electrode cell, Fig. 16·1b. Here there is no metallic connection between the two solutions, such as the platinum electrodes and wire of (a), by which the electricity might be carried, so that as the current flows through the cell the electricity is forced to pass through the high-resistant glass membrane G in order to get from one solution to the other. The e.m.f. given by the glass electrode cell will depend upon the type of ions which enter the glass at one surface and leave at the other, inasmuch as the glass is an electrolytic, not an electronic conductor; free electrons do not exist in aqueous solution nor in glass and are not involved in any phase of glass electrode theory. For the glass to act as a hydrogen electrode it is thermodynamically necessary that the net electrode reaction of the glass membrane be that of Eq. 16·1·3.

Before considering the type of ion involved and manner by which ions migrate through the glass it is first necessary to decide whether the glass can be treated as a semi-permeable membrane of negligible thickness, as was suggested by Michaelis,[1] or whether the two surfaces of the glass wall act independently of each other. By measuring the e.m.f. of the glass electrode in basic solutions where the e.m.f. is a

[1] L. Michaelis, *Naturwissenschaften* **14**, 33 (1926).

function of the concentration of sodium ions, first with no sodium ions in the solution on the other (acid) side of the glass, and second with the same sodium ion concentration in the solutions on both sides of the glass membrane the author [2] was able to demonstrate that the glass electrode does not act like a semi-permeable membrane, but that on each surface a potential difference is produced independently of the other surface. We must consider, therefore, the electrode or surface reactions at each surface of the glass wall just as in the hydrogen electrode cell, Fig. 16·1a, we considered the reactions at both platinum electrodes. Let us characterize the inside surface of the glass electrode and the inside solution (which in this chapter we shall imagine is 0.1 N hydrochloric acid), the right-hand surface of Fig. 16·1b, by the symbol ($''$), and the outer surface and solution by the symbol ($'$) and the interior of the glass itself by g.

The general equation (derived in Sec. 6·4) for the change in chemical potential of the reaction occurring at the outside wall during the passage of one faraday of electricity from the outside solution to the inside is

$$\Delta\mu' = \sum_i \int_{'}^{g} \frac{t_i}{z_i} d\mu_i \qquad [16\cdot1\cdot9]$$

where t_i is the transference number of the ith ion and z_i is the valence of the ion negative when negative. The summation is to be taken over all ionic and molecular species transferred. The valence and transference number of any molecular species are to be taken as equal to that of the ion which transfers the neutral molecule. The similar equation for the inside surface of the glass is

$$\Delta\mu'' = \sum_i \int_{g}^{''} \frac{t_i}{z_i} d\mu_i \qquad [16\cdot1\cdot10]$$

and the total change of chemical potential for the entire glass electrode cell (omitting as before liquid junction and calomel electrode reactions) is

$$\Delta\mu = \sum_i \int_{'}^{g} \frac{t_i}{z_i} d\mu_i + \sum_i \int_{g}^{''} \frac{t_i}{z_i} d\mu_i. \qquad [16\cdot1\cdot11]$$

Equation 16·1·11 is the fundamental thermodynamic equation of the glass electrode, but its evaluation presents serious difficulties in certain cases. Happily Eq. 16·1·11 is readily solved when only one ionic species is transported by the electric current across the two solution-

[2] M. Dole, *J. Am. Chem. Soc.* **53**, 4260 (1931).

glass interfaces, because under this circumstance the transference number becomes equal to unity and Eq. 16·1·11 can then be integrated.

As stated above it is necessary that reaction 16·1·3 be the only one occurring in the glass electrode cell if the glass electrode is to act as a perfect hydrogen electrode. This fundamental condition is brought about most easily by assuming that the entire current across the glass-solution interfaces is carried by the hydrogen ion, t_{H^+} equal to unity, (or by the hydroxide ion or by both acting together, see below) for then the net result of the passage of the current in the direction we are considering here, is to transfer one equivalent of hydrogen ions from the more dilute to the more concentrated solution. When t_{H^+} is equal to unity, it is easy to see that Eq. 16·1·11 reduces to Eq. 16·1·6 or to Eq. 16·1·8, the equation for the hydrogen gas electrode cell, providing $\Delta\mu_{H_2O}$ *is negligibly small* as it is in most aqueous solutions. In Sec. 16·4, we return to a consideration of the effect on the glass electrode potentials if $\Delta\mu_{H_2O}$ is not equal to zero.

However, as mentioned above there is one other way in which the fundamental reaction of the hydrogen electrode 16·1·3 can be brought about in addition to that in which the hydrogen ion only carries the electric current across the solution-glass interface. Suppose that in addition to the hydrogen ion, the hydroxyl ion can also migrate across the boundary,

$$t_{H^+} + t_{OH^-} = 1 \qquad\qquad [16·1·12]$$

instead of $t_{H^+} = 1$. Making use of the equilibrium equation

$$H_2O \rightleftarrows H^+ + OH^- \qquad\qquad [16·1·13]$$

for which we can write

$$\mu_{H^+} + \mu_{OH^-} - \mu_{H_2O} = 0 \qquad\qquad [16·1·14]$$

and

$$d\mu_{H^+} = - d\mu_{OH^-} \qquad\qquad [16·1·15]$$

since μ_{H_2O} is a constant in most aqueous solutions, we can reduce the fundamental glass-electrode equation 16·1·11 to

$$\Delta\mu = \int_{(')}^{g} t_{H^+} d\mu_{H^+} + \int_{(')}^{g} t_{OH^-} d\mu_{OH^-} + \int_{g}^{('')} t_{H^+} d\mu_{H^+}$$
$$+ \int_{g}^{('')} t_{OH^-} d\mu_{OH^-} \qquad\qquad [16·1·16]$$

or to the final desired result, Eq. 16·1·6, by means of Eqs. 16·1·12 and 16·1·15. Our present information indicates that hydroxyl ions do not take part in the electrochemical reaction of glass electrodes.

Concluding this brief account of the thermodynamics of the glass electrode we should point out that because the electrochemical reactions at the glass surface do not involve electrons, the e.m.f. of the glass electrode is unaffected by the presence of oxidizing and reducing substances and is not an oxidation-reduction potential.

16·2. The Electrode Reaction Mechanism of the Glass Electrode

The assumption that only hydrogen ions take part in the glass electrode reaction when the glass acts as a perfect hydrogen electrode is open to experimental proof. In an extensive paper entitled "Einwanderung von Ionen aus Wässriger Lösung in Glas," Quittner[3] has studied quantitatively (experimental error 5 to 10 per cent) the extent to which sodium, lithium, potassium, silver, calcium, barium, and zinc ions, as well as the hydrogen ion, can migrate into glass under the force of field strengths of 200,000 to 600,000 v./cm. Although Quittner's data were obtained under conditions of high irreversibility and cannot be treated thermodynamically or compared too closely with glass electrode data, nevertheless, they are interesting and important because they provide qualitative information of glass electrode reactions under the theoretical reversible conditions. In the case of ion migration *out of glass*, Schiller and Quittner[4] had previously demonstrated that sodium ions carried 97 to 99 per cent of the current when fields of 10^6 v./cm. were applied to ordinary glass, although in some experiments, the percentage fell as low as 69 per cent.

Quittner's experimental procedure consisted in filling the glass-bulb electrode with the solution under investigation, dipping the bulb into 0.02 N sodium sulfate which was connected by means of a salt bridge to a platinum electrode, placing within the bulb either a salt bridge to another platinum electrode or placing a platinum electrode directly into the bulb solution and running the current in such a direction that positive ions were electrolyzed out of the inside solution into the wall on the inside of the glass membrane. If sodium or ions other than the hydrogen ion carried the current exclusively across the solution-glass interface, the solution inside the bulb remained neutral unless the platinum electrode was in the bulb, in which case the solution became acid. If hydrogen ions carried the current exclusively across

[3] F. Quittner, *Ann. Physik.* [4] **85**, 745 (1928).
[4] H. Schiller, *Ann. Physik.* [4] **83**, 137 (1927).

the solution-glass interface, then the bulb solution became alkaline when a salt bridge connected it to the platinum electrode, or remained neutral if the platinum electrode was in the bulb. By titrating the test solution for its acidity or alkalinity after the electrolysis, quantitative estimates could be made of the extent to which the hydrogen or other

TABLE 16·1

PERCENTAGE OF ELECTRODE REACTION DUE TO ALKALI ION AT 52°C.
SCHOTT GLASS 59/III

DATA OF QUITTNER (1928)

Sodium Ions			Potassium Ions		
Na_2SO_4 Concn.	pH	Per Cent	K_2SO_4 Concn.	pH	Per Cent
0.001 N	Alkaline	91	0.001 N		32
0.01	Alkaline	100	0.01	Alkaline	33
			0.1		57
0.001	Acid	55	Calcium Ions		
0.01	Acid	85			
			$CaCl_2$ Concn.	pH	Per Cent
			0.01 N	Alkaline	1
Lithium Ions			Barium Ions		
Li_2SO_4 Concn.	pH	Per Cent	$Ba(NO_3)_2$ Concn.	pH	Per Cent
0.001		70	0.01 N	Alkaline	6.5
0.01	Alkaline	92			
0.1		100			

ions took part in the electrode reaction. The chief fault with Quittner's experiments was his non-control of the pH of the solutions; usually their pH continually changed during the electrolysis so that the best he could say about the electrolysis was that the experiments were carried out in either weakly acid or weakly basic solutions.

Tables 16·1 and 16·2 contain representative data from his paper (averaged results given) and it can be seen that the extent to which

TABLE 16·2

PERCENTAGE OF ELECTRODE REACTION DUE
TO SILVER, ZINC, AND COPPER IONS 52°C.

DATA OF QUITTNER (1928)

Solution	Concn.	Glass Type	pH	Per Cent
AgNO₃	N/238.3	59/III	Acid	84
AgNO₃	N/238.3	16/III	Acid	55
Zn(NO₃)₂	0.0085 N	16/III	Acid	0
CuSO₄	0.0065 N	59/III	Probably acid	0
CuSO₄	0.01067	59/III		0

the alkali ions take part in the electrode reaction is greater the greater their concentration and the more basic the solution. Divalent ions such as zinc, copper, barium, and calcium apparently do not migrate into the glasses studied (glass 59/III is a silica, borate, soda rich glass; glass 16/III is a silica, soda rich glass). Of the monovalent ions, silver, lithium, and sodium ions penetrate the glass more readily than potassium ions although the quantitative relationships depend upon the composition of the glass. When the acid concentration becomes high enough, the alkali ion transference approaches zero. This is shown in Fig. 16·2 taken from Quittner's paper.

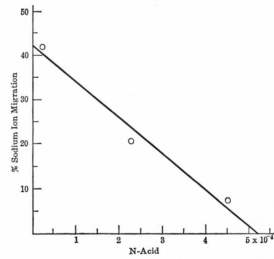

FIG. 16·2. Percentage of sodium electrode function of glass.

The percentage of the electrode reaction not due to the alkali ions is assumed to be due to the hydrogen ion. From Quittner's experiments we can conclude, therefore, that in acid solutions the hydrogen ion is the sole ion which carries the current from the solution to the glass, its transference number is unity and the glass acts as a hydrogen electrode. From the experiments in slightly acid or basic solutions containing a fairly high concentration of monovalent alkali ions, we can conclude that the current is carried to some extent by the hydrogen ion, but to a greater extent by the alkali ion, the transference number of the alkali ion tending to unity the greater its concentration and the smaller the concentration of the hydrogen ion. Under these conditions the glass electrode would act more like an alkali-ion electrode than a hydrogen electrode. The transference number of divalent ions is zero within the limits of experimental error.

From Quittner's experiments it is impossible to make any conclusions concerning the extent to which hydroxyl or other negative ions take part in glass electrode reactions, nor is it possible to estimate the extent of transfer of the solvent water molecules. Usually the question of transfer of water is unimportant because if the vapor pressure of water on both sides of the glass electrode is the same, the change in chemical potential of the water on transference will be zero and no glass electrode error will be introduced.

Thermodynamically the glass electrode problem is solved in the pH range where the transference number of the hydrogen ion is equal to unity (and $\Delta\mu_{H_2O} = 0$), but we still want to know as much as possible about the mechanism by which the glass-solution interfacial potential is developed. Here we depart from thermodynamics and enter the realm of speculation, for there is no good experimental method of studying the mechanism of electrode reactions. We probably know more concerning the mechanism of the glass electrode reaction, however, than we do concerning the mechanism of the hydrogen gas electrode reaction although very recently Walton and Wolfenden [5] have added considerable information to the hydrogen electrode problem by studying the electrolytic concentration of deuterium at various cathodes and under different conditions of temperature and current density. It would be extremely interesting to study the relative extent to which deuterium and hydrogen enter into glass electrode reactions.

We have mentioned above that the glass cannot be treated as a semi-permeable membrane, nor do we believe that it is best to consider the glass as a supercooled liquid whose surface potentials can be

[5] H. F. Walton and J. H. Wolfenden, *J. Chem. Soc.* **1937**, 1677; *Trans. Faraday Soc.* **34**, 436 (1938).

treated as ordinary liquid-junction potentials. Glass is a solid with an irregular, although definite, structure; according to Zachariasen [6] the atoms or ions in glass are linked together by essentially the same forces as in crystals and oscillate about definite equilibrium positions over large ranges of temperature. Extended three dimensional networks of silicon atoms or ions surrounded by oxygen tetrahedra form the glass structure as illustrated in Fig. 16·3, taken from Zachariasen's paper. As the glass is built up the "holes" in the open framework are occupied by cations such as the alkali cations without, however, it being required that any definite number of the cations incorporate

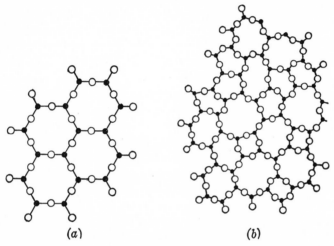

(a)   (b)

FIG. 16·3. (a) Lattice of two-dimensional crystal Al_2O_3; (b) lattice of the same compound *in vitreo*.

themselves into the framework (except enough to satisfy the requirement of electro-neutrality). The electrical current through the glass is carried by the alkali cations migrating from one equilibrium position to another, the silicon and oxygen atoms or silicate ions are held in a presumably rigid structure.

For an understanding of the glass electrode we are chiefly concerned with the equilibria that exist on the surface of the glass when the glass is in contact with an aqueous solution. By applying to the glass elec-

---

[6] W. H. Zachariasen, *J. Am. Chem. Soc.* **54**, 3841 (1932); see also B. E. Warren, H. Krutter and O. Morningstar, *J. Am. Ceram. Soc.* **19**, 202 (1936). For a general discussion of the structure of glass the reader is referred to "Crystal Chemistry," by C. W. Stillwell, McGraw-Hill Book Co., New York, 1938. See also B. E. Warren, *Chem. Rev.* **26**, 237 (1940).

trode, *mutatis mutandis*, Gurney's [7] ideas concerning energy states of ions in solution and on metal surfaces and his ideas concerning the mechanism by which interfacial potentials are produced the author [8] was able to develop a picture of glass elec-trode behavior.   When a metal ion is brought from a vacuum toward a metal, its potential energy will fall, Fig. 16·4, owing to the mirror-image attraction that exists between the metal and the ion until the close-range repulsive forces between the ion

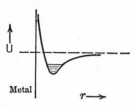

FIG. 16·4.   Potential en-ergy of ion near a metal.

and the metal come into play when the po-tential energy will rise rapidly.   Somewhere along the curve will be a potential energy minimum (or potential energy valley if one considers the phenomenon to be three-dimensional) which represents the equilib-rium position of the ion on the metal surface. The ion will oscillate or vibrate on the surface in its equilibrium position, giving rise to the various vibrational-rotational energy levels illustrated in Fig. 16·4.   Similarly, if the ion is brought from a vacuum toward a water mole-cule, Fig. 16·5, a similar potential energy-dis-

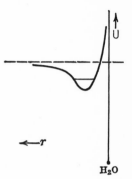

FIG. 16·5.   Potential en-ergy of ion near a water molecule.

tance curve will be obtained.   When the two curves of Figs. 16·4 and 16·5 are combined, Fig. 16·6*a*, *b*, and *c*, three possibilities exist.   If

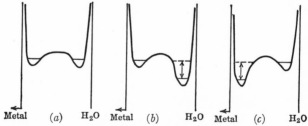

Metal   (*a*) H_2O Metal   (*b*) H_2O Metal   (*c*) H_2O

FIG. 16·6.   Combined potential energy curves of ion.

the ground level for the ion-metal is at the same height as the ground level for the ion-water combination, Fig. 16·6*a*, equilibrium will exist and there will be no net tendency for the ion to make transitions in

[7] R. W. Gurney, "Ions in Solution," Cambridge University Press, 1936; *Proc. Roy. Soc.* **A136**, 378 (1932); **A134**, 137 (1931).

[8] M. Dole, *J. Chem. Phys.* **2**, 862 (1934).

either direction, but if the ion on the metal surface is in a higher energy state than a vacant level in the solution, Fig. 16·6b, the ion will make the transition, metal to solution, charging the solution positively and the metal negatively and thus building up the potential of the interface. Figure 16·6c represents the converse case in which the metal would become positively charged and the solution negatively charged. Transitions of ions in one or the other direction will continue until the difference of electrical potential brings about equality in height of the potential energy levels, and brings the system to equilibrium. Not all the ions in the solution at any one instant will have the same potential energy, but will be presumably distributed in the various possible energy states according to the Boltzmann distribution law. Concentration of the ions will thus affect the interfacial potential.

Carrying these ideas over to the glass electrode problem, one need only to postulate that equilibrium positions for the hydrogen ion exist on the glass surface as well as in solution and that the Boltzmann factor can be applied in this case also. At equilibrium the tendency for hydrogen ions to make transitions from the solution to the glass surface will just be balanced by the repulsive forces of the interfacial potential; in this way the hydrogen electrode function is developed on the glass surface.

The mathematical treatment of the author which is closely similar to Gurney's treatment for metals will not be duplicated here in as much as it leads to the usual equations for the hydrogen electrode; interesting results were obtained, however, on applying the theory to basic solutions where transitions of ions other than the hydrogen ion have to be considered. This theory for basic solutions is given in the following section.

16·3. Theory of the Glass Electrode in Basic Solutions

In basic solutions the concentration of the hydrogen ions is extremely low, that of the alkali ion comparatively high with the result that the alkali ion takes a considerable part in the electrode reaction as the data of Quittner cited above prove. We must consider, therefore, the effect of transitions of the sodium ion to the glass surface and the mechanism by which these transitions influence the glass electrode e.m.f. When the pH is 12, let us say, there are only 10^{-12} equivalents of hydrogen ion per liter of solution, an extraordinarily small concentration; when hydrogen ions make transitions from the glass to the solution, called s-transitions, there will be relatively few to make the opposite transition, called d-transitions, but the negative charge left on the glass will attract positive ions, causing the alkali ions present in the solution to make d-transitions (solution to glass transitions) and to take the place of the hydrogen ions on the glass surface. By means of these ionic exchanges the glass will pass over from a hydrogen electrode to that of a mixed hydrogen-sodium electrode, or if the exchange has progressed far enough, to a complete sodium electrode. When the current flows across the boundary, it will be carried mostly by sodium ions and the transference number of the hydrogen ion will only be a small fraction of unity. It is possible to express these ideas, some of which have been rather vaguely advanced by other writers (for a historical review of glass electrode theories, see Dole)[9] rather precisely by means of either a statistical or thermodynamic method, the two treatments being fundamentally equivalent and leading to identical results.

If part of the glass surface is covered by sodium ions, the number of s-situations for hydrogen ions is diminished. Let the fraction of unit surface covered by hydrogen ions be γ, then the number of s-situations between the energy levels U and $U + dU$ becomes

$$\gamma \left(\frac{N_W}{RT}\right) \exp. \left\{\frac{U_{\mathrm{H}}^{og} + FE' - U}{RT}\right\} dU \qquad [16\cdot3\cdot1]$$

where N_W is the number of water molecules in contact with unit area of surface, U_{H}^{og} is the energy of the lowest quantum level of the hydrogen ion on the glass surface, F the faraday, and E' the interfacial potential taking the potential of the electrolyte as zero (the factor $1/RT$ is introduced to make Eq. 16·3·1 dimensionless). For the sodium ions we have the similar relation

$$(1 - \gamma)\left(\frac{N_W}{RT}\right)\exp. \left\{\frac{U_{\mathrm{Na}}^{og} + FE' - U}{RT}\right\} dU \qquad [16\cdot3\cdot2]$$

The number of d-situations for the hydrogen and sodium ions can be expressed by the equations

$$\frac{N_{\mathrm{H}^+}}{RT} \exp. \left\{\frac{U_{\mathrm{H}}^{os} - U}{RT}\right\} dU \qquad [16\cdot3\cdot3a]$$

$$\frac{N_{\mathrm{Na}^+}}{RT} \exp. \left\{\frac{U_{\mathrm{Na}}^{os} - U}{RT}\right\} dU \qquad [16\cdot3\cdot3b]$$

where N_{H^+} and N_{Na^+} are the number of hydrogen and sodium ions per unit area of solution in contact with the glass surface. Equating

[9] M. Dole, *J. Am. Chem. Soc.* **53**, 4260 (1931); *J. Chem. Phys.* **2**, 862 (1934); *J. Am. Chem. Soc.* **54**, 3095 (1932).

expression 16·3·1 to 16·3·3a and 16·3·2 to 16·3·3b to express a state of equilibrium and setting

$$Q_H = U_H^{os} - U_H^{og} \qquad [16·3·4]$$

and

$$Q_{Na} = U_{Na}^{os} - U_{Na}^{og} \qquad [16·3·5]$$

we obtain

$$\gamma = c_H \exp. \frac{Q_H - FE'}{RT} \qquad [16·3·6]$$

and

$$1 - \gamma = c_{Na} \exp. \frac{Q_{Na} - FE'}{RT} \qquad [16·3·7]$$

By adding we eliminate γ, the fraction of the surface covered by the sodium ions

$$c_H \exp. \frac{Q_H - FE'}{RT} + c_{Na} \exp. \frac{Q_{Na} - FE'}{RT} = 1 \qquad [16·3·8]$$

If the sodium-ion term of Eq. 16·3·8 is negligible, we obtain the equation for the hydrogen-ion function of the glass electrode,

$$c_H \exp. \frac{Q_H - FE}{RT} = 1 \qquad [16·3·9]$$

In Sec. 7·2 we defined the error of glass electrode, ΔE, by the equation

$$\Delta E = E' - E$$

Dividing Eq. 16·3·8 by 16·3·9 and rearranging we have

$$\Delta E = 2.3 \frac{RT}{F} \log \left(\frac{c_{Na} e^{(Q_{Na} - Q_H)/RT} + c_H}{c_H} \right) \qquad [16·3·10]$$

as the equation for the alkaline (sodium) error of the glass electrode given by this statistical theory. Equation 16·3·10 states that the glass electrode error will be greater the greater the concentration of sodium ions, the smaller the hydrogen-ion concentration and the higher the temperature, all in qualitative agreement with the facts. The error will also depend upon the type of ion present since the Q values are different for different ions. Equation 16·3·10 gives quantitatively the order of magnitude of the error if Q_H is greater than Q_{Na} by 15,000 calories per mole (both of these quantities must be positive, the potential energy of the ions on the glass surface being lower than in the solution). Unfortunately the quantity $Q_{Na} - Q_H$ cannot be determined by an independent experiment, nor can it be calculated; it must remain an empirical parameter chosen to fit the data.

By writing Eq. 16·3·10 in the form

$$\log (e^{F\Delta E/RT} - 1) = \log c_{Na}e^{(Q_{Na}-Q_H)/RT} + pH \qquad [16·3·11]$$

it is possible to test the theory graphically since Eq. 6·3·11 is the equation of a straight line if the pH and $\log (e^{F\Delta E/RT} - 1)$ are chosen as the variables. The author measured ΔE under conditions of constant c_{Na} so the data of Table 7·2 can be used in connection with Eq. 16·3·11. In Fig. 16·7 such a test of the theory is carried out in

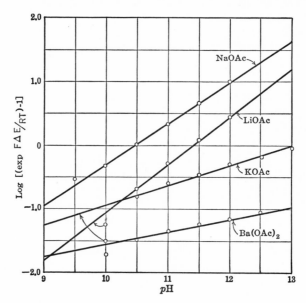

Fig. 16·7. Test of eq. 16·3·11.

connection with various acetate solutions all one normal in concentration. The linear agreement is good, except that the slope of the curves is not unity as demanded by Eq. 16·3·11. No quantitative explanation of the deviation of the slopes from unity has yet been advanced.

It is also possible to test Eq. 16·3·11 by measuring the glass electrode errors over a range of temperatures since the absolute temperature occurs as one of the parameters of the theory.

[10] M. Dole and B. Z. Wiener, *Trans. Electrochem. Soc.* **72**, 107 (1937).

In Fig. 16·8 the data of Dole and Wiener [10] for 1 N sodium phosphate solutions at 25 and 50°C. are plotted according to Eq. 16·3·11 with satisfactory agreement.   In Table 16·3 values of $Q_H - Q_{Na}$ cal-

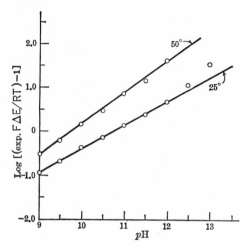

FIG. 16·8. Test of eq. 16·3·11.

culated by means of Eq. 16·3·11 from the experimental data for 1 N sodium phosphate solutions are given so that the extent of variation of the Q quantities may be seen.

TABLE 16·3

VALUES OF $Q_H - Q_{Na}$ IN K CALORIES PER MOLE

pH	0.5 cNa$_2$HPO$_4$	
	25°	50°
9	13.515	14.084
10	14.127	14.512
11	14.808	14.980
12	15.401	15.332
13	15.660	

These variations in $Q_H - Q_{Na}$ are greater than the experimental error as can be seen from the calculations tabulated in Table 16·4. Here the ΔE's at 50°C. were calculated by means of Eq. 16·3·11 taking the Q values at 25°C. at each pH as being correct.   Good agreement is obtained at high pH values in the case of the sodium solutions and at low pH values in the case of the lithium solutions, but considerable discrepancies exist in the other pH ranges.

TABLE 16·4

COMPARISON OF CALCULATED WITH OBSERVED VALUES OF ΔE IN MILLIVOLTS AT 50°C.

DATA OF DOLE AND WIENER (1937)

pH	1.0 N Li$^+$		1.0 N Na$^+$	
	$\Delta E_{obs.}$	$\Delta E_{calc.}$	$\Delta E_{obs.}$	$\Delta E_{calc.}$
9.0	....	....	7.1	14.9
9.5	8.0	6.8	12.9	23.3
10.0	17.2	13.7	25.4	36.6
10.5	30.1	23.4	39.0	50.5
11.0	46.0	39.8	58.5	65.2
11.5	67.5	59.3	75.5	81.0
12.0	97.5	80.0	104.4	101.5
12.5	125.0	102.4	.....	.....

Nicolsky [11] in his thermodynamic theory of the basic solution behavior of the glass electrode makes use of the ionic electrochemical potential, $\bar{\mu}_i$, defined in the usual way (See Sec. 6·1.)

$$\bar{\mu}_i = \mu_i + z_i F \psi \qquad [16·3·12]$$

where μ_i is the chemical potential of the ion, z_i its valence and ψ the electrostatic potential of the homogeneous phase in which the ion is immersed. Thus we can write for the ionic-exchange equilibrium existing on the glass surface (denoting the glass phase by a single prime)

$$\bar{\mu}'_{H^+} = \bar{\mu}_{H^+} \qquad [16·3·13]$$

$$\bar{\mu}'_{Na^+} = \bar{\mu}_{Na^+} \qquad [16·3·14]$$

or introducing Eq. 16·3·12

$$FE = F(\psi' - \psi) = \mu_{H^+} - \mu'_{H^+} = \mu_{Na^+} - \mu'_{Na^+} \qquad [16·3·15]$$

Since

$$\mu_i = \mu_i^o + RT \ln c_i \cdot f_i \qquad [16·3·16]$$

and

$$\mu'_i = \mu_i^{o,'} + RT \ln c'_i \cdot f'_i \qquad [16·3·17]$$

[11] B. Nicolsky, *Acta Physicochim. U. R. S. S.* **7**, 597 (1937).

we have

$$RT \ln \frac{c'_{H^+} \cdot c'_{Na^+}}{c'_{H^+} \cdot c_{Na^+}} \cdot \frac{f_{H^+} \cdot f'_{Na^+}}{f'_{H^+} \cdot f_{Na^+}} = \mu^{o,'}_{H^+} - \mu^o_{H^+} + \mu^o_{Na^+} - \mu^{o,'}_{Na^+} = RT \ln K$$

$$[16\cdot3\cdot18]$$

The constant K, which Nicolsky calls "the constant of the sodium- and hydrogen-ion exchange" is the usual mass action law constant for the equilibrium reaction

$$H^+(\text{solution}) + Na^+(\text{glass}) \rightleftarrows H^+(\text{glass}) + Na^+(\text{solution}) \quad [16\cdot3\cdot19]$$

From $16\cdot3\cdot15$

$$FE = \mu^o_{H^+} - \mu^{o,'}_{H^+} + RT \ln \frac{c_{H^+} \cdot f_{H^+}}{c'_{H^+} \cdot f'_{H^+}} \qquad [16\cdot3\cdot20]$$

The concentration of the hydrogen and sodium ions in the glass and their activity coefficients are unknown, but the activity coefficients in the glass phase may be eliminated by defining the $\mu^{o,'}$ values in such a way that the f'_i's are equal to unity. Probably the activity coefficient of a sodium ion in the glass depends almost entirely on its interaction with its nearest anion, and very little on the replacement of other sodium ions by hydrogen ions. We can consider, therefore, the ionic activity coefficients in the glass constant, and, by choice of the appropriate $\mu^{o,'}_i$ equal to unity.

Since electro-neutrality exists in the glass phase, we can write

$$c'_{H^+} + c'_{Na^+} = c'_o \qquad [16\cdot3\cdot21]$$

where c'_o is a constant.

From Eqs. $16\cdot3\cdot18$ and $16\cdot3\cdot21$ we can obtain the equation

$$\frac{c_{H^+}f_{H^+}}{c'_{H^+}} = \frac{c_{Na^+} \cdot f_{Na^+}K + c_{H^+} \cdot f_{H^+}}{c_o} \qquad [16\cdot3\cdot22]$$

which, when introduced into Eq. $16\cdot3\cdot20$ gives

$$FE = \mu^o_{H^+} - \mu^{o,'}_{H^+} - RT \ln c_o + RT \ln (c_{Na^+} \cdot f_{Na^+}K + c_{H^+} \cdot f_{H^+}) \quad [16\cdot3\cdot23]$$

or

$$E = E^o + \frac{RT}{F} \ln (c_{Na^+} \cdot f_{Na^+}K + c_{H^+} \cdot f_{H^+}). \qquad [16\cdot3\cdot24]$$

If the concentration, c_{Na^+}, of the sodium ion in the aqueous solution is zero, Eq. $16\cdot3\cdot24$ reduces to the usual hydrogen electrode equation.

$$E = E^o + \frac{RT}{F} \ln c_{H^+} \cdot f_{H^+} = E^o - 2.3 \frac{RT}{F} pH \qquad [16\cdot3\cdot25]$$

Subtracting $16\cdot3\cdot25$ from $16\cdot3\cdot24$ we obtain an equation identical with $16\cdot3\cdot10$ which was derived on the basis of Gurney's statistical method (with the exception that activity coefficients were omitted from 16·3·10).

If the hydrogen-ion concentration is very low, pH high, Eq. 16·3·24 reduces to

$$E = \text{const.} + \frac{RT}{F} \ln c_{Na^+} \cdot f_{Na^+} \qquad [16·3·26]$$

the equation of a pure sodium electrode. In the case of glass electrodes composed of glass of certain types, the sodium electrode function is highly developed and Eq. 16·3·26 is verified (at least roughly) but with Corning 015 glass, no one has yet proved that the electrodes give potentials entirely independent of the pH even in solutions of high pH and high sodium-ion concentration.

For intermediate cases of mixed electrode functions, Nicolsky makes the following approximate calculations. In basic solutions of sodium hydroxide,

$$c_{Na^+} \cdot f_{Na^+} \sim c_{OH} \cdot f_{OH} = \frac{K_W}{c_{H^+} \cdot f_{H^+}} \qquad [16·3·27]$$

substituting this relation into 16·3·24, we obtain

$$E = E^o + \frac{RT}{F} \ln \left\{ c_{H^+} f_{H^+} + \frac{K\,K_W}{c_{H^+} \cdot f_{H^+}} \right\} \qquad [16·3·28]$$

This equation reduces at high pH to the following simple expression

$$E = \text{const.} - \frac{RT}{F} \ln c_{H^+} \cdot f_{H^+} = \text{const.} + 2.3 \frac{RT}{F} p\text{H} \qquad [16·3·29]$$

By comparing Eq. 16·3·29 with Eq. 16·3·25 we see that the e.m.f. of the glass electrode cell first increases with rise of pH (taking the sign of the saturated calomel electrode) and then decreases; hence the e.m.f.-pH curve should go through a maximum in the case of the experiments where the sodium-ion concentration is *not* maintained constant, e.g., sodium hydroxide added to hydrochloric acid. Such a maximum has been frequently observed.

Other mathematical equations for the alkaline solution behavior have been given by Gross and Halpern,[12] Urban and Steiner,[13] Jewstropiev and Suikovskaja,[14] and Powney and Jordan.[15]

[12] P. Gross and O. Halpern, *J. Chem. Phys.* **2**, 136 (1934).

[13] F. Urban and A. Steiner, *J. Phys. Chem.* **35**, 3058 (1931).

[14] Jewstropiev and Suikovskaja, *Works of State Optical Institute (Leningrad)* **10**, 23 (1934) (Quoted by Nicolsky).

[15] J. Powney and D. O. Jordan, *J. Soc. Chem. Ind.* **56**, 133T (1937); D. O. Jordan, *Trans. Faraday Soc.* **34**, 1305 (1938).

The equation for the glass electrode errors published by Jordan is an especially useful one inasmuch as it serves as a more convenient tool for the calculation of glass electrode-alkaline correction factors than does Eq. 16·3·10. This equation, which is (see Sec. 7·4).

$$\log \Delta E = A\, pH' + B \log m - C \qquad [16\cdot3\cdot30]$$

where A, B, and C are empirical constants, m the concentration of alkali ion and pH' is the erroneous pH as observed with the glass electrode, has no exact theoretical basis, but can be easily shown to be an approximate form of Eq. 16·3·11 by expanding the exponential term of the latter in a series, dropping all terms of the expansion beyond the first, and substituting pH' for pH. These two approximations introduce errors acting in opposite directions and so tend to make the resulting equation more valid; in fact, the agreement of the equation with the data is surprisingly good, see Fig. 16·9, except at the very high pH values where it fails completely (because in this range pH' becomes practically constant).

In Sec. 4·2 and Fig. 4·5 we have discussed the glass-solubility measurements as a function of pH carried out by Hubbard, Hamilton, and Finn [16] who found that the solubility-pH curve had a trend very similar to that of the ΔE-pH curve;

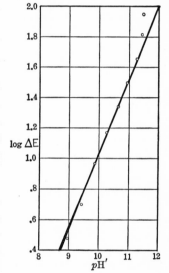

FIG. 16·9. Test of eq. 16·3·30 for 1 N Na$^+$ solutions. (Data of Dole and Wiener, 1937.)

that is, the rapid attack of the glass by the hot (80°) alkaline solution began at a pH of 8 or 9 and increased markedly with rising pH.   On the basis of this and other analogies to be mentioned in Sec. 16·4, Hubbard, Hamilton, and Finn concluded, "In all cases that have been studied voltage departures of the glass electrode have been found to be associated with marked changes in the solubility of the glass. This leads the authors to believe that the variations in magnitude of the voltage departures of the glass electrode in the presence of different ions are primarily caused by solubility differences of the glass produced by these ions and not by an

[16] D. Hubbard, E. H. Hamilton, and A. N. Finn, *J. Research Natl. Bur. Standards*, **22**, 339 (1939).

equilibrative response of the electrode to ions other than hydrogen."
However, the authors did not consider the effect of solubility differences on the thermodynamic aspects of the glass electrode discussed
above, nor did they suggest a mechanism by which change of solubility
could affect the e.m.f. Furthermore, it is possible that ionic exchanges
of hydrogen and alkali ion between the glass and the water solution
might be responsible for the glass corrosion as well as for the voltage
departures. Sodium silicate is more soluble than silicic acid and as
sodium ions exchange with hydrogen ions, giving the glass surface a
mixed electrode function, the glass surface also becomes more soluble.
At not too high pH values or temperatures the ionic surface equilibrium
is probably established more rapidly than the glass dissolves, so that
although we are not dealing with complete equilibrium in the strict
thermodynamic sense, the e.m.f. data are reproducible and do have
theoretical significance.

16·4. Theory of the Glass Electrode in Acid and Nonaqueous Solutions

In studying the negative errors exhibited by the glass electrode in
very acid, strong salt or nonaqueous solutions, the author [17] found
that these errors did not depend in any direct way upon the concentration of positive, negative or hydrogen ions, and he concluded, therefore, that the negative errors must be caused by a decrease in the
chemical potential or vapor pressure of the water in the solution in
contact with the glass surface. This conclusion was tested by adding
ethyl alcohol to the solution at constant pH, and measuring the error
which was found to be negative in sign and entirely similar to the
errors produced by adding concentrated acids to the solution. If the
chemical potential of the water is lowered by adding a concentrated
salt solution, negative errors are again observed even at intermediate
pH values.

The only mechanism, by which, thermodynamically, a change in the
chemical potential of the water can affect the e.m.f. of the glass electrode in a different way than it affects the e.m.f. of a hydrogen electrode and thus produce an error of the glass electrode is by water
taking part in the glass electrode reaction. We know that water is
not involved in the hydrogen electrode reaction; that is, we know that
water is not transferred from one solution to the other via the hydrogen
gas electrodes, but there is a distinct possibility that water takes part
in the glass electrode reaction and that as the hydrogen ion migrates
from the solution to the glass surface it carries water along with it.

[17] M. Dole, *J. Am. Chem. Soc.* **54**, 3095 (1932).

Although thermodynamics is not concerned with the mechanism of electrode reactions, it is essential that one know the final and initial states of the system in order to derive the correct e.m.f. equations. Instead of writing the glass electrode reaction as

$$H^+(0.01N) \xrightarrow{\text{H}_2} H^+(0.1N)$$

as we did in Sec. 16·1, perhaps we should write it as

$$H^+(0.01N) + H_2O(P'_{H_2O}) \xrightarrow{p(H_2O)^+} H^+(0.1N) + H_2O(P''_{H_2O})$$

where the symbol $p(H_2O)^+$ over the arrow indicates that the unit that is to be transferred is the proton hydrated with one molecule of water. The change in chemical potential for the reaction as written is

$$\Delta\mu = \mu_{H^+(0.1N)} - \mu_{H^+(0.01N)} + \mu_{H_2O(P'')} - \mu_{H_2O(P')} \quad [16\cdot4\cdot1]$$

On introducing the concentration, activity coefficients, vapor pressures, and e.m.f. we obtain

$$E = \frac{2.303RT}{F} \log \frac{m_{H^+(0.01N)}\gamma_{H^+(0.01N)}}{m_{H^+(0.1N)}\gamma_{H^+(0.1N)}} + \frac{2.303RT}{F} \log \frac{P'_{(H_2O)}}{P''_{(H_2O)}} \quad [16\cdot4\cdot2]$$

Since the chemical potential of the water can be represented by the equation

$$\mu_{H_2O} = \mu^o_{H_2O} + RT \ln P_{H_2O} \quad [16\cdot4\cdot3]$$

where P_{H_2O} is the vapor pressure of the water at the temperature T and μ^o is a constant independent of concentration but not of temperature, or total external pressure. Equation 16·4·3 is valid as long as the water vapor behaves as a perfect gas which it does closely enough for all the purposes of this book.

Equation 16·1·8 is the equation of the true hydrogen electrode and if we subtract it from 16·4·2 we obtain an equation for the error of the glass electrode as a function of the vapor pressure of the water provided hydrogen is transferred as the current flows from one solution to the other through the glass electrode as a proton hydrated with one molecule of water. Thus

$$\Delta E = E_{(16\cdot4\cdot2)} - E_{(16\cdot1\cdot8)} = \frac{2.303RT}{F} \log \frac{P'_{(H_2O)}}{P''_{(H_2O)}} \quad [16\cdot4\cdot4]$$

Equation 16·4·4 is identical with Eq. 8·2·1 if we maintain the vapor pressure of the solution inside the glass electrode practically equal to that of pure water, $P'' = P_o$, for then we can write Eq. 16·4·4

$$\Delta E = 2.3 \frac{RT}{F} \log a_{H_2O} \qquad [16·4·5]$$

where a_{H_2O} is the activity of the water in the outside solution,

$$a_{H_2O} = \frac{P'}{P_o} \qquad [16·4·6]$$

Equation 16·4·5 predicts that the negative errors of the glass electrode should be directly proportional to the logarithm of the activity of the water, the slope of the line being equal to 2.3 RT/F or 0.05914 at 25°C.

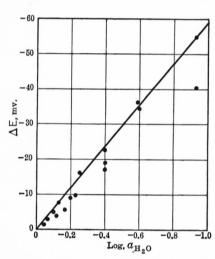

FIG. 16·10. Negative errors of the glass electrode as a function of activity of the water.

In Fig. 16·10 the solid line represents the errors calculated by means of Eq. 16·4·5 (in this calculation no constants were chosen to make the theory fit the data) while the solid circles are the experimental points. The data necessary to prepare this graph were taken from Table 8·1. The agreement seems to be good enough to substantiate the postulate that as hydrogen ions migrate from the solution to the glass surface, one water molecule per proton is carried along.

The theory can be further tested by measuring the negative errors as a function of temperature. If the errors are produced by migration of ions other than the hydrogen ion into glass as they are in alkaline solution, we might expect the negative errors to be much greater at the higher temperatures by analogy with the behavior in the alkaline region, but if the errors are produced by a decrease in the vapor pressure of water, there will not be much change on going to the higher temperatures because the vapor pressure ratios do not change very much with change of temperature. Dole and Wiener [18] measured the negative errors of the glass electrode at 50°C. in sulfuric acid solutions,

[18] M. Dole and B. Z. Wiener, *Trans. Electrochem. Soc.* **72**, 107 (1937).

and found no appreciable increase in the errors over those at 25°C. (See Fig. 9·6.) Thus the water transference theory of the negative errors of Corning 015 glass electrodes seems to be well substantiated.

When glass electrodes exhibit no negative errors in solutions of low water activity, we can conclude that the hydrogen ion migrates through the glass as an unhydrated proton.

Hubbard, Hamilton, and Finn [19] discovered that the solution attack on Corning 015 glass becomes zero at a pH of 8 and at lower pH values, between 2 and 6, the solution causes a slight swelling of the glass. In solutions of still lower pH, in the very acid range, the swelling of the glass is repressed, the attack-pH curve having a trend similar to that of the glass electrode error-pH curve, see Fig. 4·6, for the acid solutions studied. Strong salt solutions and alcoholic solutions also repress the swelling as well as produce a negative error of the glass electrode. Furthermore, some glasses which cause neither a swelling nor an attack of the glass exhibit no voltage departures in the acid range. Thus there is a general correlation between the glass solubility studies of Hubbard, Hamilton, and Finn and the electromotive behavior of the glass electrode, but there seems to be no direct evidence that glass electrode errors in acid, strong salt, and nonaqueous solutions are caused by the repression of the swelling. In all of these solutions the activity of the water is reduced with the consequent production of the glass electrode error, and possibly the swelling of the glass is also reduced for the same reason. In the case of Hubbard, Hamilton, and Finn's glass A for which the negative glass electrode error is zero, we can assume that water cannot penetrate the glass either to produce a swelling or a glass-electrode error.

The attack of the glass by the hydrogen fluoride solutions is probably so vigorous that thermodynamic equilibrium is prevented from being established.[20,21]

[19] D. Hubbard, E. H. Hamilton, and A. N. Finn, *J. Research Natl. Bur. Standards*, **22**, 339 (1939).

[20] For an interesting study of the electromotive behavior of glass electrodes of different compositions in fused lead chloride containing lithium, sodium, and potassium salts see B. v. Lengyel and A. Sammt, *Z. physik. Chem.* **181A**, 55 (1937).

[21] G. Haugaard, *J. Phys. Chem.* **45**, 148 (1941), has recently published data which indicate that sodium ions from a fresh glass surface exchange with hydrogen ions of the solution until equilibrium with respect to both this reaction and the establishment of the electrode e.m.f. has been attained.

CHAPTER 17

SIGNIFICANCE AND STANDARDIZATION OF THE pH SCALE

17·1. Why Do We Measure pH Numbers?

Before giving specific details for the standardization of glass electrodes and before describing the general methods for the standardization of the pH scale itself, let us consider the purpose of pH measurements and the uses to which pH values are put. Some of the significance of pH will then be understood, more of it when standardization methods have been scrutinized and finally our concept will become complete after a short discussion of attempts to develop a general acidity scale valid for all solvents.

Listing the uses of pH determinations in the order of their frequency we have:

First, pH measurements are carried out to indicate relative changes in acidity or alkalinity from sample to sample, from day to day in the same sample, or to bring different samples to the same pH value. Thus we measure the pH of blood of a patient as a measure of corresponding physiological changes in the organism; we measure the pH of food preparations to detect any variation from the norm, we measure the pH continuously so that variations in pH taking place within a few seconds can be discovered and automatically recorded. This type of pH measurement we shall call *relative* pH *measurements;* they are perhaps the most important practically, but at the same time the most difficult to interpret theoretically.

Second, we frequently make what may be called definite pH measurements in which we are more interested in the exact value of the pH than we are in small variations. If we wish to compare our pH numbers with those obtained by other workers on similar media, we have to standardize our method by some previously adopted procedure, because comparison of numbers based on different standards and obtained under different experimental conditions would be meaningless. Perhaps we can say that most published pH values are of this class; the authors present their material with the expectation that other workers will be able to reproduce their results and that their work is of some permanent significance. To make *definite p*H *measurements,* may be said to be the goal of most of those scientists who intend to preserve for posterity a record of their studies of acidity.

Third, having made definite *p*H measurements, not a few calculate or attempt to calculate from the *p*H the activity (concentration × activity coefficient) of the hydrogen ion. We group in this class all calculations of *pK* or ionization constants of acids and bases since under the usual experimental conditions the ionization constant can be obtained rather directly once the activity of the hydrogen ion is known. Application of the knowledge of the hydrogen ion activity obtained by *p*H measurements to other types of aqueous equilibria also belongs in this group of *p*H uses; for example, calculation of the extent of salt hydrolysis, of the role of the hydrogen ion in acid-base equilibria in the blood, of the role of the hydrogen ion in protein and colloidal chemistry and of the hydrogen-ion activity of buffer solutions, the latter being of interest in studies of oxidation-reduction potentials and of the kinetics of certain reactions, etc. Then, again, we may wish to calculate relative changes in hydrogen-ion activity from the measurement of relative *p*H values in addition to the more important *definite hydrogen-ion activity* calculations.

Fourth and finally, from the measurement of *p*H we may wish to find the *concentration of the hydrogen ion* as distinct from its activity. Although in all aqueous solution equilibria it is the activity of the hydrogen ion which enters the mass action law equations, nevertheless in certain reaction rate studies, we may require a knowledge of the hydrogen-ion concentration, [1] particularly if the rate of reaction is to be determined by measuring the rate of acid formation.   In all acid-base potentiometric titrations, we are measuring total equivalents of acid or base originally present in the solution, which we get from a sudden change in the hydrogen-ion concentration at the so-called end point of the titration; but in such titrations the e.m.f. usually changes so rapidly with only a minute change in the composition of the solution, ionic strength or "thermodynamic environment" practically constant, that changes in hydrogen-ion activity are equal to changes in hydrogen ion concentration and we cannot distinguish between the two.

We can, therefore, group the uses of *p*H measurements into several distinct classes which should be clearly recognized inasmuch as the method of standardization of the *p*H scale or of one's individual

---

[1] For an extensive discussion of the much debated question concerning the importance of activity or concentration in kinetics see S. Glasstone, "Recent Advances in Physical Chemistry," Second Edition, P. Blakiston's Son & Co., Philadelphia, 1933, p. 473.

apparatus and the significance of the pH numbers are partly determined by the subsequent applications we wish to make of them.

17·2. Sörensen's First Standardization of the pH Scale

In 1909 Sörensen [2] first defined the pH with the words "Für die Zahl p schlage ich den Namen, 'Wasserstoffionenexponent' und die Schreibweise pH vor. Unter dem Wasserstoffionen-exponenten (pH) einer Lösung wird dann der Briggsche Logarithmus des reziproken Wertes des auf Wasserstoffionen bezogenen Normalitätsfaktors der Lösung verstanden." Mathematically

$$pH = - \log c_{H^+} \quad \text{(Sörensen)} \quad [17·2·1]$$

Sörensen standardized his pH scale by e.m.f. measurements of the cells

$$\text{Pt, H}_2 \left|
\begin{matrix} x \ N \ \text{HCl} \\ (0.1 - x) \ N \ \text{NaCl} \end{matrix} \right|\left|
y \ N \ \text{KCl} \right|\left| 0.1 \ N \ \text{KCl} \right| \text{HgCl} \left| \text{Hg} \ [17·2·A] \right.$$

from which the pH can be calculated if the exact relation between e.m.f. and pH is known. (In cell 17·2·A x was varied from zero to 0.09 and y had the values 1.75 and 3.5). But to know this latter relationship one must know the concentration of hydrogen ions in the cell solution in order to calculate the pH according to Eq. 17·2·1 and thereby to discover the exact mathematical connection between the known pH and the measured e.m.f. Sörensen believed that the normality of the hydrochloric acid multiplied by the fraction ionized (degree of dissociation) α, as calculated from conductance ratios gave one the concentration of the hydrogen ions.

From Kohlrausch's conductance measurements on 0.1 N hydrochloric acid at 18°C., Sörensen found α_{HCl} to be 0.9165 and he assumed that α_{HCl} was also equal to this value in all mixtures of $x \ N$ HCl + $(0.1 - x) \ N$ NaCl. For 0.01 N hydrochloric acid Sörensen took α_{HCl} equal to 0.9661.

The equation for the e.m.f. of his cell 17·2·A (written as one would write it today) is

$$E = E^{o,\prime} - 2.3 \frac{RT}{F} \log c_{H^+} \cdot f_{H^+} + E_x \quad [17·2·2]$$

(compare Eq. 2·1·1) where E_x is the unknown liquid-junction potential, and f_{H^+} is the activity coefficient of the hydrogen ion. If $\log c_{H^+} \cdot f_{H^+}$ and E_x are known, $E^{o,\prime}$ can be calculated and the pH

[2] S. P. L. Sörensen, *Biochem. Z.* **21**, 131, 201 (1909).

scale as determined by the hydrogen electrode becomes standardized. Sörensen's treatment was equivalent to setting

$$c_{H^+} \cdot f_{H^+} = \alpha_{HCl} N_{HCl} \qquad [17\cdot2\cdot3]$$

which we know today is erroneous, although this error is not as serious as it might seem. To eliminate E_x from $17\cdot2\cdot2$ Sörensen measured the e.m.f. of cell $17\cdot2\cdot A$ when the salt bridge-potassium chloride concentration was 1.75 N and 3.5 N, and then extrapolated the e.m.f. to infinite values of the salt-bridge concentrations where E_x was assumed to be zero. This procedure is called the Bjerrum [3] extrapolation, but when it has been applied, there is no definite assurance that the liquid-junction potential has been brought to zero. As an illustration of Sörensen's method some of his data are given in Table 17·1.

TABLE 17·1

STANDARDIZATION OF THE pH SCALE AT 18°C.

DATA OF SÖRENSEN (1909)

N_{HCl}	N_{NaCl}	$c_{H^+}(\alpha N_{HCl})$	-0.0577 $\log c_{H^+}$	$E_{1.75}$	$E_{3.5}$	$E\infty$	$E^{o,\prime}$
0.1	0	0.09165	0.0599	0.4066	0.4020	0.3974	0.3375
0.05	0.05	0.04583	0.0773	0.4219	0.4184	0.4149	0.3376
0.005	0.095	0.004583	0.1350	0.4733	0.4733	0.4733	0.3383
0.01	0	0.009661	0.1163	0.4599	0.4571	0.4543	0.3380

He selected 0.3377 as his best value of $E^{o,\prime}$ and calculated the pH from the equation (at 18°C., using hydrogen saturated with water vapor)

$$p\text{H} = \frac{E^{\infty}_{(17\cdot2\cdot A)} - 0.3377}{0.0577} \qquad [17\cdot2\cdot4]$$

where $E^{\infty}_{17\cdot2\cdot A}$ is the e.m.f. of cell $17\cdot2\cdot A$ containing the test sample in place of the hydrochloric acid-sodium chloride mixture when extrapolated to the value of the e.m.f. at infinite concentration of the salt bridge-potassium chloride solution. (In his measurements of the pH of standard buffer solutions Sörensen did not always find it necessary to attempt to eliminate the liquid-junction potential in this way, only in the case of the most acid and the most basic solutions.)

[3] N. Bjerrum, *Z. physik. Chem.* **53**, 428 (1905).

TABLE 17·2

COMPARISON OF SOME pH SCALE STANDARDIZATIONS AT 25°C.

(NOTE: Some of these data are calculated or estimated from combinations of other data. For the $E^{o,\prime}$ values an attempt to eliminate the liquid-junction potential has been made. The E^o values include the liquid-junction potential.)

Cell (E.M.F. in Volts)	Sörensen 1909, 1924	Scatchard 1925	Clark 1928	MacInnes 1938	Hitchcock 1937	Recommended Value
0.1 N KCl $\mid$ HgCl $\mid$ Hg $E^{o,\prime}$	+0.3376	+0.3352	....	......	......	......
Acid $\parallel$ Sat. KCl $\parallel$ 0.1 N KCl $\mid$ HgCl $\mid$ Hg E^o	......	+0.3372	+0.3376	......	+0.3362	......
Buffer $\parallel$ Sat. KCl $\parallel$ 0.1 N KCl $\mid$ HgCl $\mid$ Hg E^o	......	......	......	+0.3358	+0.3353	0.3355
Acid $\parallel$ Sat. KCl $\mid$ HgCl $\mid$ Hg E^o	......	+0.2454	+0.2458	......	+0.2450	+0.2450
Buffer $\parallel$ Sat. KCl $\mid$ HgCl $\mid$ Hg E^o	......	......	......	+0.2446	+0.2441	+0.2443
pH of 0.05 c $KHC_8H_4O_4$ (Phthalate)	......	......	3.974	4.000	4.008	4.005
pH of 0.1 N HCl	1.04 (From conductance at 18°C.)	1.075	1.075	......	1.085	......

Sörensen's scheme of standardization is open to three criticisms; first, $\alpha \cdot N_{HCl}$ is now known not to give the concentration of the hydrogen ions in 0.1 N hydrochloric acid, in fact hydrochloric acid is probably completely dissociated at this concentration; second, he gave no thought to elimination of the activity coefficient of the hydrogen ion from equation 17·2·2 because this function was not in general use at that time; third, the liquid-junction potential was probably not completely eliminated. Yet it is interesting to note that some of these errors counterbalanced with the result that his $E^{o,'}$ for the 0.1 N calomel half cell is not very much in error; in other words, his $E^{o,'}$ is very close to the E^o commonly accepted today. In Table 17·2 we have collected some standard values of various half cells, as well as other data for comparison purposes. Note the close agreement between Sörensen's value 0.3376 (with liquid junction supposedly eliminated) and Clark's 1928 E^o for the 0.1 N calomel electrode containing the liquid-junction potentials between standard half cell and test solution.[4]

17·3. Scatchard's Standardization of the pH Scale

Passing over a considerable amount of work between the years 1909 to 1924 we come to the experiments of Scatchard[5] on the revision of some single electrode potentials published in 1925. Since his extensive work has been of some influence on pH measurements, let us briefly review the method he followed.

He first made e.m.f. measurements of the cell

$$\text{Pt, H}_2 \mid \text{HCl} \mid \text{AgCl} \mid \text{Ag} \qquad [17·3·A]$$

over a range of acid concentrations, and calculated the E^o to be 0.2226 at 25 °C. by the extrapolation method already described in Sec. 1·3.

The standard electrode potentials commonly determined by physical chemists and those tabulated in the International Critical Tables are based on the concentration scale moles per thousand grams of water rather than on the usual normality scale (equivalents per liter of solution). E^o values, activity coefficients and pH standardizations in aqueous solution will vary slightly with the concentration definitions used; the error involved depends on the temperature, being larger the more the density of the solvent differs from unity. For nonaqueous solutions it

---

[4] As stated in our list of conventions in Chapter I, a liquid junction in a cell is designated by the symbol ‖ ; this symbol signifies further that the liquid-junction potential is included in the measured e.m.f. Only in the half cells labeled $E^{o,'}$, of Table 17·2 have attempts been made to eliminate the liquid-junction potential.

[5] G. Scatchard, *J. Am. Chem. Soc.* **47**, 696 (1925).

is decidedly important to distinguish carefully between these concentration units; for water E^o on the weight scale is greater than E^o on the volume molar scale by 0.13, 0.52 and 2.58 mv. at 25, 50 and 100°, respectively, the general equation being

$$E^o \text{ (weight scale)} = E^o \text{ (volume scale)} - \frac{2.3\,RT}{z_iF} \log d_o$$

where d_o is the density of the solvent, and z_i is the valence of the ion under consideration.

In using Scatchard's data which are based on the weight molal scale, we ultimately define, therefore, pH in terms of moles of hydrogen ion per 1000 g. of solvent.

Scatchard next made e.m.f. measurements of the cell

$$\text{Hg} \mid \text{HgCl} \mid \text{Sat. KCl} \parallel \text{HCl} \mid \text{AgCl} \mid \text{Ag} \qquad [17\cdot3\cdot\text{B}]$$

also over a range of acid concentrations. Reproducible liquid-junction potentials between the acid and saturated potassium chloride solutions were obtained by means of flowing junctions. The e.m.f. of cell 17·3·B is given by the equation

$$E = -\,E^{o,'}_{\text{Sat.Cal.}} + E^{o}_{\text{Ag}|\text{AgCl}} - E_x - 2.3\,\frac{RT}{F} \log m_{\text{Cl}^-}\cdot\gamma_{\text{Cl}^-} \quad [17\cdot3\cdot1]$$

or

$$E + 2.3\,\frac{RT}{F} \log m_{\text{Cl}^-} = E^{o}_{\text{Ag}|\text{AgCl}} - E^{o,'}_{\text{Sat.Cal.}} - E_x - 2.3\,\frac{RT}{F} \log \gamma_{\text{Cl}^-}$$

$$[17\cdot3\cdot2]$$

where E_x is the unknown liquid-junction potential.

At zero concentration the right-hand member of Eq. 17·3·2 becomes equal to $E^{o}_{\text{Ag}|\text{AgCl}} - E^{o,'}_{\text{Sat.Cal.}} - E_x$ since $\log \gamma_{\text{Cl}^-}$ vanishes in the limit; furthermore, knowing $E^{o}_{\text{Ag}|\text{AgCl}}$, we can find $E^{o,'} + E_x$.

By plotting $E + 2.3\,\dfrac{RT}{F} \log m_{\text{Cl}^-}$ as a function not of the square root of the concentration (Scatchard's data were not obtained in dilute enough solutions to use the square root limiting law) but as a function of $(A\sqrt{m} - Bm)$ where A and B are constants, Scatchard was able to extrapolate his $\left(E + 2.3\,\dfrac{RT}{F} \log m_{\text{Cl}^-} \right)$ values to zero concentration and so obtain the desired quantity, $E^{o}_{\text{Ag}|\text{AgCl}} - E^{o,'}_{\text{Sat.Cal.}} - E_x$. This extrapolation is rather a peculiar one, because the liquid-junction potential probably does not remain constant in very dilute solutions, but actually rises.[6]

[6] D. A. MacInnes, D. Belcher, and T. Shedlovsky, *J. Am. Chem. Soc.* **60**, 1094 (1938).

In Table 17·3 Scatchard's data are given, as well as the experimental deviations from the average e.m.f. of each cell and deviations of $E + 2.3 \dfrac{RT}{F} \log m_{Cl^-}$ from the theoretical curve used for extrapolation.

TABLE 17·3

STANDARDIZATION OF THE pH SCALE AT 25°C.

DATA OF SCATCHARD (1925)

m	E (average) (cell 17·3·B)	Deviation from average (mv.)	$-(E + 2.3$ $RT/F \log m_{Cl^-})$	Deviation from curve (mv.)
0.0100	0.09783	0.03	0.02047	−0.39
0.01002	0.09801	0.07	0.02022	−0.14
0.01010	0.09750	0.04	0.02055	−0.58
0.01031	0.09686	0.02	0.02066	−0.94
0.04986	0.05965	0.03	0.01737	0.01
0.05005	0.05954	0.03	0.01739	−0.01
0.09642	0.04421	0.01	0.01587	0.02
0.09772	0.04387	0.10	0.01587	0.00
0.09834	0.04378	....	0.01580	0.05
0.2030	0.02669	0.00	0.01427	−0.02
0.3063	0.01675	0.01	0.01365	0.01
0.3981	0.01018	0.03	0.01348	0.03
0.5009	0.00399	0.05	0.01377	−0.15
0.5013	0.00409	0.02	0.01365	−0.03
0.6367	−0.00237	0.01	0.01397	0.06
0.9377	−0.01393	0.01	0.01559	0.00
1.0008	−0.01602	0.02	0.01600	0.00
1.5346	−0.03100	0.13	0.02000	0.00

The value of $-(E + 2.3 \, RT/F \log m_{Cl^-})$ at zero concentration accepted by Scatchard is $+0.0228$ mv. which when added to his value of $+0.2226$ found for the E^o of the half cell $Cl^- \mid AgCl \mid Ag$ gives $+0.2454$ as the value of $E^{o,'} + E_x$, or as we defined it in Sec. 2·1, the value of E^o, the standard electrode potential of the saturated calomel electrode *including the liquid-junction potential.* Hence from measurements of our standard pH cell

$$\text{Pt, H}_2 \mid \text{test sample} \parallel \text{Sat. KCl} \mid \text{HgCl} \mid \text{Hg} \qquad [17·3·C]$$

the pH can be calculated at 25° by the equation

$$p\text{H} = \frac{E - E^o}{2.3RT/F} = \frac{E_{17·3·C} - 0.2454}{0.05914} \qquad [17·3·3]$$

Clark,[7] in recommending the E^o for the cell 17·3·C to be used in pH calculations, was undoubtedly influenced by the work of Scatchard and adopted $+0.2458$ as the E^o of the saturated calomel electrode including liquid-junction potential. This figure of 0.2458 was actually obtained by subtracting 0.0918, the e.m.f. of the cell

$$\text{Hg} \mid \text{HgCl} \mid \text{Sat. KCl} \parallel 0.1 \; m \; \text{KCl} \mid \text{HgCl} \mid \text{Hg} \quad [17·3·D]$$

found by Fales and Mudge,[8] from the E^o of the cell, 0.3376 at 25°C.,

$$\text{Pt, H}_2 \mid \text{H}^+ \parallel \text{Sat. KCl} \parallel 0.1 \; N \; \text{KCl} \mid \text{HgCl} \mid \text{Hg} \quad [17·3·E]$$

calculated from the data of Sörensen (See Table 17·2). Thus we see that the more recent and theoretically more nearly correct approach of Scatchard is in good agreement with the earlier pH standards.

There are, however, three important criticisms of this calibration of the pH scale. The first is due to the fact that Scatchard did not make measurements in sufficiently dilute solutions to apply the simple limiting square root law of Debye and Hückel; instead he found it necessary to use an empirical extension of this equation and to use the data at the concentrations 0.05 m and above to determine the shape of the curve. Second, there is, as usual, the liquid-junction potential uncertainty which comes into Scatchard's work in an uncertain way. According to Eq. 17·3·2 and to Scatchard's method of extrapolation it is necessary that

$$E^o_{\text{Ag|AgCl}} - E^{o,'}_{\text{Sat.Cal.}} - E_x - 2.3 \frac{RT}{F} \log \gamma_{\text{Cl}^-} = k + A\sqrt{m} - Bm$$

$$[17·3·4]$$

for his treatment to be of accurate significance. We know that in very dilute solutions

$$-2.3 \frac{RT}{F} \log \gamma_{\text{Cl}^-} = A\sqrt{m} \qquad [17·3·5]$$

and since the term Bm becomes negligible at the lowest concentrations

$$E^o_{\text{Ag|AgCl}} - E^{o,'}_{\text{Sat.Cal.}} - E_x \qquad [17·3·6]$$

should be equal to the constant k. But if the liquid-junction potential E_x is not a constant, independent of the concentration, Scatchard's method of extrapolation is open to serious doubt. Examining his data given in Table 17·3, it appears that the $E + 2.3 \; (RT/F) \log m_{\text{Cl}^-}$ values deviate much more from the theoretical curve at 0.01 m than

[7] W. M. Clark, "The Determination of Hydrogen Ions," Third Edition, Williams and Wilkins Co., Baltimore, 1928.

[8] H. A. Fales and W. A. Mudge, *J. Am. Chem. Soc.* **42**, 2434 (1920).

one would expect experimentally. That is, the experimental fluctuations are considerably smaller than the calculated deviations from the curve. If the liquid-junction potential at 0.01 m is larger than expected on the basis of the theoretical curve (the sign of the liquid-junction potential is such that the acid solution is negative) a deviation in the direction found by Scatchard could be explained.

The third objection to Scatchard's work is that he employed acid solutions throughout and did not also determine E^o from cells containing buffer solutions. There is considerable evidence at hand (see below) that the liquid-junction potential of the boundary acid ‖ saturated potassium chloride solution is larger than that of the boundary buffer solution ‖ saturated potassium chloride solution. Actually most pH measurements made in industry or in medicine are those of buffer solutions or of solutions containing salts rather than of strong acids; it would have been better, therefore, if a pH standard obtained through the use of buffer solutions had been selected. Cohn [9] and Cohn, Heyroth, and Menkin [10] were apparently the first to realize this and we shall now consider their method of pH standardization which has recently been elaborated most extensively by Hitchcock and Taylor [11] as well as by MacInnes, Belcher, and Shedlovsky.[12] (The germ of this method is to be seen in an early paper of Hastings and Sendroy.) [13]

17·4. Cohn's Method of pH Standardization

Reduced to its simplest statement, Cohn's method of pH standardization may be said to consist in finding the hydrogen-ion activity of a buffer solution, rather than that of a strong acid, by calculations based on the Debye-Arrhenius theory of dissociation, and then selecting the value of E^o to use in the e.m.f.-pH equation which will give experimentally the calculated pH of the buffer. As an example, let us take acetic acid-sodium acetate buffers which Cohn, Heyroth, and Menkin [10] first studied.

The dissociative equilibrium

$$HAc \rightleftarrows H^+ + Ac^-$$ [17·4·1]

[9] E. J. Cohn, *J. Am. Chem. Soc.* **49**, 173 (1927).

[10] Cohn, Heyroth, and Menkin, *J. Am. Chem. Soc.* **50**, 696 (1928).

[11] D. I. Hitchcock and A. C. Taylor, *J. Am. Chem. Soc.* **59**, 1812 (1937); **60**, 2710 (1938).

[12] D. A. MacInnes, D. Belcher, and T. Shedlovsky, *J. Am. Chem. Soc.* **60**, 1094 (1938).

[13] A. B. Hastings and J. Sendroy, Jr., *J. Biol. Chem.* **65**, 445 (1925).

where HAc represents undissociated acetic acid and Ac⁻ the acetate ion (CH_3COO^-) can be mathematically expressed by the thermodynamically exact mass-action law equation

$$K = \frac{m_{H^+} \cdot \gamma_{H^+} \cdot m_{Ac^-} \cdot \gamma_{Ac^-}}{m_{HAc} \, \gamma_{HAc}} \qquad [17 \cdot 4 \cdot 2]$$

where m is the concentration in moles per 1000 g. solvent and γ the activity coefficient. Taking logarithms of Eq. 17·4·2 we have

$$\log K = \log m_{H^+} \cdot \gamma_{H^+} + \log \frac{m_{Ac^-}}{m_{HAc}} + \log \frac{\gamma_{Ac^-}}{\gamma_{HAc}} \qquad [17 \cdot 4 \cdot 3]$$

or

$$p\text{H} - \log \frac{m_{Ac^-}}{m_{HAc}} = pK + \log \frac{\gamma_{Ac^-}}{\gamma_{HAc}} = pK' \qquad [17 \cdot 4 \cdot 4]$$

At zero concentration the left-hand side of Eq. 17·4·4, which in accordance with the usual practice we shall designate by pK', must equal pK since all activity coefficients are by definition equal to unity in infinitely dilute solutions. If the ionic strength is not too great, we can calculate γ_{Ac^-} by means of the Debye-Hückel limiting law; the thermodynamic dissociation constant pK can also be found by theoretically exact experimental methods. If, in dilute solutions, γ_{HAc} is set equal to unity, pK' and the pH can then be calculated since $\log \frac{m_{Ac^-}}{m_{HAc}}$ is known from the relations

$$m_{Ac^-} = m_{Na^+} + m_{H^+} \qquad [17 \cdot 4 \cdot 5]$$

$$m_{HAc} = \text{total acetate} - m_{Ac^-} \qquad [17 \cdot 4 \cdot 6]$$

where m_{H^+} is a small correction term, easily estimated from the pH measurements using approximate activity coefficients usually calculated from the Debye theory. Knowing the pH of the buffer solution, the E^o value of the e.m.f.-pH equation can be found from hydrogen electrode measurements on the same buffer solution and the pH scale standardized. Actually, however, measurements of pH of buffer solutions are most frequently made over a range of concentration so great that graphical methods are used to estimate E^o.

In the experimental work to be described in this section, the normality (volume) concentration scale was used so that we shall now use the symbols c and f in place of m and γ. (K on the volume-concentration scale equals K on the weight-concentration scale multiplied by the density of the solvent.)

Suppose f_{HAc} is set equal to zero and $\log f_{Ac^-}$ replaced by some function of the ionic strength μ (defined by Eq. 1·3·16) such as

$$- \log f_{Ac^-} = 0.5\sqrt{\mu} \qquad [17\cdot4\cdot7]$$

valid for dilute solutions of uniunivalent salts at 25°C. according to the Debye theory or such as

$$+ \log f_{Ac^-} = - \frac{0.5\sqrt{\mu}}{1 + B\sqrt{\mu}} + C\mu \qquad [17\cdot4\cdot8]$$

valid for higher concentrations. In Eq. 17·4·8 B and C are empirical constants.

Making use of Eq. 17·4·7, Eq. 17·4·4 becomes

$$pK' = pK - 0.5\sqrt{\mu} \qquad [17\cdot4\cdot9]$$

From electrometric measurements of pH, pK' can be calculated by Eq. 17·4·4; these values of pK' can then be plotted over a range of values of the square root of the concentration and the curve extrapolated to zero concentration to give pK, the true dissociation constant of the acid. Since pK is known from independent measurements, the validity of the extrapolation and the validity of the pK' values can be tested. If the pH has been incorrectly determined in the electrometric measurements, the extrapolation of pK' to zero concentration will not give the true value of pK; in this case E^o values of the equation

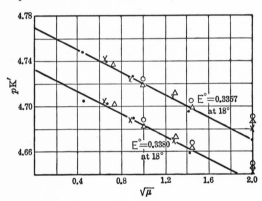

FIG. 17·1. Diagram illustrating Cohn's method of extrapolation.

$$pH = \frac{E - E^o}{2.3RT/F} \qquad [17\cdot4\cdot10]$$

can be altered until the electrometric pH numbers give values of pK' which extrapolate to the correct pK.

In Fig. 17·1 the calculations of pK' by Cohn, Heyroth, and Menkin are reproduced, the lower curve resulted from pH measurements, using 0.3380 as the E^o of the 0.1 N calomel electrode at 18° (the value recommended by Sörensen), and the upper curve, using 0.3357 to calculate the pH. Extrapolating the lower curve to zero concentration gives

$$pK = 4.733$$

or

$$K = 1.85 \times 10^{-5}$$

while from the upper curve we have,

$$pK = 4.77$$

$$K = 1.7 \times 10^{-5}$$

Harned and Ehlers [14] and MacInnes and Shedlovsky [15] have measured the true dissociation constant of acetic acid at 25° with very close agreement. Harned and Ehlers extended their measurements over the temperature range 0 to 35°C. with the results quoted in Table 17·4.

TABLE 17·4

DISSOCIATION CONSTANT OF ACETIC ACID (WEIGHT-CONCENTRATION SCALE)

DATA OF HARNED AND EHLERS (1932)

Temp. °C.	0	5	10	15	20	25	30	35
$K \times 10^5$.......	1.653	1.699	1.727	1.743	1.751	1.754	1.755	1.750

At 18° it is readily seen that the dissociation constant of acetic acid is much nearer 1.7×10^{-5} than 1.85×10^{-5} which means that it is better to use E^o equal to 0.3357 than 0.3380; as indeed was the recommendation of Cohn, Heyroth, and Menkin.

Recently Hitchcock and Taylor [16] have applied Cohn's method to a number of systems and to concentration ranges such that they find it necessary to set

$$\log \frac{f_{HA}}{f_{A^-}} = 0.5\sqrt{\mu} - C\mu \qquad [17\cdot4\cdot11]$$

and to plot

$$E - k\,pK + k \log \frac{c_{HA}}{c_{A^-}} + k\,A\sqrt{\mu} \qquad [17\cdot4\cdot12]$$

[14] H. S. Harned and R. W. Ehlers, *J. Am. Chem. Soc.* **54**, 1350 (1932).
[15] D. A. MacInnes and T. Shedlovsky. *J. Am. Chem. Soc.* **54**, 1429 (1932).
[16] D. I. Hitchcock and A. C. Taylor, *J. Am. Chem. Soc.* **59**, 1812 (1937).

as a function of μ, obtaining E^o at zero concentration, rather than to plot

$$E - k\,pK + k\log\frac{c_{HA}}{c_{A^-}} \qquad [17\cdot4\cdot13]$$

as a function of $\sqrt{\mu}$. (k is equal to 0.05914 and A 0.506 at 25° C.)

They confirm the conclusions of Cohn, Heyroth, and Menkin that the E^o value for the 0.1 N calomel electrode is too high if thermodynamic dissociation constants are to be determined from pH measurements on buffer solutions, and suggest the value 0.3355 for use at 25°C.

Actually, Hitchcock and Taylor made measurements using the saturated calomel electrode. Their determinations of E^o at 25° of the saturated calomel electrode including the liquid junction potential for a number of systems are given in Table 17·5. Each solution was

TABLE 17·5

STANDARDIZATION OF THE pH SCALE AT 25° E^o OF THE SATURATED
CALOMEL ELECTRODE

DATA OF HITCHCOCK AND TAYLOR (1937)
(Concentrations in moles per liter)

Stock Solution before Dilution	0.0993 CH_3COOH 0.0991 CH_3COOK	0.0251 CH_3COOH 0.0999 CH_3COONa	0.1001 CH_3COOH 0.0994 CH_3COONa	0.4071 CH_3COOH 0.0996 CH_3COONa	0.025 KH_2PO_4 0.025 Na_2HPO_4
E^o	0.2442	0.2441	0.2441	0.2440	0.2442

Stock Solution	0.05 $Na_2B_4O_7$	0.0999 $CH_2OHCOOLi$ 0.0500 HCl	0.1 HCl	0.01 HCl 0.09 KCl	0.01 HCl 0.09 NaCl
E^o	0.2440	0.2443	0.2450	0.2445	0.2441

diluted with water in order to obtain a range of E values to carry out the necessary extrapolation to zero concentration. Very close agreement can be seen to exist between the different E^o values for the various series with the exception of two of the solutions containing the relatively high concentrations of hydrochloric acid. These data of Hitchcock and Taylor confirm the statements in the previous section to the effect that standardizations of the pH scale based on hydrochloric acid solutions give values for E^o different from what one finds using buffer solutions (or solutions containing much salt).

MacInnes, Belcher, and Shedlovsky [17] have also applied Cohn's method in the standardization of the 0.1 N calomel electrode, using sodium acetate-acetic acid buffers at 12, 25 and 38°C. and sodium chloroacetate-chloroacetic acid buffers at 25°C. Their data are collected in Table 17·6.

TABLE 17·6

STANDARDIZATION OF THE pH SCALE

(E^o of the 0.1 N calomel electrode including liquid-junction potentials of saturated potassium chloride salt bridge)

DATA OF MacINNES, BELCHER, AND SHEDLOVSKY (1938)

Solutes	CH₃COOH, CH₃COO Na			CH₂ClCOOH CH₂ClCOO Na
Temp.........	12	25	38	25
E^o...........	0.3364	0.3358	0.3352	0.3357

Since MacInnes, Belcher, and Shedlovsky determined the difference in e.m.f. between the saturated potassium chloride calomel electrode and the 0.1 N calomel electrode at the three temperatures, the E^o values of the former electrode can be calculated and compared with Hitchcock's data given in Table 17·5 (for a comparison at 25° see Table 17·2).

The difference between the data of Table 17·7 and 17·5 at 25° amounts to 0.5 mv. or 0.008 pH unit. If we accept the data of Hitchcock and MacInnes, we can use the resulting average E^o values with the feeling that the uncertainty in the pH scale is less than 0.01 pH unit, at least as determined by this method. It is interesting to note that the earlier (1928) recommendation of Cohn and co-workers, namely, that the E^o of the 0.1 N calomel electrode (including saturated potassium chloride salt-bridge liquid-junction potentials) be taken as 0.3357 at 18° agrees well with the recommendation of MacInnes, Belcher, and Shedlovsky, namely, 0.3361 (interpolated).

The difference between these new standardizations of the pH scale and the old scale that has long been in use is approximately 0.03 pH

[17] D. A. MacInnes, D. Belcher, and T. Shedlovsky, *J. Am. Chem. Soc.* **60**, 1094 (1938).

unit. Thus Clark [7] gives as the pH of 0.05c potassium acid phthalate at 25°, 3.974, MacInnes exactly 4.000, and Hitchcock, 4.008 (see Table 17·2). Undoubtedly the conclusions of Cohn, Hitchcock,

TABLE 17·7

STANDARDIZATION OF THE pH SCALE

(E^o of the saturated calomel electrode)

DATA OF MACINNES, BELCHER, AND SHEDLOVSKY (1938)

(Acetic acid-sodium acetate buffers)

Temp.	12	25	38
$\Delta E^o = (E^o_{0.1 N} - E^o_{Sat.})$..........	0.0834	0.0912	0.0977
$E^o_{Sat.}$......................	0.2530	0.2446	0.2375

MacInnes, and their co-workers are much nearer the truth than the old estimate of Clark, Sörensen, etc. and we shall adopt their recommendations in this book. Before listing our final recommendations, however, we wish to point out certain peculiarities of Cohn's method of pH standardization.

In all these methods requiring extrapolation to infinite dilution it is usually necessary to make an arbitrary choice concerning the extrapolation technique. We are led to wonder if other functions would extrapolate to the same values of E^o. MacInnes, Belcher, and Shedlovsky find that they have to use in their extrapolation equations values of the constant in the Debye limiting activity-coefficient equation which are somewhat larger than the theoretical. They also believe that a possible expected curvature in their plotted lines is eliminated by a compensating variation in liquid-junction potential so that linear curves are obtained. Thus the liquid-junction potential uncertainty enters into the problem rather indefinitely. The data of Hitchcock and Taylor were obtained over a higher concentration range, were extrapolated to zero concentration by a different function, and therefore probably compensate for the liquid-junction potential to a greater or less extent than in MacInnes' case. Perhaps the discrepancy of 0.5 mv. between the two investigations is to be explained in this way.

In MacInnes' case the liquid-junction potential contained in the E^o for the saturated calomel electrode is presumably that of the junction saturated potassium chloride ‖ buffer of concentration 0.01μ or less, while in Hitchcock's case it is of the junction potassium chloride ‖ buffer of concentration 0.1μ or less. If the pH of more concentrated solutions must be measured, the liquid-junction potential uncertainty cannot be so completely avoided in the calculations as it would be at lower concentrations by use of the new value of E^o.

17·5. Glass Electrode Standardization Recommendations

There are two distinct methods by which glass electrodes may be standardized, or what amounts to the same thing, two ways in which the constant E^o of the pH equation for the glass electrode

$$p\mathrm{H} = \frac{E - E^o}{2.3RT/F} \qquad [17·5·1]$$

may be determined. The first and most exact method and the method which gives us *definite* pH readings is to measure accurately the asymmetry potential and other e.m.f.'s existing in the cell; then to calculate E^o as described below. The second, and most commonly followed method is to measure the e.m.f. of the glass electrode cell when it contains a buffer of known pH; the E^o of Eq. 17·5·1 is then readily calculated. This second method is more convenient than the first as it does not require a knowledge of the asymmetry potential or of the potentials existing within the glass electrode, such as the inner reference electrode potential. It is not, however, as precise as the first method although the pH values so obtained are *definite* pH values provided no mistake has been made in the pH of the known buffer.

If pH measurements are made with the glass electrode by means of the following cell

Ag|AgCl|0.1 N HCl|glass| test sample ‖ Sat. KCl|HgCl|Hg   [17·5·A]

the pH can be calculated from Eq. 17·5·1 whose E^o is determined as follows: Cell 17·5·A may be considered as consisting of the cell

Ag | AgCl | 0.1 N HCl | H$_2$, Pt   [17·5·B]

whose e.m.f.[5] at 25° is equal to −0.3524 v. and of the cell

Pt, H$_2$ | test sample ‖ Sat. KCl | HgCl | Hg   [17·5·C]

whose e.m.f. at 25° is given by the equation

$$E = 0.2443 + 2.3(RT/F)\,p\mathrm{H} \qquad [17·5·2]$$

Adding the e.m.f. of cell 17·5·C to that of 17·5·B we have as the equation of our glass electrode-pH cell,

$$E = -0.1081 + \frac{2.3RT}{F} pH \qquad [17\cdot5\cdot3]$$

or

$$pH = \frac{E + 0.1081}{2.3RT/F} \qquad [17\cdot5\cdot4]$$

where the E^o of Eq. 17·5·1 is now seen to be equal to -0.1081. In adopting 0.2443 for the standard e.m.f. of cell 17·5·C we have averaged Hitchcock's recommendation of 0.2441 with MacInnes' recommendations of 0.2446 thereby obtaining a value which is probably within the limits of error of each investigation.

The asymmetry potential which in general exists across all glass electrode membranes must be taken into consideration in all accurate measurements. The asymmetry potential defined as being the e.m.f. of the cell

Ag | AgCl | 0.1 N HCl | glass | 0.1 N HCl | AgCl | Ag   [17·5·D]

(See Sec. 1·5.)

should be added to the e.m.f. of cell (17·5·A) to eliminate this error.

In this way definite (as distinguished from relative) pH measurements can be made with the glass electrode alone; by this statement we mean that the pH of the solution or of standard buffer does not have to be measured first with the hydrogen electrode. Of course correct pH measurements with the glass electrode can be made by this method only over the range of pH where the e.m.f. of the glass electrode is unaffected by the presence of ions other than the hydrogen ion, or is unaffected by change in vapor pressure of the water.

Usually, however, one knows neither the acid concentration of the hydrochloric acid within the glass electrode nor the asymmetry potential of the glass electrode, so that the E^o of Eq. 17·5·1 cannot be obtained merely by calculation; it must be found by an actual pH measurement of a buffer solution of known pH. We recommend the use of potassium acid phthalate buffer of concentration 0.05 mole per liter, (10.21 grs. weighed in air per liter of solution at 25° C.) whose pH has been found most recently to be 4.005 at 25° C., (average of Hitchcock's and MacInnes' data) Knowing the e.m.f. of cell 17·5·A when the test sample is 0.05 M potassium acid phthalate, the E^o is readily calculated from the equation

$$E_o = E - \frac{2.3RT}{F} pH. \qquad [17\cdot5\cdot5]$$

(This recommendation is for the glass electrode only; phthalate buffers give difficulties when used in connection with the hydrogen electrode.)

The standardization procedure recommended by manufacturers of commercial glass electrodes is not uniform, but varies from one set of directions to another by the equivalent of 0.03 pH unit. We recommend that all users of commercial glass-electrode equipment adopt the same value for the pH of 0.05 M $C_6H_4 (COO)_2$ HK, namely 4.005 at 25° C. and correct for the asymmetry potential using this value of the phthalate buffer.

A good grade of solid phthalate should be used, Bureau of Standards phthalate or recrystallized phthalate dried at 110° in an oven.

In order to make sure that both the electrical system and glass electrode cell are functioning without error, it is also, in addition, necessary to check the e.m.f. or pH reading occasionally by measuring the pH of a buffer of pH around 8 or 9. According to the recently published data of Hitchcock and Taylor,[18] 0.05 M $Na_2B_4O_7$ has a pH of 9.180 at 25° C. This solution is made in the following way: First air-dry the $Na_2B_4O_7 \cdot 10H_2O$, then dry the hydrated salt to constant weight in a big desiccator over a saturated sodium bromide [19] solution which gives the correct vapor pressure of water for the salt. Weigh the salt as $Na_2B_4O_7 \cdot 10H_2O$; 19.07 grams weighed in air per liter of solution. The sodium error of Corning 015 glass electrodes is negligible as the author has been able to show by direct comparison of the glass and hydrogen electrode in this solution.[20]

The above recommendations are all for the glass electrode at 25° C. At other temperatures the glass electrode can be easily standardized by means of the 0.05 M phthalate buffer whose pH from 12 to 38° has been studied by MacInnes, Belcher, and Shedlovsky.[21] Correcting the data of the latter to conform to the average selected for 25° we can list the pH of the phthalate buffer at 12, 25 and 38° as 4.005, 4.005 and 4.02.[22] A private communication of Dr. W. J. Hamer to Bacon, Hensley, and Vaughn contains the following equation for the pH at the phthalate buffer as a function of the absolute temperature T,

$$p\text{H} = 5.13 \log T + \frac{1519.62}{T} + 0.01092T - 17.039 \qquad [17 \cdot 5 \cdot 6]$$

[18] D. I. Hitchcock and A. C. Taylor, *J. Am. Chem. Soc.* **59**, 1812 (1937).

[19] I. M. Kolthoff, *J. Am. Chem. Soc.* **48**, 1447 (1926).

[20] M. Dole. Unpublished data.

[21] D. A. MacInnes, D. Belcher, and T. Shedlovsky, *J. Am. Chem. Soc.* **60**, 1094 (1938); see also D. I. Hitchcock and A. C. Taylor, *ibid.*, 60, 2710 (1938).

[22] The National Technical Laboratories, Pasadena, Calif., is prepared to deliver buffer solutions having known pH values up to 100° C.

Equation 17·5·6 is valid to 0.002 pH unit from 0° to 60° C. If we maintain our entire glass electrode-calomel electrode cell at a uniform temperature, the E^o can be calculated by means of Eq. 17·5·5 from the e.m.f. of the cell containing the phthalate buffer.

If the pH of highly ionized acid solution containing no salt is to be determined, the glass electrode should be standardized using 3.98 as the pH of 0.05 M potassium acid phthalate and 0.2450 as the E^o of cell 17·5·C. All the evidence seems to indicate that the liquid-junction potential between highly ionized acid solutions and saturated potassium chloride is sufficiently different from that between buffer solutions and saturated potassium chloride solutions to justify the use of the different pH values of the standard buffer.

17·6. Glass Electrode Standardization Recommendations for Non-aqueous Solutions

The problem of standardization of glass electrode e.m.f. measurements on nonaqueous solutions in terms of pH or of hydrogen-ion activity of nonaqueous solutions is also the problem of standardizing other hydrogen-ion electrode data, but this is a problem that has never been solved, nor can ever be solved until some sound method of measuring or calculating single electrode or single phase boundary potentials has been developed. Thermodynamically, the problem is insoluble, since on transferring a hydrogen ion from one solvent to another, we do both electrical and chemical work, and these two kinds of work cannot be separately estimated or measured. Unless theoretical calculations are able to solve the problem for us in a sound and convincing way, we suspect that scientists will be unable to come to an agreement as to the definition and assumptions adopted.

There is no theoretical reason why the method of Cohn for the standardization of the aqueous pH scale could not be used for the standardization of any nonaqueous pH scale; the E^o so determined would then be related to thermodynamic equations expressing the equilibria which exist in that particular solvent. However, hydrogen-ion activities in the nonaqueous solutions giving such pH numbers would not necessarily be equal to hydrogen-ion activities corresponding to equal pH numbers pertaining to aqueous solutions, because the standard reference solution in each case would be composed of a different solvent.

As far as the author is aware, no one has as yet standardized any non-aqueous pH scale by the method of Cohn; indeed, it is only within the last year that the aqueous scale has been so standardized.

In our judgment we believe that at the present time the best recommendation for standardization of the glass electrode as applied to non-aqueous solution is to use the same value of E^o as is used in aqueous solution experiments.[23] In other words, calculate the pH of the non-aqueous solution from the e.m.f. in exactly the same way that the pH of aqueous solutions is calculated if the measurements are made in the same way with a potassium chloride salt bridge, but be sure to state the method used. Such pH numbers can then be corrected to more reasonable values in the future by means of an additive correction factor if necessary or desirable. We make this recommendation because of the fact that the dials of many commercial pH electrometers are graduated already in terms of pH and are standardized in terms of the aqueous pH scale. Nonaqueous pH measurements will undoubtedly be made with these instruments. Another reason for making this arbitrary recommendation is that nonaqueous solvents are so diverse and different in their properties that any single recommendation could not be exact for all solvents, and until the proper standardization technique is worked out for a particular solvent, we might just as well adhere to the water standard for that solvent, erroneous though it be.

In the next section we discuss the significance of such pH measurements.

17·7. The Significance of pH.

Most routine measurements of pH are of the relative type; that is, the whole glass-electrode cell is occasionally calibrated with a buffer of known pH so that we do not know the exact e.m.f. of the separate parts of the cell in relation to one another, we do not know to what extent these separate e.m.f.'s may be changing, and we do not know how accurately the pH is being measured between calibrations. Nevertheless, these routine data have an important practical if empirical significance, because the pH values so obtained are carefully correlated with other observable properties of the solution under investigation, such as the enzymatic activity of the system, or its taste, or its ore-flotation power to quote a few examples. Provided our electrochemical measurements are accurate enough to reproduce any desired pH, it is usually neither necessary nor desirable to attempt to calculate hydrogen-ion activity or hydrogen-ion concentration of the solution.

[23] If the activity of water is low in the nonaqueous solvent, glass electrodes made of Corning 015 glass will give erroneous e.m.f. readings as compared to hydrogen electrodes, see Chapter 8; there is a possibility, however, that electrodes made of different types of glass might function more accurately in nonaqueous solvents.

Although it is unnecessary to go beyond the pH to the hydrogen-ion concentration, still our pH measurements tell us whether our hydrogen-ion concentration is too large or too small, whether we need add more base or more acid to bring the solution to the desired pH. In fact, from many relative pH measurements we can calculate quite accurately the change in hydrogen-ion concentration in going from one pH to the next; this statement is true if the salt concentration is fairly large in comparison to the hydrogen-ion concentration and if the salt concentration remains nearly constant as the pH is changed, for then neither the liquid-junction potential nor the hydrogen-ion activity coefficient changes sufficiently to invalidate the statement that

$$\Delta p\text{H} = - \Delta \log N_{\text{H}^+} \qquad [17\cdot7\cdot1]$$

We might ask what are these relative pH numbers in terms of physical realities? Actually, they are calculated or automatically obtained from e.m.f. values, these e.m.f.'s being the combination of various electric potential differences existing in the cell which are complicated functions of the composition and concentration of the system under investigation and of the temperature and pressure.

If the glass electrode has been carefully and accurately calibrated or if the related e.m.f.'s of the separate components of the glass electrode cell have been measured, *definite* pH values can be obtained. As already stated many times no exact thermodynamic significance can be given to these numbers, yet in the Cohn method of standardizing the pH scale, E^o values are chosen so that hydrogen-ion activities calculated from the pH by the equation

$$p\text{H} = - \log c_{\text{H}^+} \cdot f_{\text{H}^+} \qquad [17\cdot7\cdot2]$$

yield the thermodynamically correct weak acid dissociation constants when substituted in the law of mass action equation. No more exact significance than this can be attributed to pH numbers, and to understand the extent of and to reproduce in one's own measurements the thermodynamic validity of Eq. 17·7·2 the exact conditions, solution concentrations, etc., used in the determination of E^o must be studied.

Now if we measure the pH of solutions not so similarly constituted with respect to solvent, ionic strength, and mobility of ions present, then our pH numbers will lose the exact significance given by Eq. 17·7·2 to the extent that the liquid-junction potential in the cell differs from the liquid-junction potentials in the cells measured by

Hitchcock, MacInnes and co-workers. What is the order of magnitude of error involved? Of course, it is impossible to answer this last question exactly, and any approximate estimates that we might make will depend upon the concentration and composition of the solution involved. From calculations given by Hamer,[24] the difference in the potentials of the liquid junctions

$$\text{Sat. KCl} \parallel 0.1 \; N \; \text{HCl}$$

and

$$\text{Sat. KCl} \parallel 0.1 \; N \; \text{KCl}$$

is of the order of magnitude of a few millivolts at 25° C. At higher concentrations the difference would be greater. It is for this reason that we recommended in the previous section that a slightly different pH scale be used when measuring the pH of highly ionized acid solutions. But even this latter recommendation will produce pH numbers having decreased significance in terms of Eq. 17·7·2 when the concentration becomes greater than tenth normal.

The pH of a solution at one temperature is of significance only in relation to the standard of reference at that temperature; if we try to compare the pH of a solution at two different temperatures, we find that our e.m.f. measurements includes an unknown e.m.f. produced by the thermal gradient in the salt bridge, an e.m.f. which is sufficient to render uncertain the thermodynamic significance of the measurement. This thermal e.m.f. is probably of the same order of magnitude as the liquid-junction potential.

We now come to a consideration of the significance of pH measurements on nonaqueous solutions.

When the e.m.f. measurement includes the potential difference at the junction of an aqueous solution and a nonaqueous solution, all significance of the pH in terms of Eq. 17·7·2 is lost. Thus, phase-boundary potentials can amount to as much as 0.1 v. or more with a corresponding uncertainty in the pH (in terms of Eq. 17·7·2), of one or more pH units. This can be seen in the work of Hall and Conant [25] who measured the e.m.f. of a chloranil electrode (platinum in contact with a saturated solution of tetrachloroquinone and tetrachlorohydroquinone) in acid solutions in glacial acetic acid in reference to the aqueous saturated potassium chloride calomel electrode, and attempted to calculate the pH of these nonaqueous solutions with reference to the water standard. Although they used a salt bridge composed of a

[24] W. J. Hamer, *Trans. Electrochem. Soc.* **72**, 45 (1937).
[25] N. F. Hall and J. B. Conant, *J. Am. Chem. Soc.* **49**, 3047 (1927).

supersaturated solution of lithium chloride in glacial acetic acid, so that their cell was built up as follows

| Hg | HgCl | KCl Sat. in water | LiCl Supersat. in acetic acid + gelatin | Acid in glacial acetic acid | $C_6Cl_4O_2$ $C_6Cl_4(OH)_2$, Pt | [17·7·A] |

they felt that their phase-boundary potential was not eliminated. They therefore did not calculate the pH from the equation applicable to aqueous solutions (at 25°)

$$p\text{H} = \frac{0.418 - E}{0.0591} \qquad [17·7·3]$$

but from the equation

$$p\text{H}^{(\text{HAc})} = \frac{0.566 - E}{0.0591} \qquad [17·7·4]$$

Thus they assign the value +0.148 v. to allow for the phase-boundary and liquid-junction potentials existing in the cell and for any difference in the standard electrode potential of the chloranil electrode in the two solvents. However, this correction factor was chosen in a rather arbitrary way, namely, to give values for the pH of an equimolar mixture of pyridine (strong base) and pyridine acetate in the glacial acetic acid which would be nearly equal to the pK_A of acetic acid in water, and to give values for the strengths of anhydro bases such as urea which would be nearly the same in the two solvents.

The pH function is not one which lends itself to exact thermodynamic definition in terms of the composition and concentration of the solution; it can only be defined in terms of electromotive force. Hammett and Deyrup,[26] however, have advanced an "acidity function" defined by the equation

$$\text{H}_o = -\log c_{\text{H}^+} \cdot f_{\text{H}^+} \cdot \frac{f_\text{B}}{f_{\text{BH}^+}} \qquad [17·7·5]$$

which has "operational significance" and which can be measured particularly easily by such substances as basic indicators in different solvents provided that the ratio of the activity coefficients of the indicator base and acid indicator ion, $f_\text{B}/f_{\text{BH}^+}$ is the same for all bases in the same solution (this assumption is not necessary if the proper extrapolation technique is used). Unfortunately the H_o function is

[26] L. P. Hammett and A. J. Deyrup, *J. Am. Chem. Soc.* **54**, 2721 (1932); L. P. Hammett, "Physical Organic Chemistry," McGraw-Hill Book Co., New York, 1940.

not capable of exact expression in terms of e.m.f. measurements and is, therefore, of no interest to us here. (Parenthetically, it might be remarked that indicators have been chiefly used in the past to measure acidity of non-aqueous solutions, see the review, "Acidity in Non-Aqueous Solution" by Kilpatrick.[27])

In addition to the liquid-junction and phase-boundary potential uncertainties, we should mention again the fact that temperature fluctuations, errors in forming the liquid junction and application of the glass electrode to solutions where the glass electrode does not act like a hydrogen electrode can impair or destroy the significance of glass electrode pH measurements.

[27] M. Kilpatrick, *Trans. Electrochem. Soc.* **72**, 95 (1937).

APPENDIX I

A	[1·3]	Empirical constant
a	[8·2]	Activity
B	[1·3]	Empirical constant
C	[3·4]	Empirical constant
c	[1·3]	Concentration in moles per liter of solution
D	[1·2]	Dielectric constant
E	[1·3]	Electromotive force in volts
E^o	[1·3]	Standard electrode potential
F	[1·3]	The faraday
f	[16·3]	Activity coefficient
f	[1·2]	Force
G	[6·4]	Gibbs free energy
G_m	[3·4]	Mutual conductance
I	[3·4]	Current in amperes
K	[2·3]	Ionization constant
K	[4·1]	Empirical constant
K_A	[15·2]	Acid Ionization constant
K_B	[15·2]	Base Ionization constant
k	[1·3]	Boltzmann's constant
ln	[1·3]	Natural logarithm
log	[1·3]	Briggsian logarithm
m	[1·3]	Moles per 1000 grams of solvent
N	[1·1]	Normality; equivalents per liter of solution
N	[1·3]	Avogadro's number
P	[4·1]	Back e.m.f.
P	[8·3]	Vapor pressure
p		Symbol for $-\log$
Q	[4·1]	Empirical constant
q	[1·2]	Charge on ions
R	[1·3]	Constant of the perfect gas law
R	[3·4]	Resistance in ohms
r	[1·2]	Distance
S	[3·4]	Galvanometer sensitivity
T	[1·3]	Absolute temperature
t	[6·1]	Transference number
t	[9·1]	Centigrade temperature

U	[16·3]	Potential energy
u	[6·1]	Mobility of positive ion
V	[8·3]	Volume
V_A	[15·2]	Volume of acid
V_B	[15·3]	Volume of base
v	[6·1]	Mobility of negative ion
Z	[3·4]	Impedance
z	[1·3]	Valence (taken positive for a negative ion)
α	[1·1]	Fraction of ionization
γ	[1·3]	Activity coefficient
ϵ	[1·3]	Unit positive charge
κ	[4·1]	Specific conductance
Λ	[1·1]	Equivalent conductance
Λ_0	[1·1]	Equivalent conductance at zero concentration
μ	[1·3]	Chemical potential
$\bar{\mu}$	[6·1]	Electrochemical potential
μ	[3·4]	Voltage amplification
μ_i^o	[1·3]	Standard ionic chemical potential
μ	[1·3]	Ionic strength
Π	[8·3]	Osmotic pressure
π	[1·3]	Ratio of circumference to diameter of circle
ψ	[16·1]	Electrostatic potential

APPENDIX II

A CONSISTENT SET OF VALUES OF THE GENERAL PHYSICAL CONSTANTS
AND RATIOS (AS OF AUGUST, 1939) *

Velocity of light.............. $c = (2.99776 \pm 0.00004) \times 10^{10}$ cm. sec.$^{-1}$

Electronic charge............ $\epsilon = (4.8022 \pm 0.0010) \times 10^{-10}$ abs. e.s.u.

$\epsilon/c = (1.60193 \pm 0.00033) \times 10^{-20}$ abs. e.m.u.

Specific electronic charge... $\epsilon/m = (1.7591 \pm 0.0005) \times 10^{7}$ abs. e.m.u.g.$^{-1}$

$(\epsilon/m)c = (5.2734 \pm 0.0015) \times 10^{17}$ abs. e.s.u.g.$^{-1}$

Faraday constant (chemical atomic
weight scale)............... $F = 96494 \pm 10$ int-coul.g $-$ equiv.$^{-1}$

$= 96480 \pm 10$ abs-coul.g $-$ equiv.$^{-1}$

$= 9648.0 \pm 1.0$ abs. e.m.u.g $-$ equiv.$^{-1}$

Avogadro's number......... $N = \dfrac{Fc}{\epsilon}$ $(6.0227 \pm 0.0014) \times 10^{23}$ mole^{-1}

Gas constant.............. $R = (8.31450 \pm 0.00043) \times 10^{7}$ erg. deg.$^{-1}$ mole^{-1}

$= 8.31450$ absolute joules deg.$^{-1}$·mole^{-1}

$= 8.31283$ international joules deg.$^{-1}$·mole^{-1}

Ice point (absolute scale).... $T_0 = 273.15 \pm 0.01°$ K

1 International ohm............ $= 1.00048 \pm 0.00002$ absolute ohm

1 International ampere.......... $= 0.99986 \pm 0.00002$ absolute ampere

1 International volt............. $= 1.00034 \pm 0.00003$ absolute volt

1 International joule............ $= 1.00020 \pm 0.000045$ absolute joule

Mechanical equivalent of heat... $= 4.1847 \pm 0.0008$ absolute joules cal.$^{-1}_{15}$

$$2.3026 \frac{RT}{F} \text{ at } 25° \text{ C.} = 0.05916_3 \pm 0.000012 \text{ absolute volt}$$

$$2.3026 \frac{RT}{F} \text{ at } 25° \text{ C.} = 0.05914_3 \pm 0.000012 \text{ international volt}$$

Boltzmann constant $k = \dfrac{R}{N} = (1.38052 \pm 0.00033) \times 10^{-16}$ erg. deg.$^{-1}$

Dielectric constant of water† at 25° C., $D = 78.54$

* Private communication from Professor R. T. Birge. Some of the ratios have been calculated
from Birge's constants.

† J. Wyman, Jr. *Phys. Rev.* **35,** 623 (1930).

APPENDIX III

VALUES OF 2.3026 RT/F IN ABSOLUTE VOLTS AT DIFFERENT TEMPERATURES

(The values given in parentheses are in units of International Volts)

°C	°K	2.3026 RT/F	°C	°K	2.3026 RT/F
0	273.15	0.05420 (0.05418)	36	309.15	0.06135 (0.06133)
2	275.15	0.05460 (0.05458)	37	310.15	0.06154 (0.06152)
4	277.15	0.05500 (0.05498)	38	311.15	0.06174 (0.06172)
6	279.15	0.05540 (0.05537)	40	313.15	0.06214 (0.06212)
8	281.15	0.05579 (0.05577)	42	315.15	0.06254 (0.06252)
10	283.15	0.05619 (0.05617)	44	317.15	0.06293 (0.06291)
12	285.15	0.05658 (0.05656)	46	319.15	0.06333 (0.06331)
14	287.15	0.05698 (0.05696)	48	321.15	0.06373 (0.06371)
16	289.15	0.05738 (0.05736)	50	323.15	0.06412 (0.06410)
18	291.15	0.05777 (0.05776)	55	328.15	0.06512 (0.06509)
20	293.15	0.05817 (0.05815)	60	333.15	0.06611 (0.06609)
22	295.15	0.05857 (0.05855)	65	338.15	0.06710 (0.06708)
24	297.15	0.05897 (0.05895)	70	343.15	0.06809 (0.06807)
25	298.15	0.05916 (0.05914)	75	348.15	0.06909 (0.06906)
26	299.15	0.05936 (0.05934)	80	353.15	0.07008 (0.07005)
28	301.15	0.05976 (0.05974)	85	358.15	0.07107 (0.07105)
30	303.15	0.06016 (0.06014)	90	363.15	0.07206 (0.07204)
32	305.15	0.06055 (0.06053)	95	368.15	0.07305 (0.07303)
34	307.15	0.06095 (0.06093)	100	373.15	0.07405 (0.07402)

In regard to the use of international or absolute units Dr. George W. Vinal of the National Bureau of Standards has kindly written us as follows: "Quoting from the concluding paragraphs of a paper by Mr. E. C. Crittenden, *Electrical Engineering* 59, 163 (1940), 'The decision made by the official international organization dealing with weights and measures to adopt the absolute practical electrical units in place of the present international units on January 1, 1940, could not be carried out on that date because agreement had not been reached on exact values for the absolute units.' What actually happened was that the Germans reported in June, 1939, that they had not completed their absolute measurements and they were unwilling to agree on numerical values." The war has delayed indefinitely any further international discussion of this problem. The National Bureau of Standards is still issuing standardization certificates on the basis of international units.

APPENDIX IV

STANDARD ELECTRODE POTENTIALS OF E. M. F. CELLS USED
IN pH MEASUREMENTS*

Half Cell	Tempera-ture	E. M. F. E^o
Buffer ‖ sat. KCl ∣ HgCl ∣ Hg	25°	0.2443
Acid ‖ sat. KCl ∣ HgCl ∣ Hg	25°	0.2450
Buffer ‖ sat. KCl ‖ 0.1 N KCl ∣ HgCl ∣ Hg	25°	0.3355
Acid ‖ sat. KCl ‖ 0.1 N KCl ∣ HgCl ∣ Hg	25°	0.3362
Buffer ‖ sat. KCl ∣ HgCl ∣ Hg	$t°$ C.†	$E^o \doteq 0.2601$ $- 6.02 \times 10^{-4}\, t$ $- 1.15 \times 10^{-6}\, t^2$

Buffer ($t°$ C.) ‖ KCl (sat.) ($t°$ C.) ‖
  ‖ KCl (sat.) (25° C.) ∣ HgCl (25° C.) ∣ Hg (25° C.) .... E^o $= 0.2651$
                      $- 7.98 \times 10^{-4}\, t$
                      $- 1.23 \times 10^{-6}\, t^2$

* For the standard electrode potentials of the quinhydrone electrode see Table 9·3.
† Values of this half-cell at definite temperatures are given in Table 9·5.

APPENDIX V

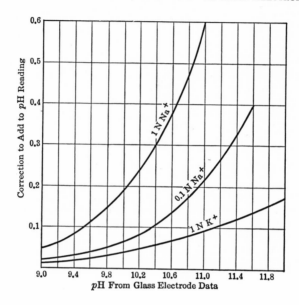

APPENDIX VI

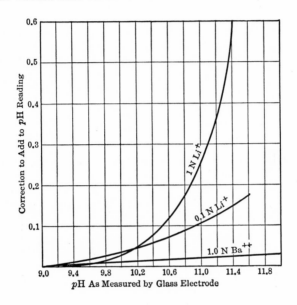

311

APPENDIX VII

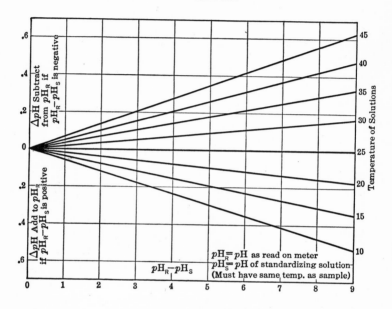

312

APPENDIX VIII

Dissociation Constants of Acids at 25° C.

Substance	$K_1 \times 10^5$	$K_2 \times 10^{11}$	Reference*
	Inorganic Acids		
HSO_3^-	1150		S and N
H_2SO_3	1200		S and N
H_3PO_4	751.6	6226	H and O
H_3BO_3	5.79×10^{-5}		H and O
HIO_3	17300		D
H_2CO_3	0.0454	5.61	M and B
	Organic Acids		
Formic	17.72	....	H and O
Acetic	1.754	....	H and O
Propionic	1.336	....	H and O
α-Butyric	1.515	....	H and O
Chloracetic	137.9	....	H and O
Glycolic	14.75		H and O
Lactic	13.74		H and O
Cyanacetic	350.	....	M
Benzoic	6.312	....	B and K
Cyanbenzoic	31.	....	K, W, and L
o-Chlorobenzoic	122	....	M
o-Nitrobenzoic	600	....	M
3,5-Dinitrobenzoic	150	....	M

* B and K, Brockman and Kilpatrick, *J. Am. Chem. Soc.* 56, 1483 (1934); D, C. W. Davies, *J. Phys. Chem.* 29, 977 (1925); H. and O. Harned and Owen, *Chem. Rev.* 25, 31 (1939); K, W, and L. H. D. Kirschman, B. Wingfield, and H. J. Lucas, *J. Am. Chem. Soc.* 52, 23 (1930); M, D. A. MacInnes, *ibid.* 48, 2068 (1926); M and B, MacInnes and Belcher, *ibid.* 55, 2630 (1933), S and N, M. S. Sherrill and A. A. Noyes, *J. Am. Chem. Soc.* 48, 1861 (1926).

APPENDIX IX

DISSOCIATION CONSTANTS OF WATER AT DIFFERENT TEMPERATURES

Harned and Owen, *Chem. Rev.* **25**, 31 (1939)

$t°$ C.	0	5	10	15	20	25	30
$K_w \times 10^{14}$	0.1133	0.1846	0.2920	0.4503	0.6809	1.008	1.468
$t°$ C.	35	40	45	50	55	60	
$K_w \times 10^{14}$	2.089	2.917	4.018	5.474	7.297	9.614	

APPENDIX X*

pH Values of Standard Buffer Solutions

Solution	pH$_{25°C}$.	pH$_{38°C}$.
0.05 M KHC$_8$H$_4$O$_4$ phthalate	4.005	4.02
0.1 N HCl	1.085	1.082
0.1 M KH$_3$ (C$_2$O$_4$)$_2$·2H$_2$O tetroxalate	1.480	1.495
0.01 N HCl + 0.09 N HCl	2.075	2.075
0.1 N CH$_3$ COOH + 0.1 N CH$_3$ COONa	4.643	4.64
0.025 M KH$_2$PO$_4$ + 0.025 M Na$_2$HPO$_4$·2H$_2$O	6.855	6.835
0.05 M Na$_2$B$_4$O$_7$·10H$_2$O	9.180	9.070

* Hitchcock and Taylor, *J. Am. Chem. Soc.* **60**, 2712 (1938) and from MacInnes, Belcher, and Shedlovsky, *ibid.*, **60**, 1099 (1938). Values from the two investigations were averaged when duplicated in the two papers.

Natural numbers.	0	1	2	3	4	5	6	7	8	9	PROPORTIONAL PARTS								
											1	2	3	4	5	6	7	8	9
10	0000	0043	0086	0128	0170	0212	0253	0294	0334	0374	4	8	12	17	21	25	29	33	37
11	0414	0453	0492	0531	0569	0607	0645	0682	0719	0755	4	8	11	15	19	23	26	30	34
12	0792	0828	0864	0899	0934	0969	1004	1038	1072	1106	3	7	10	14	17	21	24	28	31
13	1139	1173	1206	1239	1271	1303	1335	1367	1399	1430	3	6	10	13	16	19	23	26	29
14	1461	1492	1523	1553	1584	1614	1644	1673	1703	1732	3	6	9	12	15	18	21	24	27
15	1761	1790	1818	1847	1875	1903	1931	1959	1987	2014	3	6	8	11	14	17	20	22	25
16	2041	2068	2095	2122	2148	2175	2201	2227	2253	2279	3	5	8	11	13	16	18	21	24
17	2304	2330	2355	2380	2405	2430	2455	2480	2504	2529	2	5	7	10	12	15	17	20	22
18	2553	2577	2601	2625	2648	2672	2695	2718	2742	2765	2	5	7	9	12	14	16	19	21
19	2788	2810	2833	2856	2878	2900	2923	2945	2967	2989	2	4	7	9	11	13	16	18	20
20	3010	3032	3054	3075	3096	3118	3139	3160	3181	3201	2	4	6	8	11	13	15	17	19
21	3222	3243	3263	3284	3304	3324	3345	3365	3385	3404	2	4	6	8	10	12	14	16	18
22	3424	3444	3464	3483	3502	3522	3541	3560	3579	3598	2	4	6	8	10	12	14	15	17
23	3617	3636	3655	3674	3692	3711	3729	3747	3766	3784	2	4	6	7	9	11	13	15	17
24	3802	3820	3838	3856	3874	3892	3909	3927	3945	3962	2	4	5	7	9	11	12	14	16
25	3979	3997	4014	4031	4048	4065	4082	4099	4116	4133	2	3	5	7	9	10	12	14	15
26	4150	4166	4183	4200	4216	4232	4249	4265	4281	4298	2	3	5	7	8	10	11	13	15
27	4314	4330	4346	4362	4378	4393	4409	4425	4440	4456	2	3	5	6	8	9	11	13	14
28	4472	4487	4502	4518	4533	4548	4564	4579	4594	4609	2	3	5	6	8	9	11	12	14
29	4624	4639	4654	4669	4683	4698	4713	4728	4742	4757	1	3	4	6	7	9	10	12	13
30	4771	4786	4800	4814	4829	4843	4857	4871	4886	4900	1	3	4	6	7	9	10	11	13
31	4914	4928	4942	4955	4969	4983	4997	5011	5024	5038	1	3	4	6	7	8	10	11	12
32	5051	5065	5079	5092	5105	5119	5132	5145	5159	5172	1	3	4	5	7	8	9	11	12
33	5185	5198	5211	5224	5237	5250	5263	5276	5289	5302	1	3	4	5	6	8	9	10	12
34	5315	5328	5340	5353	5366	5378	5391	5403	5416	5428	1	3	4	5	6	8	9	10	11
35	5441	5453	5465	5478	5490	5502	5514	5527	5539	5551	1	2	4	5	6	7	9	10	11
36	5563	5575	5587	5599	5611	5623	5635	5647	5658	5670	1	2	4	5	6	7	8	10	11
37	5682	5694	5705	5717	5729	5740	5752	5763	5775	5786	1	2	3	5	6	7	8	9	10
38	5798	5809	5821	5832	5843	5855	5866	5877	5888	5899	1	2	3	5	6	7	8	9	10
39	5911	5922	5933	5944	5955	5966	5977	5988	5999	6010	1	2	3	4	5	7	8	9	10
40	6021	6031	6042	6053	6064	6075	6085	6096	6107	6117	1	2	3	4	5	6	8	9	10
41	6128	6138	6149	6160	6170	6180	6191	6201	6212	6222	1	2	3	4	5	6	7	8	9
42	6232	6243	6253	6263	6274	6284	6294	6304	6314	6325	1	2	3	4	5	6	7	8	9
43	6335	6345	6355	6365	6375	6385	6395	6405	6415	6425	1	2	3	4	5	6	7	8	9
44	6435	6444	6454	6464	6474	6484	6493	6503	6513	6522	1	2	3	4	5	6	7	8	9
45	6532	6542	6551	6561	6571	6580	6590	6599	6609	6618	1	2	3	4	5	6	7	8	9
46	6628	6637	6646	6656	6665	6675	6684	6693	6702	6712	1	2	3	4	5	6	7	7	8
47	6721	6730	6739	6749	6758	6767	6776	6785	6794	6803	1	2	3	4	5	5	6	7	8
48	6812	6821	6830	6839	6848	6857	6866	6875	6884	6893	1	2	3	4	4	5	6	7	8
49	6902	6911	6920	6928	6937	6946	6955	6964	6972	6981	1	2	3	4	4	5	6	7	8
50	6990	6998	7007	7016	7024	7033	7042	7050	7059	7067	1	2	3	3	4	5	6	7	8
51	7076	7084	7093	7101	7110	7118	7126	7135	7143	7152	1	2	3	3	4	5	6	7	8
52	7160	7168	7177	7185	7193	7202	7210	7218	7226	7235	1	2	2	3	4	5	6	7	7
53	7243	7251	7259	7267	7275	7284	7292	7300	7308	7316	1	2	2	3	4	5	6	6	7
54	7324	7332	7340	7348	7356	7364	7372	7380	7388	7396	1	2	2	3	4	5	6	6	7

Natural numbers	0	1	2	3	4	5	6	7	8	9	PROPORTIONAL PARTS								
											1	2	3	4	5	6	7	8	9
55	7404	7412	7419	7427	7435	7443	7451	7459	7466	7474	1	2	2	3	4	5	5	6	7
56	7482	7490	7497	7505	7513	7520	7528	7536	7543	7551	1	2	2	3	4	5	5	6	7
57	7559	7566	7574	7582	7589	7597	7604	7612	7619	7627	1	2	2	3	4	5	5	6	7
58	7634	7642	7649	7657	7664	7672	7679	7686	7694	7701	1	1	2	3	4	4	5	6	7
59	7709	7716	7723	7731	7738	7745	7752	7760	7767	7774	1	1	2	3	4	4	5	6	7
60	7782	7789	7796	7803	7810	7818	7825	7832	7839	7846	1	1	2	3	4	4	5	6	6
61	7853	7860	7868	7875	7882	7889	7896	7903	7910	7917	1	1	2	3	4	4	5	6	6
62	7924	7931	7938	7945	7952	7959	7966	7973	7980	7987	1	1	2	3	3	4	5	6	6
63	7993	8000	8007	8014	8021	8028	8035	8041	8048	8055	1	1	2	3	3	4	5	5	6
64	8062	8069	8075	8082	8089	8096	8102	8109	8116	8122	1	1	2	3	3	4	5	5	6
65	8129	8136	8142	8149	8156	8162	8169	8176	8182	8189	1	1	2	3	3	4	5	5	6
66	8195	8202	8209	8215	8222	8228	8235	8241	8248	8254	1	1	2	3	3	4	5	5	6
67	8261	8267	8274	8280	8287	8293	8299	8306	8312	8319	1	1	2	3	3	4	5	5	6
68	8325	8331	8338	8344	8351	8357	8363	8370	8376	8382	1	1	2	3	3	4	4	5	6
69	8388	8395	8401	8407	8414	8420	8426	8432	8439	8445	1	1	2	2	3	4	4	5	6
70	8451	8457	8463	8470	8476	8482	8488	8494	8500	8506	1	1	2	2	3	4	4	5	6
71	8513	8519	8525	8531	8537	8543	8549	8555	8561	8567	1	1	2	2	3	4	4	5	5
72	8573	8579	8585	8591	8597	8603	8609	8615	8621	8627	1	1	2	2	3	4	4	5	5
73	8633	8639	8645	8651	8657	8663	8669	8675	8681	8686	1	1	2	2	3	4	4	5	5
74	8692	8698	8704	8710	8716	8722	8727	8733	8739	8745	1	1	2	2	3	4	4	5	5
75	8751	8756	8762	8768	8774	8779	8785	8791	8797	8802	1	1	2	2	3	3	4	5	5
76	8808	8814	8820	8825	8831	8837	8842	8848	8854	8859	1	1	2	2	3	3	4	5	5
77	8865	8871	8876	8882	8887	8893	8899	8904	8910	8915	1	1	2	2	3	3	4	4	5
78	8921	8927	8932	8938	8943	8949	8954	8960	8965	8971	1	1	2	2	3	3	4	4	5
79	8976	8982	8987	8993	8998	9004	9009	9015	9020	9026	1	1	2	2	3	3	4	4	5
80	9031	9036	9042	9047	9053	9058	9063	9069	9074	9079	1	1	2	2	3	3	4	4	5
81	9085	9090	9096	9101	9106	9112	9117	9122	9128	9133	1	1	2	2	3	3	4	4	5
82	9138	9143	9149	9154	9159	9165	9170	9175	9180	9186	1	1	2	2	3	3	4	4	5
83	9191	9196	9201	9206	9212	9217	9222	9227	9232	9238	1	1	2	2	3	3	4	4	5
84	9243	9248	9253	9258	9263	9269	9274	9279	9284	9289	1	1	2	2	3	3	4	4	5
85	9294	9299	9304	9309	9315	9320	9325	9330	9335	9340	1	1	2	2	3	3	4	4	5
86	9345	9350	9355	9360	9365	9370	9375	9380	9385	9390	1	1	2	2	3	3	4	4	5
87	9395	9400	9405	9410	9415	9420	9425	9430	9435	9440	0	1	1	2	2	3	3	4	4
88	9445	9450	9455	9460	9465	9469	9474	9479	9484	9489	0	1	1	2	2	3	3	4	4
89	9494	9499	9504	9509	9513	9518	9523	9528	9533	9538	0	1	1	2	2	3	3	4	4
90	9542	9547	9552	9557	9562	9566	9571	9576	9581	9586	0	1	1	2	2	3	3	4	4
91	9590	9595	9600	9605	9609	9614	9619	9624	9628	9633	0	1	1	2	2	3	3	4	4
92	9638	9643	9647	9652	9657	9661	9666	9671	9675	9680	0	1	1	2	2	3	3	4	4
93	9685	9689	9694	9699	9703	9708	9713	9717	9722	9727	0	1	1	2	2	3	3	4	4
94	9731	9736	9741	9745	9750	9754	9759	9763	9768	9773	0	1	1	2	2	3	3	4	4
95	9777	9782	9786	9791	9795	9800	9805	9809	9814	9818	0	1	1	2	2	3	3	4	4
96	9823	9827	9832	9836	9841	9845	9850	9854	9859	9863	0	1	1	2	2	3	3	4	4
97	9868	9872	9877	9881	9886	9890	9894	9899	9903	9908	0	1	1	2	2	3	3	4	4
98	9912	9917	9921	9926	9930	9934	9939	9943	9948	9952	0	1	1	2	2	3	3	4	4
99	9956	9961	9965	9969	9974	9978	9983	9987	9991	9996	0	1	1	2	2	3	3	3	4

AUTHOR INDEX

ACREE, S. F., 104, 118, 162, 166, 170, 215
ADAIR, G. S., 195
AMIS, E. S., 21, 142, 175
ANDERSON, J. S., 18
ANSON, M. L., 40, 55–57, 87
ARRHENIUS, S., 1, 2, 6, 9, 289
ATKIN, W. R., 216, 217
AUERBACH, FR., 246, 253

BACON, 156, 165, 298
BAECKSTRÖM, S., 247
BAIER, W. E., 208
BALL, E. G., 173
BARCROFT, J., 195
BARENNE, J. G. DUSSER DE, 199–201, 232
BARNES, C. R., 209
BARRON, 185
BARTH, G., 51, 53
BAUER, K. J., 243
BAXTER, W. P., 153, 156, 166
BECK, F. F., 199
BECKMAN, A. O., 78, 132, 134, 135, 151–153, 156–158, 165, 166, 168, 191, 211, 216, 227
BEDFORD, M. H., 93
BEHRMANN, V. G., 191
BELCHER, D., 13, 30, 70, 71, 79, 80, 96, 114, 139, 140, 156, 160, 185–188, 191, 241, 242, 289, 294, 295, 298, 313, 315
BEL'GOVA, M. A., 144
BELL, R. A., 229, 231
BENNET, R. D., 29
BENZ, E. W., 193
BIILMANN, E., 19
BIRGE, R. T., 307
BJERRUM, N., 4, 14, 283
BLAIR, J. S., 35, 36, 115, 116, 204–208
BLANK, I. H., 199
BLUM, E., 72–78, 82, 132, 151, 152
BORELIUS, G., 27
BOWLES, J. A. C., 246
BRADFIELD, R., 221
BRASS, P. D., 212, 213
BRIGGS, D. R., 48, 88, 89

BRITTON, H. T. S., 84, 90, 242
BROCKMAN, 313
BRÖNSTED, 6
BROWN, A. S., 100, 101
BROWN, H., 51–53
BROWN, H. F., 173, 174
BROWN, W. E. L., 28, 64, 184
BUCHBÖCK, G., 30, 139
BURR, H. S., 193
BURTON, J. O., 170, 215

CADY, H. P., 175
CAMERON, A. E., 87
CAMERON, D. H., 214
CAMPAIGNE, E. E., 194
CARDWELL, W. T., 153
CARMODY, W. R., 100
CARR, C. J., 199
CARVER, D. H., 223
CARY, H. H., 153, 166
CASTLE, 190
CHALON, O. T., 224
CHERRY, R. N., 47–49, 51, 53, 56
CLARK, W. M., 11, 14, 15, 16, 22, 24, 25, 113, 183, 185, 284, 285, 288, 295
CLARKE, B. L., 247, 248, 250, 251, 253
COHN, E. J., 289–295, 299, 301
COLEMAN, 222
COMPTON, A. H., 40, 234
COMPTON, K. G., 247, 248
CONANT, J. B., 302
CORZO, R. H., 154
COWPERTHWAITE, I. W., 125, 247
COX, C. D., 245, 247
CRANSTON, J. A., 173, 174
CREMER, M., 25
CRITTENDEN, E. C., 308
CROWTHER, E. M., 220, 221
CULLEN, G. E., 183–185
CZERWINSKI, J., 218

DALLEMAGNE, M. J., 154
DAVENPORT, J. E., 242, 244, 245, 254
DAVIDSON, G. F., 223

DAVIES, C. W., 313
DEAN, H. L., 219, 220
DEBYE, P., 6, 8, 9, 289, 290, 291, 295
DEEDS, F., 29, 69, 70, 89, 90, 153, 154, 192, 196, 197, 229
DERIBERE, M., 214
DEYRUP, A. J., 303
DILLON, R. F., 81
DINSMORE, R. P., 212
DOBROSCKY, I. D., 96, 238, 241
DOLAZALEK, 40
DuBOIS, D., 56, 117, 189–191
DuBRIDGE, L. A., 51–53
DuBUISSON, M., 201, 232
DuNOÜY, P. LeC., 16
DUNN, M. S., 242, 249
DÜRICHEN, W., 46, 47, 54, 55, 62, 63, 235, 236
DUSPIVA, F., 240

EARLE, I. P., 183
EASTMAN, E. D., 253
EDWARDS, E. G., 169, 170, 173–176
EHLERS, R. W., 164, 167, 292
ELDER, L. W., 29, 65, 67, 79, 208
ELLIS, J. H., 102, 104, 167
ELLIS, S. B., 29, 55, 57, 60, 61, 82, 170, 171, 173, 174
ETIENNE, A. D., 226, 255
EVANS, D. P., 169, 170, 173–176
EVANS, R. M., 242, 244, 245, 254
EVSEYEVICH, 134

FALES, H. A., 101, 165, 288
FALK, K. G., 191
FAY, M., 191
FERGUSON, A. L., 109–112
FERGUSON, J. B., 79
FINN, A. N., 68, 83, 131, 138, 143–145, 154, 275, 279
FITCH, R. H., 192, 196–199
FOKIMA, E. A., 242
FOSBINDER, R. J., 29
FOSDICK, L. S., 194, 239
FREUNDLICH, H., 27
FRIEDENTHAL, H., 22
FRITSCH, A., 217–219
FUGIMOTO, T., 187, 188
FUHRMANN, F., 21
FUJITA, A., 244
FUOSS, 4

GABBARD, J. L., 21, **72**, 93, 123, 142, 155, 174
GARDINER, W. C., 123, 124, 126, 155, 156, 161
GARMAN, R. L., 38, 39, 95, 96
GEBAUER-FUELNEGG, E., 22
GERKE, R. H., 103
GIBBS, 160
GIRAUT-ERLER, L., 253
GLASSTONE, 281
GOLDMAN, L., 216, 217
GOODE, K. H., 41
GOODHUE, L. D., 29, 56, 60, 61, 142
GOODMAN, E. N., 195
GRANGER, F. S., 19
GREVILLE, G. D., 56
GRIFFITH, R. L., 223
GROSS, P., 274
GUCKER, F. T., 33
GUGGENHEIM, E. A., 107, 108, 110, 111
GURNEY, R. W., 3, 5, 266, 267, 273

HABER F., 19, 25–27, 64, 78, 85, 86, 92, 199, 227, 235, 237
HALL, N. F., 247, 302
HALPERN, O., 274
HAMER, W. J., 156, 160, 298, 302
HAMILTON, E. H., 68, 83, 131, 138, 143–145, 154, 275, 279
HAMMET, L. P., 4, 303
HANLON, R. T., 228
HARING, M. M., 56
HARNED, H. S., 162–164, 167, 292, 313, 314
HARRIS, I., 191
HARRISON, G. B., 86
HARRISON, W. H., 210
HARTMANN, M. L., 99
HARTSUCH, P. J., 96
HASSELBALCH, 183
HASTINGS, A. B., 184, 289
HAUGAARD, G., 70, 83, 181, 189, 190, 219, 279
HAVARD, R. E., 181
HEIDELBERG, Q. S., 63
HEINTZE, S. G., 220, 221
HELMHOLTZ, 160
HENDERSON, L. J., 180
HENDERSON, P., 108, 109
HENNY, K., 54
HENSLEY, 156, 165, 298

HERDY, O., 78
HEUKELEKIAN, H., 228
HEYROTH, 289, 291–293
HIGHBERGER, J. H., 115
HILL, A. V., 28
HILL, S. E., 29, 48, 58, 59, 131, 178
HIMWICH, 190
HINTON, C. L., 212
HISSINK, D. J., 220, 221
HITCHCOCK, D. I., 104, 160, 284, 289, 292–298, 302, 315
HITCHENS, R., 109–112
HIXON, R. M., 142
HOLLEY, C. E., Jr, 123, 129, 131
HORN, F., 65
HOROVITZ, K., 28, 64, 65, 70
HORWITT, M. K., 191
HUBBARD, D., 68, 83, 131, 138, 143–145, 154, 275, 279
HÜCKEL, E., 6, 290
HUGHES, W. S., 27, 64–66, 79, 124
HULETT, G. A., 104, 234, 235
HULL, H. G., 228
HUMPHREYS, R. G., 154
HURD, C. B., 223

INGHAM, J. W., 242
INGLE, J. D., 175
INGOLS, R. S., 228
IZMAÏLOV, N. A., 144

JACQUES, A. G., 176
JELLINEK, K., 218
JENSEN, M. A., 247
JEWSTROPIEV, 274
JOHNSON, R. P., 33
JOHNSON, S., 1
JOHNSON, W. C., 97
JONES, GRINNELL, 99
JONES, P. T., 247
JORDAN, D. O., 81, 123, 124, 129, 130, 136, 137, 155–158, 217, 226, 274, 275.
JORDAN, H. F., 212, 213
JOSEPH, G. H., 208
JULIUS, W. H., 33, 34

KAHLER, H., 69, 70, 89, 90, 153, 154, 192, 196–199, 229
KARGIN, W. A., 242
KELLER, W. H., 93
KELM, E. F., 68

KEMPF, 199
KERRIDGE, P. M. T., 29, 40, 57, 82, 87, 181, 184, 191, 238
KIEHL, S. J., 29, 35, 55, 57, 60, 61, 82, 170, 171, 173, 174
KILPATRICK, M., 304, 313
KILPI, S., 253
KING, C. E., 193
KIRSCHMAN, H. D., 313
KLEMENSIEWICZ, Z., 25–27, 64, 78, 85
KLINE, G. M., 118
KOENIG, F. O., 108
KOHLRAUSCH, 282
KOLTHOFF, I. M., 23, 298
KOSSEL, 3
KRAISSL, F., 88, 152
KRANTZ, J. C., 199
KRATZ, L., 86
KRAUS, L, 4
KRONIG, 197
KRUTTER, H., 265
KRYUKOV, A. A., 86
KRYUKOV, P. A., 86

LAMB, A. B., 111, 176
LANDIS, Q., 212
LANE, C. T., 193
LANFORD, O. E., 35
LANGMUIR, 3
LARSON, A. T., 111
LAUG, E. P., 80, 181, 183, 185, 188, 189, 241
LAUNER, H. F., 224, 225
LENGYEL, B., 72–78, 82, 132, 151, 152, 279
LEWIS, G. N., 3, 6, 9, 164
LINDEMANN, 40
LONGSWORTH, L. G., 114, 233–235
LOSHAKOFF, A., 242, 249
LUBS, H. A., 11, 24, 25
LUCAS, H. J., 313
LUNDSTEEN, E., 181, 189, 190
LUPTON, J. M., 81, 242, 244, 252, 255
LYMAN, 185

McCLENDON. J. F., 194, 195
McCULLOCH, W. S., 199–201, 232
McGAVACK, J., 212
McGEORGE, W. T., 219
McGUIRE, G., 191

MCILVAINE, 204
MACINNES, D. A., 13, 29, 30, 40, 65, 68–71, 79, 80, 82, 92–96, 100, 101, 111, 114, 118, 125, 126, 131, 139, 140, 156, 160, 185, 186, 191, 199, 233–235, 238–242, 247, 248, 284, 286, 289, 292, 294, 295, 297, 298, 302, 313, 315
MCLAUGHLIN, G. D., 214
MACLAGAN, N. F., 56
MARSHALL, C., 193
MATHESON, H., 170, 215
MEACHAM, M. R., 118
MELLANBY, J., 9
MENKIN, 289, 291–293
METCALF, G. F., 42, 43, 47
MICHAELIS, L., 11, 38, 39, 96, 185, 241, 244, 258
MIRSKY, A. E., 40, 55–57, 87
MOREY, G. W., 68
MORNINGSTAR, O., 265
MORRISON, J., 242
MORTON, C., 29, 42, 60, 85, 89–91, 98, 114, 115, 162, 230–232, 242, 253
MOUQUIN, H., 38, 39, 95, 96
MOYER, H. V., 226
MUDGE, W. A., 101, 165, 288
MÜLLER, FR., 46, 47, 54, 55, 62, 63, 235, 236
MUSSER, R., 199
MYERS, 184

NAFTEL, J. A., 22, 221
NELSON, J. M., 19
NERNST, W., 14
NEUMANN, R. S., 242
NEUSS, J. D., 242
NEWTON, E. B., 177
NEWTON, R. C., 203
NICHOLS, M. L., 38, 39, 95
NICOLSKY, B., 134, 272–274
NIMS, L. F., 193, 199–201, 232
NOTTINGHAM, W. B., 33, 44, 59, 236
NOYES, A. A., 313
NUNGESTER, W. J., 199

O'BRIEN, H., 185, 188, 189, 241
OSTERBERG, A. E., 196
OWEN, 313, 314

PAÏC, M., 94, 240, 245–247
PARKS, L. R., 209

PARSONS, T. R., 181
PARSY, G., 99, 101, 145, 147, 149, 219
PARTRIDGE, H. M., 29, 246
PASSINSKI, A. H., 72, 78, 134
PASTEUR, L., 1
PCHELIN, V. A., 158
PENICK, D. B., 47, 51, 53
PETERS, J. P., 180, 190
PICKFORD, G. E., 241
PIERCE, J. A., 21
PLANCK, M., 107–109
PLEASS, W. B., 216, 219
PLEIJEL, H., 107
PORTER, R. E., 150
POWNEY, J., 81, 124, 155, 157, 158, 226 274
PRICE, J. W., 184
PULFRICH, 83

QUIGLEY, J. P., 195
QUITTNER, F., 138, 261–264, 267

RAMBO, A. I., 222
RANDALL, M., 9, 103, 164
REBBECK, J. W., 79
REICHERT, J. S., 228
RENSE, W. A., 63
RICHTER, H., 154
RIEMANN, W., 242
RITTENBERG, S. C., 117, 211
ROBERTS, R. M., 120, 123, 129, 131
ROBERTSON, G. R., 38, 39
ROBINSON, H. W., 184
ROBINSON, R. A., 84, 90, 242
ROE, C. P., 212, 213
ROLLER, P. S., 249, 253
RONA, 27
ROSEBURY, F., 56, 118, 119
ROSENTHAL, H. G., 154
ROSENTHAL, S., 229
ROTHSCHILD, LORD, 104
ROWLAND, B. W., 223
RUBIN, E. L., 191
RUMBOLD, J. S., 212
RUSS, R., 19

SAECHTLING, H., 154
SALM, E., 22
SAMMT, A., 279
SANDERS, H. L., 123, 124, 12o, 155, 156, 161

SCATCHARD, G., 104, 111, 112, 167, 284–289
SCHEMPF, J. M., 38, 39, 95
SCHICKTANZ, S. T., 226, 255
SCHILLER, H., 28, 64, 261
SCHNEIDER, J., 65
SCHOLLENBERGER, C. J., 221
SCHWABE, K., 78, 153, 173, 237, 242, 251, 252
SEEKLES, L., 189–191
SENDROY, J., JR., 180, 184–189, 191, 289
SHAW, 211
SHEDLOVSKY, L., 194
SHEDLOVSKY, T., 100, 101, 156, 160, 185–188, 191, 289, 292, 294, 295, 298, 315
SHERRILL, M. S., 313
SHUTT, W. S., 191
SILLEN, L. G., 108
SLOBOD, R. L., 82
SMITH, D. M., 242, 244, 252, 255
SMITH, G. F., 58
SMOLCZYK, E., 246, 253
SNYDER, A. J., 226
SOKOLOV, S. I., 72
SÖRENSEN, S. P. L., 9–11, 14, 17, 24, 25, 282–285, 288, 292, 295
STADIE, W. C., 29, 43, 57, 185, 188, 189, 241
STARLING, S. G., 40
STEINER, A., 132, 274
STILLWELL, C. W., 265
STOCK, C. C., 173
SUGDEN, J. A., 229, 231
SUIKOVSKAJA, 274
SULLIVAN, V. R., 58
SWENSON, T. L., 211

TAYLOR, A. C., 104, 160, 289, 292, 293, 295, 298, 315
TAYLOR, P. B., 108, 109
TAYLOR, W. C., 152
THIESSE, X., 191
THOMPSON, B. J., 42, 43, 47
THOMPSON, F. C., 216, 217
THOMPSON, M. R., 22, 101, 191, 226
THOMSON, J. J., 3

URBAN, F., 132, 274

VAN DYKE, H. B., 29
VAN LENTE, K., 109–112
VAN SLYKE, D. D., 180, 190
VARNEY, P. L., 92
VAUGHN, 156, 165, 298
VERAIN, M., 191
VICKERS, H. E. J., 229, 231
VILLARS, D. S., 176–178
VINAL, G. W., 38, 308
VOEGTLIN, C., 192, 196–199, 229
VOIGTMAN, E. H., 223
VON STEIGER, A. L., 28, 65, 184

WALKER, R. H., 219, 220
WALL, H. C., 37, 223, 224
WALLACE, E. C., 215
WALTON, H. F., 264
WARREN, B. E., 265
WATERS, 102
WATSON, F. J., 81
WATSON, H. B., 175, 176
WHITNAH, C. H., 232–234
WIEGAND, W. B., 226
WIENER, B. Z., 123, 124, 128, 129, 153, 155–159, 270, 271, 278
WINGFIELD, B., 104, 162, 166, 313
WINTER, P. K., 226
WOLFENDEN, J. H., 264
WOLFERS, D., 194
WOLFF, 102
WOOTEN, L. A., 247, 248, 250, 251, 253
WRIGHT, D. D., 162, 163
WRIGHT, W. H., 29, 65, 67
WYMAN, J., 53, 116, 307

YEH, Y. L., 111
YORSTON, F. H., 223
YOSHIMURA, H., 80, 83, 89, 181, 183, 187–189, 241
YOUDEN, W. J., 96, 238, 241
YOUNG, L. E., 103

ZACHARIASEN, W. H., 75, 265
ZIEGLER, A., 191
ZIMMERMAN, J., 65
ZOBELL, C. E., 117, 211

Acetic acid, dissociation constants of, 292, 313
    in buffer solutions, 293, 294
    titration curves for, 246
Acid errors of glass electrode, corrections for, 144, 145
    defined, 139
    equation for, 141, 144, 278
    in hydrogen fluoride, 131, 132, 143
    in solutions, chloride, 140, 142, 143
        sulfate, 140, 142, 143
    temperature variation, 158, 159
    theory of, 276–279
Acid mixtures, analysis of, 251–253
    in nonaqueous solutions, 252, 253
Acidity, Arrhenius' theory of, 1–3
    Brönsted definition of, 6
    significance of, in relation to pH, 280
Acidity function, 303
Acids, behavior of glass electrode in, 139–145
    dissociation constants of, 313
    theory of glass electrode in, 276–279
Activity coefficient, Debye equation for, 8, 9
    definition of, 7
    determination of, 6–9
    empirical equations for, 9, 291, 292
    in relation to pH, 281
    "mean," 7
Advantages, 30
    in biological chemistry, 179, 185
Agar-potassium chloride jelly, for salt bridge, 110, 244
    in salt bridge, 111
Air bath, constant temperature, 119
Alkali loss, 82, 83
Alkaline errors, as a function of pH, 128–134
    corrections for, 310, 311
    definition of, 127
    equations for, 136, 158, 269, 274
    in lime liquors containing sodium ions, 216–218

Alkaline errors, method of measuring, 124
    methods of avoiding, 132–137
    mixture of sodium and barium ions and, 130
    negative ions and, 131
    positive ions and, 130–132
    qualitative explanation of, 137
    table of, 128
    temperature variation of, 155–158
    theory of, 267–276
Alcohols, errors of glass electrode in, 141, 142
    theory of glass electrode behavior in, 276–279
    titrations in, 254, 255
Amino acids, titrations of, 249
Ammonium ion errors, 86, 131
Amplifying circuits, balanced-tube circuits, 62, 229, 236
    circuit with negative feedback, 63
    electron beam circuit of Hill, 58–59
    impulse-type circuits, 60, 61, 230
    internally compensated, Barth's, 52
        DuBridge and Brown's, 51–54
        Penick's, 52
        Wyman's, 52–54
    multiple tube, 58–63
    single tube, Brigg's, 48
        Cherry's, 48, 49
        Hill's, 48
Analysis, of acids, 243–251
    in nonaqueous solutions, 254, 255
    of acid mixtures, 251–253
Antimony-antimony oxide electrode, 22
    in dairy products, 209
    in latex, 213
Asymmetry potential defined, 12–13
    effect of annealing on, 67
    function, of composition, 66
        of pH, 69
        of time, 81
    glass thickness, 67, 69, 70
    temperature variation, 154, 155
    values of, 67, 69

Automatic *p*H control, 232–237
　　balanced Wheatstone-bridge circuit
　　　　for, 236
　　cell for, 233
　　quadrant electrometer circuit for, 233
Automatic *p*H recording, 193, 200, 201

Barium ions, glass electrode errors of, 128
　　correction graph for, 311
　　migration into glass, 262
Baths, plating, acid and alkaline, 226
Bean sprout brine, hydrogen swelled,
　　　*p*H measurements of, 207, 208
Beef serum, 189
Behavior, electromotive, 66–78
Bjerrum extrapolation, 283
Blood, 185, 186
　　cells for the determination of *p*H of,
　　　　188, 190, 191, 192
　　equilibria in, 180
　　first acid change, 181
　　glycolysis in, 181
　　*p*H of, as affected by carbon dioxide-
　　　　bicarbonate ratio, 180
　　　normal limits, 180
　　reduced, 186, 187
　　technique of handling, 181, 182
Blood corpuscles, effect on *p*H measure-
　　　ments, 190
Boiler water, *p*H determination of, 223,
　　　227, 228
Brine solutions, *p*H measurement of, 210
Brönsted definition of acidity, 6
Buffer solutions, standardization, 297,
　　　298
　　*p*H values of, 315
Bulb glass electrodes, 85–89
　　thin wall, 87
Buttermilk, *p*H measurement of, 209
Butter serum, *p*H measurement of, 209,
　　　211

Calcium ions, effect on coagulation of
　　　blood, 192
　　errors, 130
　　　equation for, 137
　　migration into glass, 262

Calomel electrode, 16
　　cells for, 16, 26, 114–116, 171, 211,
　　　　227, 232, 239
　　method of preparing saturated, 102–
　　　　104
　　polarization of, 104
　　preparation of calomel, 102, 103
　　standard electrode potentials of, 284,
　　　　293–295, 309
　　temperature variation of, 166
Cannula, for blood *p*H work, 192
Capillary and capillary-tip glass elec-
　　　trodes, 96, 97, 196, 211, 239
Carbon, colloidal, *p*H determination of,
　　　226
Cell, differential titration, 247, 248
　　electrode vessels for, 16, 26, 114–116,
　　　　171, 211, 227, 232, 239
　　for automatic *p*H control, 233
　　for blood *p*H determination, 188, 190–
　　　　192
　　for continuous *p*H recording, 232
　　micro, 29, 188, 190, 191, 239–241
　　micro-titration, 243
　　sign conventions, 11–13
　　temperature coefficient of, 167, 168
　　titration, 243–246
Cheese, *p*H determination of, 211
Chemical potential, defined, 7, 257
Chlorine, *p*H of solutions of, 170
Chocolate syrup, canned, *p*H measure-
　　　ment of, 204–206
Clark cell, 16, 185
Cleaning, 81, 82, 222, 223
Colorimetric determination of *p*H, 22–25
　　C correction for, 184
　　compared with glass electrode, in
　　　　horse serum, 191
　　in oil emulsions, 146, 147
　　errors of, 24, 25
　　H correction for, 184
　　in blood, 183, 184, 191
　　in peroxide solutions, 228
　　in soap solutions, 226
　　theory of, 23, 24
Continuous *p*H recording, 200, 229–232
　　balanced Wheatstone-bridge circuit
　　　　for, 229
　　ballistic amplifier for, 230, 231

Continuous pH recording, cell for, 232
Copper ions, migration into glass, 263
Corning 015 glass, asymmetry potentials of, 15, 81, 154, 155
  composition of, 68
  effect of drying, 80, 81, 188
  electrical resistance of, 71, 80, 152, 153
  solubility in distilled water, effect upon pH, 170, 171
Cleaning technique, 81, 82, 222, 223
Corrosion, at high temperature, 153, 154
Coulomb's law, 4
Cream, pH measurement of, 209

Dairy products, 209
Debye theory of solution, 8
Definite pH measurements, 280, 281, 296, 297
Devitrification of glass, 153, 154
Differential titrations, 247–251
  equation for, 249
Dioxan, 255
Disadvantages, 32
Dissociation constants, defined, 290
  of acetic acid, 292
  of acids, table of, 313
  of water, table of, 314
Drying, effect, 80, 81
Drying technique, 188

Electric resistance of glass, as a function of composition, 69, 74, 79
  as a function of temperature, 75, 151–153
  comparison of d.-c. and a.-c. resistance, 71
  effect on e.m.f. measurements, 36, 151
  equation for, 75, 152
  water content, 80
Electrode, antimony-antimony oxide, 22, 209, 213
  calomel, see Calomel electrode
  definition of, 14
  Hydrogen, see Hydrogen electrode
  Platinum-platinic chloride, 99
  Potential, mechanism of, 266, 267
  Quinhydrone, see Quinhydrone electrode

Electrode, Reference electrodes, for glass electrodes, 98–104
  Silver chloride, 98–101
Electrometer tubes, characteristics of, 47
Electrometers, see also Amplifiers
  Compton, 40
  Electrostatic, 39, 40
  Vacuum-tube, balanced-tube circuit, 62, 229, 236
    difficulties of, 50, 51
    electron-beam amplifier, 58, 59
    impulse-type circuits, 60, 61, 230
    internally compensated circuits, 51–54
    multiple-tube circuit, 58–63
    negative feedback circuit, 63
    single-tube circuits, 46–54
    theory of, 41–46
E.m.f., mechanism of production, 266
  Relation to chemical potential and free energy, 7
Emulsions, glass electrode in, 145–149
Energy levels, ionic, in water, 266
  on glass, 267
  on metal surface, 266
Equations, Debye theory of activity coefficients, 8, 9
  empirical, for activity coefficients, 9, 291, 292
  for acid error, 141, 144, 278
  for alkaline error, 136, 158, 269, 274
  for calculation of pH, 17, 155, 297
  for differential titration maxima, 249
  for saturated calomel electrode, 156
  for temperature correction, 161
  for the pH of 0.05 c potassium acid phthalate, 298
  Gibbs–Helmholtz, 160
  Henderson–Hasselbalch, 180
  Henderson liquid junction, 108
  Thermodynamic liquid junction, 122
Errors, of acid solutions, 139–145, 158, 159, 278
  of alkaline solutions, 127–137, 155–158, 216–218, 267–276
  of electrical leaks, 89–92, 177, 178
  of glass solubility, 169–172
  of grid currents, 43, 47

Errors, of inadequate shielding, 56, 57
  of nonaqueous solutions, 141–145
  of salt solutions, 140, 142
  of standard cell e.m.f. changes, 35, 37
  of temperature fluctuations, 161, 162, 166
  previous history and, 225
Ethyl alcohol, 141, 142
Exchange force, 5

Ferric chloride, hydrolysis of, measurement of, 176
Fibrin deposits, 192
Flow rate, effect on pH measurements, 172, 173, 193
Flowing junctions, 111–113
  Vessels for, 112, 227
Fluoride ion, 131

Galvanometers, critical damping resistance, 46, 49, 50
  potentiometer circuit, 38, 39
  precautions in use of, 32
  supports, 33, 34
    Julius suspension, 33, 34
Gibbs–Helmholtz equation, 160
Glass, see also Corning 015
  composition of, 65, 66, 68–70, 72, 74, 78, 143
  electrical properties of, 66–78
  electric resistance as a function of temperature, 74, 75, 80, 151–153
  electrical resistance of, 66, 69, 71, 74, 75
  for glass electrode, 64–78
  solubility of, 82–85
  Structure of, 265
  Swelling of, 84, 279
  Water content, 78–81
Glycerol, influence on glass electrode, 194
Glycine, formol titration, 249
Grapefruit juice, canned, pH measurement of, 206, 207
Grid currents and e.m.f. measurements, 42, 43, 47
  table of, 47
Gurney theory of electrode potentials, 266

History, 25–30
Humidity, high, 177, 178
  effect on measurements, 54, 176–178, 197
Hydration energy, 3, 4
Hydrochloric acid, effect on liquid-junction potentials, 112, 289, 293
  effect on quinhydrone, 163
  temperature coefficient of cells containing, 162–164, 167
Hydrogen electrode, advantages, 17
  Clark cell, 15, 16
  defined, 14
  disadvantages, 17, 18
  duNoüy cell, 16
  equations for, 16, 17
  history, 14
  in beef blood serum, 189
  in blood, 182, 183
  in dairy products, 209
  in distilled or tap water, 170
  in lemon and orange juices, 208
  in lime liquors, 216, 218
  in magnesium sulfate solution, 175
  in reduced whole blood, 186, 187
  in rubber latex, 212
  in sea water, 173
  in soap solutions, 226
  in sucrose solutions, 175
  technique, 15
  thermodynamics of, 256–258
Hydrogen fluoride, thermodynamic equilibrium, 279
  effect, 131, 132, 143
Hydrogen ion, colorimetric method of determining, 10
  defined, 5
  definition of pH, 9, 10
  migration into glass, 262, 263
  nature of, 3
Hydrogen-ion concentration, relation of pH to, 280, 281, 300–304
Ice cream mix, pH measurement of, 209
Indicators, see also Colorimetric method of pH determination
  advantages, 24, 25
  disadvantages, 24, 25
  theory of, 23, 24

Insulation, humidity, 177, 178
  of glass electrode stems, 89–92
  of input circuits, 53–56
  switches, 54–56
Interionic theory of Debye, 6
Ion migration into glass, 261–264
  alkali ions, 262
  silver, zinc, and copper, 263
Ionic strength, defined, 9
  principle of, 9
Ionization, Arrhenius' theory of, 1–3
  degree of, 2
  law of mass action equation for, 290
  mechanism of, 3–6

Ketones, halogenated, aqueous solutions,
    of, 175–176
  measurement of hydrolysis, 176

Latex, rubber, effect, 213, 214
  pH determination of, 212–214
Leads, insulated beaded cable, 56
  insulation of, 55, 56
Leather extract, pH measurement of, 215
Lemon juice, 208
Lime liquors, 216–218
Liquid junctions, apparatus for in cells,
    114–117
  asbestos fiber type, 117, 211
  crystallization of potassium chloride
    in, 117
  derivation of equation for, 120–122
  experimental studies of, 109–113
  Flowing, 111–113
  Salt bridges, 111
  Theory of liquid-junction potentials,
    105–109, 120–122
  Types of, 107–109
    Ground-glass stopper, 117
Liquid-junction potential, equation for,
    108, 122
  in pH scale standardization, 282, 283,
    285, 288, 289, 295, 296, 299, 302
  method of eliminating, 283
Lithium ions, migration into glass, 262
Lithium-ion error, correction graph for,
    311
  equation for, 136, 137
  table of, 128

Magnesium sulfate solutions, 175
Meat-packing plant, glass electrode in,
    203
Meats, pH determination of, 211
Mechanism, 261–267
  in solutions, basic, 267, 268, 273
    acid, 276–279
Membrane type glass electrodes, 92–95
Micro apparatus for pH determina-
    tion, 29, 188, 190, 191, 239–241
Micro-titration cell, 243
Micro-glass electrode, for blood pH
    measurements, 191
Milk, pH measurement of, 209
Mold, prevention of growth of, 177

Nonaqueous solution errors, equation
    for, 141, 144, 145
  explanation of, 145
  in alcoholic solutions, 141, 142
  in dioxan, 255
  in glycerol, 194
  method of avoiding, 144
  theory of, 276–279
Nonaqueous solutions, analysis of acid
    mixtures in, 252, 253
  theory of glass electrode in, 276–279
  titrations of acid in, 254, 255

Oil, as the constant temperature bath
    liquid, 57, 178
Orange juice, 208

Paper extracts, pH determination of,
    224, 225
Paper industry, 223
pH, calculation of, at higher tempera-
    tures, 161
  definition of, 10, 282, 301
  in nonaqueous solutions, 302–304
  micro-determinations of, 29, 188, 190,
    191, 238–241
  of aqueous soap solutions, 226
  of beef serum, 189
  of blood, 180–193
  of blood in vivo, 192, 193
  of blueprint sensitizing solution, 226
  of canned grapefruit juice, 206, 207
  of canned tomato juice, 204, 205

pH, of cerebral cortex, 199, 200
  of chlorine solutions, 170
  of coffee infusions, 208
  of contraceptive jellies, 194
  of dairy products, 209
  of dental plaque, 194
  of dilute phosphate buffers, 172–174
  of dyestuffs, 224
  of emulsions of sulfonated oils, 145–150
  of hydrogen-swelled bean sprout brine,
      207–208
  of hypochlorite solutions, 223
  of lemon and orange juices, 208
  of lime liquors, 216–218
  of living tissue, 196–199
  of paper extracts, 224, 225
  of potassium chloride solutions, 173,
      174
  of pure water, 169–174
  of reduced whole blood, 186, 187
  of rubber latex, 213, 214
  of salt solutions, 174, 175
  of sea water, 173
  of skin, 199
  of soils, 219–222
  of stomach content, 194
  of sulfonated oils, 150
  of tanning liquors, 215
  of unbuffered and slightly buffered
      solutions, 169–174
  of Walker sarcoma, 199
  significance of, 300–304
pH measurements, rapidity of, 189, 193
  relative, 280
  stomach, 195
pH scale, standard electrode potentials
      for, 284, 309
  Standardization of, 282–296
  Cohn's method, 289–296
  Scatchard's method, 285–289
  Sörensen's method, 282–285
Phase boundary potentials, 105, 106, 120
  in pH measurements of nonaqueous
      solutions, 303
Pipet-type glass electrode, 170, 171
Potassium acid phthalate, 298
  pH of 0.05 c solutions, at 25° C., 284,
      315
    at various temperatures, 160, 298

Potassium acid phthalate, pH, of 0.05 c
      solutions, directions for preparing,
      297
Potassium chloride, for salt bridge, 118
  solution creep, 118
Potassium ion, migration into glass,
      262
Potassium-ion error, 130, 132, 137
  correction graph for, 310
Potentiometer, calibration of, 35, 36
  galvanometer circuit, 38, 39
  Poggendorf, theory of, 34, 35
  precautions in use of, 35
Pressure effects, 228
Proteins, effect of, 210

Quadrant electrometer, for automatic
      pH control, 233
  in glass electrode circuit, 39, 40
Quinhydrone, effect on pH, 207, 221
Quinhydrone electrode, advantages, 21
  defined, 18
  disadvantages, 21
  effect of manganese dioxide upon, 220,
      222
  equation for, 19–21
  history, 19
  in blood, 183
  in canned chocolate syrup, 204–206
  in canned grapefruit juice, 206, 207
  in canned tomato juice, 204, 205
  in dairy products, 209, 210
  in distilled or tap water, 170
  in hydrogen-swelled bean sprout brine,
      207, 208
  in magnesium sulfate solutions, 175
  in oil emulsions, 147
  in protein solution, 179
  in rubber latex, 212
  in sea water, 173
  in silicic acid gels, 222
  in soils, 220–222
  in sucrose solutions, 175
  in the measurement of jam pH, 212
  in the paper industry, 224
  in urine, 194
  reaction with hydrochloric acid, 163
  temperature coefficient of, 162
  theory of, 21

Reaction rates, measurements, 175, 176
Reference electrodes, 98–104
  temperature coefficient of, 162–168
Resistance, *see* Electric resistance of glass
  electrical measuring circuit for, 67
Reversibility, 123, 124
Rubber latex, 213, 214

Salt bridge, agar-potassium chloride jelly for, 244
  capillary hooks for, 243
  potential of liquid junctions, 111
Salt errors, 140, 142
Saturated calomel electrode, 16, 102–104
  standard electrode potential of, 166, 284, 293–295, 309
  temperature coefficient of, 165, 166
Semi-solids, pH measurement of, 210, 211
Sign conventions, 11–13
Significance of pH, in aqueous solutions, 300–302
  in nonaqueous solutions, 302–304
Silicate solutions, 175
Silver chloride electrode, 98–101
  temperature coefficient of, 163, 164
Silver ions, migration into glass, 263
Skin, surface of, pH determination of, 199
Skin potentials, 192, 195, 197
Soap solutions, pH determination of, 226
Sodium borate, $Na_2B_4O_7 \cdot 10H_2O$, 298
  pH of 0.05 c solution, 298, 315
Sodium ion, migration out of and into glass, 261, 262
Sodium-ion errors, 129–134
  as a function of temperature, 155–158
  correction graph for, 310
  equation for, 158, 159, 269, 274, 275
  theory of, 267–276
Sodium silicate, effect, 222
Soils, effect of drying and rewetting, 219
  pH measurement of, 219–222
Solutions, nonaqueous, 81
  magnesium sulfate, 175
  silicate, 175
  soap, 226
  sucrose, 175
Spear-type glass electrode, 196, 211

Spiral-type glass electrode, 96
Stability, high temperature, 153, 154
Standard cell, calibration, 37
  commercial, 37
  precautions in use of, 38
  Weston, 37
Standard electrode potentials, for calomel electrodes, 284, 309
  saturated, as function of temperature, 166
  method of determining, 6–9, 282–296
  of the quinhydrone electrode, 162
  table of, 309
Standardization, 296–300
  asymmetry potentials, 297
  in nonaqueous solutions, 299, 300
  of pH scale, 282–296
  table for, 284, 309
Stearic acid, titration of, in n-butanol, 254
Stomach pH measurements, 195
Streaming potential, pH measurements, 171
Sucrose, glass, quinhydrone and hydrogen electrodes in solutions of, 175
Sulfonated oils, composition of, 146
  emulsions of, 145–149
  pH of, 150
Sulfuric acid, 140, 142, 143, 159
Supports, 57
Surface e.m.f., as a function of temperature, 159–162
Swelling of glass, in acid and nonaqueous solutions, 279
  Repression of, 84
Switches, 50
  construction of, 55–56
  insulation, 54–55
  shielding of, 55–56

Tanning liquors, 215, 216
Temperature, correction curves for pH meters, 312
Temperature effects, errors in acid and nonaqueous solution, 159
  alkaline, 155–158
  on corrosion, 153, 154
  on asymmetry potential, 154, 155
  variation of glass resistance, 151–153

Tetramethyl ammonium-ion error, 131
Theory, 256–279
  comparison with hydrogen electrode,
    256–261
  corrosion of glass, 275, 276
  equation for, in alkaline range, 270,
    272–275
  in acid and nonaqueous solutions, 276–
    279
  of Gurney, 267–269
Thermodynamics, 256–261
  in solutions, acid, 277
    alkaline, 272, 273
Thompson glass electrode, for blood pH
    measurements, 191
Tissue pH measurements, 196–199
Titration cells, 243–246
  for differential titrations, 247, 248
  for volatile acids, 245
Titrations potentiometric, 242–249
  in nonaqueous solutions, 254, 255
  micro-titration cell, 243
Tomato juice, canned, pH measurement
    of, 204, 205
Transference experiments on glass, 261–
    264
Treatment, effect of, 225
Tropics, 177

Types, bulb, 85–89
  bulb, thin wall, 87
  capillary, 96, 97
  capillary, tip, 196
  membrane, 92–95
  pipet, 88, 89, 171
  spear, 196, 211
  spiral, 96

Urine, 194

Vacuum tubes, electrometer, character-
    istics of, 47
  electron beam, 59
  FP-54, 42, 43, 47, 49, 54
  Screen grid (6C6), 68

Water, in glass, 78–81
  pH of, 170, 172, 174
  transfer into glass, 264
  vapor pressure of, 276–279
Water bath, constant temperature, by
    circulating water, 116
  gas heated, 188
Wulff, pH apparatus, 146, 147

Zinc ions, migration into glass, 263

A 3 C 9
20 - 55
Cu(3 5) : 1

∨w1s ⅞ l⅞